A2-Level

Biology

for AQA

The Complete Course for AQA

Contents

Introduction

How to use this book i

How Science Works

1. The Scientific Process 1
2. Scientific Evidence 3
3. Science and Decision Making 6

Unit 4

Section 1: Ecosystems and Populations

1. Ecosystems 7
2. Variation in Population Size 10
3. Investigating Populations 13
4. Analysing and Interpreting
   Distribution Data 19
5. Human Populations 21
Exam-style Questions 27

Section 2: Energy Supply

1. Storing and Releasing Energy 29
2. Photosynthesis and the Light-dependent
   Reaction 31
3. Light-independent Reaction 36
4. Limiting Factors in Photosynthesis 39
5. Respiration 43
Exam-style Questions 52

Section 3: Energy Flow & Nutrient Cycles

1. Energy Transfer and Energy Loss 54
2. Farming Practices and Productivity 59
3. The Carbon Cycle and Global Warming 62
4. The Effects of Global Warming 66
5. The Nitrogen Cycle and Eutrophication 70
Exam-style Questions 75

Section 4: Succession and Conservation

1. Succession 77
2. Conservation 81
3. Conservation Evidence and Data 85
Exam-style Questions 89

Section 5: Inheritance, Selection and Speciation

1. Genetic Terms 91
2. Genetic Diagrams — Simple
   Monohybrid Crosses 93
3. Genetic Diagrams — Sex-linked
   and Multiple Allele Crosses 96
4. Genetic Pedigree Diagrams 99
5. The Hardy-Weinberg Principle 100
6. Allele Frequency and Speciation 104
Exam-style Questions 109

Unit 5

Section 1: Responding to the Environment

1. Survival and Response   111
2. Nervous and Hormonal Communication   112
3. Chemical Mediators   116
4. Receptors   117
5. The Nervous Impulse   121
Exam-style Questions   **126**
6. Synaptic Transmission   128
7. Effectors — Muscles   133
8. Control of Heart Rate   140
9. Responses in Plants   142
Exam-style Questions   **147**

Section 2: Homeostasis

1. Homeostasis Basics   149
2. Control of Body Temperature   153
3. Control of Blood Glucose Concentration   157
4. Control of the Menstrual Cycle   161
Exam-style Questions   **165**

Section 3: Genetics

1. DNA and RNA   167
2. Protein Synthesis   170
3. The Genetic Code and Nucleic Acids   174
4. Regulation of Transcription
   and Translation   178
Exam-style Questions   **182**
5. Mutations   184
6. Mutations and Cancer   187
7. Diagnosing and Treating Cancer and
   Genetic Disorders   188
8. Stem Cells   192
9. Stem Cells in Medicine   195
Exam-style Questions   **199**

Section 4: Gene Technology

1. Making DNA Fragments   201
2. Gene Cloning   205
3. Genetic Engineering   209
4. Genetic Fingerprinting   212
5. Locating and Sequencing Genes   216
6. DNA Probes in Medical Diagnosis   221
7. Gene Therapy   224
Exam-style Questions   **228**

Exam Help

1. Exam Structure   230
2. Command Words   230
3. Answering the Essay Question   231
4. Answering Data Questions   231
5. Graph Skills   235

Reference

Answers   236
Glossary   263
Acknowledgements   269
Index   271

How to use this book

Learning Objectives
- These tell you exactly what you need to learn, or be able to do, for the exam.
- There's a specification reference at the bottom that links to the AQA specification.

Examples
- These are here to help you understand the theory.
- You don't need to learn them unless it says so in the text.

Tips
These are here to help you understand the theory.

Learning Objectives:
- Know that photosynthesis is the main route by which energy enters an ecosystem.
- Understand how energy is transferred through the trophic levels in food chains and food webs and is dissipated.
- Know that net productivity is defined by the expression, Net productivity = Gross productivity – Respiratory loss
- Be able to quantify the efficiency of energy transfer between trophic levels.
- Understand pyramids of numbers, biomass and energy and their relationship to their corresponding food chains and webs.

Specification Reference 3.4.5

Tip: The producers are at the bottom of the food chain and energy moves up through the food chain as it passes between trophic levels.

Tip: Remember, the primary consumer is the first consumer in a food chain, the secondary consumer is the second consumer in the food chain, and the tertiary consumer is the third consumer.

1. Energy Transfer and Energy Loss

Plants get their energy from the sun, and animals get their energy by eating plants or other animals. But some energy is always lost as it moves between organisms — and you can show this using some nifty equations and diagrams.

Ecosystems and energy
An ecosystem includes all the organisms living in a particular area and all the non-living (abiotic) conditions. The main route by which energy enters an ecosystem is **photosynthesis** (e.g. by plants, see p. 29). (Some energy enters sea ecosystems when bacteria respire chemicals from deep sea vents.)

During photosynthesis plants convert sunlight energy into a form that can be used by other organisms — plants are called **producers** (even though they're only converting the energy, not producing it). Energy is transferred through the living organisms of an ecosystem when organisms eat other organisms, e.g. producers are eaten by organisms called **primary consumers**. Primary consumers are then eaten by **secondary consumers** and secondary consumers are eaten by **tertiary consumers**. Each of the stages (e.g. producers, primary consumers) is called a **trophic level**.

Food chains and **food webs** show how energy is transferred through an ecosystem. Food chains show simple lines of energy transfer. Food webs show lots of food chains in an ecosystem and how they overlap.

Example
The example below shows a food chain (red box) and a food web (blue box).

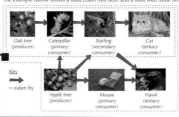

| Oak tree (producer) | Caterpillar (primary consumer) | Starling (secondary consumer) | Cat (tertiary consumer) |

Key
= eaten by

| Apple tree (producer) | Mouse (primary consumer) | Hawk (tertiary consumer) |

Energy locked up in the things that can't be eaten (e.g. bones, faeces) gets recycled back into the ecosystem by microorganisms called **decomposers** — they break down dead or undigested material (see page 62).

54 Unit 4: Section 3 Energy Flow & Nutrient Cycles

---

3. Conservation Evidence and Data

You need to be able to evaluate data on conservation. Sometimes though, it can be a bit tricky — especially when data sets show conflicting trends...

Evaluating evidence on conservation
You need to be able to evaluate any evidence or data about conservation projects and research that the examiners throw at you — so here's an example I made earlier...

Example
In recent years, native British bluebells have become less common in woodland areas. It's thought that this is due to the presence of non-native Spanish bluebells, which compete with the native species for a similar niche.

An experiment was carried out to see if removing the invasive Spanish species would help to conserve the native species. Each year for 15 years the percentage cover of native species was estimated in a 50 m by 50 m area of woodland using random sampling and 250, 1 m² quadrats. After five years, all the Spanish bluebells were removed. A similar sized control woodland in which the Spanish bluebells remained untouched was also studied. The results are shown below.

Figure 1: Percentage cover of native British bluebells in a woodland.

Figure 2: Control experiment.

You might be asked to:
Describe the data
- For the first five years, the percentage cover of native bluebells fell from 50% to around 25%. After the Spanish species was removed, it increased from 25% to around 45% in ten years.
- The control experiment shows a fairly steady drop in native bluebell percentage cover from 60% to 20% over the 15 years.

Draw conclusions
The removal of Spanish bluebells resulted in an increase in the percentage cover of native bluebells over a ten year period. This suggests that the recent decrease in native British bluebells is due to competition with the Spanish bluebells.

Learning Objectives:
- Be able to evaluate evidence and data concerning issues relating to the conservation of species and habitats and consider conflicting evidence.
- Be able to explain how conservation relies on science to inform decision-making.

Specification Reference 3.4.7

Tip: A niche is the role of a species within its habitat (see page 7). If you need a reminder about using quadrats, take a look at page 14.

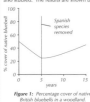

Figure 3: Some attempts to conserve British bluebells (top) have involved removing Spanish bluebells (bottom).

Unit 4: Section 4 Succession and Conservation 85

How Science Works
- How Science Works is a big part of A2 Biology. There's a whole section on it at the front of the book.
- How Science Works is also covered throughout the book wherever you see this symbol.

HOW SCIENCE WORKS

Exam Tips
There are tips throughout the book to help with all sorts of things to do with answering exam questions.

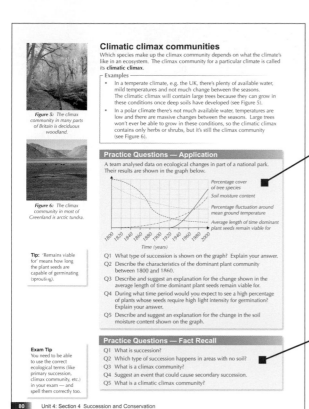

Climatic climax communities

Which species make up the climax community depends on what the climate's like in an ecosystem. The climax community for a particular climate is called its **climatic climax**.

Examples

- In a temperate climate, e.g. the UK, there's plenty of available water, mild temperatures and not much change between the seasons. The climatic climax will contain large trees because they can grow in these conditions once deep soils have developed (see Figure 5).
- In a polar climate there's not much available water, temperatures are low and there are massive changes between the seasons. Large trees won't ever be able to grow in these conditions, so the climatic climax contains only herbs or shrubs, but it's still the climax community (see Figure 6).

Figure 5: The climax community in many parts of Britain is deciduous woodland.

Figure 6: The climax community in most of Greenland is arctic tundra.

Tip: 'Remains viable for' means how long the plant seeds are capable of germinating (sprouting).

Practice Questions — Application

A team analysed data on ecological changes in part of a national park. Their results are shown in the graph below.

- Percentage cover of tree species
- Soil moisture content
- Percentage fluctuation around mean ground temperature
- Average length of time dominant plant seeds remain viable for

Time (years)

Q1 What type of succession is shown on the graph? Explain your answer.
Q2 Describe the characteristics of the dominant plant community between 1800 and 1860.
Q3 Describe and suggest an explanation for the change shown in the average length of time dominant plant seeds remain viable for.
Q4 During what time period would you expect to see a high percentage of plants whose seeds require high light intensity for germination? Explain your answer.
Q5 Describe and suggest an explanation for the change in the soil moisture content shown on the graph.

Exam Tip
You need to be able to use the correct ecological terms (like primary succession, climax community, etc.) in your exam — and spell them correctly too.

Practice Questions — Fact Recall

Q1 What is succession?
Q2 Which type of succession happens in areas with no soil?
Q3 What is a climax community?
Q4 Suggest an event that could cause secondary succession.
Q5 What is a climatic climax community?

Practice Questions — Application

- Annoyingly, the examiners expect you to be able to apply your knowledge to new situations — these questions are here to give you plenty of practice at doing this.
- All the answers are in the back of the book (including any calculation workings).

Practice Questions — Fact Recall

- There are a lot of facts to learn for A2 Biology — these questions are here to test that you know them.
- All the answers are in the back of the book.

Glossary

There's a glossary at the back of the book full of all the definitions you need to know for the exam, plus loads of other useful words.

Exam-style Questions

- Practising exam-style questions is really important — you'll find some at the end of each section.
- They're the same style as the ones you'll get in the real exams — some will test your knowledge and understanding, some will test that you can apply your knowledge and some will test How Science Works.
- All the answers are in the back of the book, along with a mark scheme to show you how you get the marks.

Exam Help

There's a section at the back of the book stuffed full of things to help with your exams.

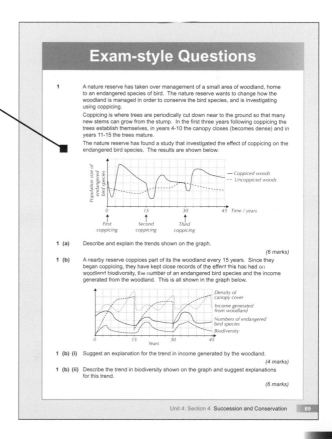

Exam-style Questions

1   A nature reserve has taken over management of a small area of woodland, home to an endangered species of bird. The nature reserve wants to change how the woodland is managed in order to conserve the bird species, and is investigating using coppicing.

Coppicing is where trees are periodically cut down near to the ground so that many new stems can grow from the stump. In the first three years following coppicing the trees establish themselves, in years 4-10 the canopy closes (becomes dense) and in years 11-15 the trees mature.

The nature reserve has found a study that investigated the effect of coppicing on the endangered bird species. The results are shown below.

— Coppiced woods
-- Uncoppiced woods

1 (a)   Describe and explain the trends shown on the graph.
(6 marks)

1 (b)   A nearby reserve coppices part of its woodland every 15 years. Since they began coppicing, they have kept close records of the effect this has had on woodland biodiversity, the number of an endangered bird species and the income generated from the woodland. This is all shown in the graph below.

- Density of canopy cover
- Income generated from woodland
- Numbers of endangered bird species
- Biodiversity

1 (b) (i)   Suggest an explanation for the trend in income generated by the woodland.
(4 marks)

1 (b) (ii)   Describe the trend in biodiversity shown on the graph and suggest explanations for this trend.
(6 marks)

Published by CGP

Editors:
Charlotte Burrows, Emma Elder, Rosie McCurrie, Rachael Rogers,
Camilla Simson, Hayley Thompson, Jane Towle.

Contributors:
Gloria Barnett, Jessica Egan, James Foster, Julian Hardwick, Derek Harvey,
Stephen Phillips, Adrian Schmit, Sophie Watkins.

ISBN: 978 1 84762 788 9

With thanks to Janet Cruse-Sawyer, Mary Falkner, Philip Rushworth and Hayley Thompson for the proofreading.
With thanks to Anna Lupton and Laura Jakubowski for the copyright research.

www.cgpbooks.co.uk

Printed by Elanders Ltd, Newcastle upon Tyne.
Clipart from Corel®

1. The Scientific Process

Science tries to explain how and why things happen. It's all about seeking and gaining knowledge about the world around us. Scientists do this by observing things, developing theories and then testing them to see if they're correct — this is the scientific process. There are five main stages...

1. Developing theories

A **theory** is a possible explanation for something. Theories usually come about when scientists observe something and wonder why or how it happens. (Scientists also sometimes form a model too — a simplified picture of what's physically going on.)

Tip: A theory is only scientific if it can be tested.

┌ **Examples** ─────────────────────

- Darwin came up with his theory of evolution by natural selection after observing wildlife (e.g. finches) and fossils during a trip around South America and the Galapagos Islands.

- The theory that smoking causes lung cancer was developed after it was observed that many people who contracted lung cancer also smoked.

- John Snow came up with the theory that cholera is transmitted in water, rather than air, after observing lots of cases of cholera clustered around a water pump.

- Edward Jenner came up with the idea that being infected with cowpox protected you from getting smallpox after observing that milkmaids didn't get smallpox.

Figure 1: *The doctor, John Snow.*

Tip: Sometimes data from one experiment can be the starting point for developing a new theory.

2. Testing the theories

The next step is to make a **prediction** or **hypothesis** — a specific testable statement, based on the theory, about what will happen in a test situation. Then an experiment or study is carried out to provide evidence that will support the prediction (or help to disprove it). If it's disproved it's back to the drawing board — the theory is modified or a completely new one is developed.

Tip: The results of one experiment can't prove that a theory is true — they can only suggest that it's true. They can however disprove a theory — show that it's wrong.

┌ **Examples** ─────────────────────

- Louis Pasteur designed an experiment to test his idea that 'germs' in the air caused disease and decomposition. He boiled two flasks of broth, both of which were left open to the air. One of the flasks had a curved neck (see Figure 2) to trap any airborne bacteria so they couldn't get into the broth. The broth in the flask with the curved neck stayed fresh, whereas the other broth went off. This provided evidence to support his theory. (After more evidence like this modern microbiology was born.)

- Edward Jenner tested his idea that getting cowpox protected people from getting smallpox by infecting a boy with cowpox, then exposing him to smallpox. The boy didn't get smallpox, which provided evidence to support his theory. (Eventually this lead to the development of a smallpox vaccine.)

Figure 2: *Pasteur's experiment — the flask with the curved neck stayed fresh.*

3. Communicating the results

The results are then published — scientists need to let others know about their work. Scientists publish their results in **scientific journals**. These are just like normal magazines, only they contain scientific reports (called papers) instead of the latest celebrity gossip.

Tip: Some well known biological journals are Nature, The Lancet and the British Medical Journal.

Scientific reports are similar to the lab write-ups you do in school. And just as a lab write-up is reviewed (marked) by your teacher, reports in scientific journals undergo **peer review** before they're published. The report is sent out to peers — other scientists who are experts in the same area. They examine the data and results, and if they think that the conclusion is reasonable it's published. This makes sure that work published in scientific journals is of a good standard.

Tip: Scientific findings are also communicated at conferences around the world.

But peer review can't guarantee the science is correct — other scientists still need to reproduce it. Sometimes mistakes are made and flawed work is published. Peer review isn't perfect but it's probably the best way for scientists to self-regulate their work and to publish quality reports.

Tip: Other scientists need to reproduce results to make sure they're reliable — see the next page for more.

4. Validating the theory by more testing

Other scientists read the published theories and results, and try to test the theory themselves in order to validate it (back it up). This involves:

- Repeating the exact same experiments.
- Using the theory to make new predictions and then testing them with new experiments.

Tip: Even negative results are communicated — knowing that something is wrong improves scientific knowledge.

Examples

- In 1998 a study was published that linked the MMR vaccine to autism (a developmental disorder). Other scientists then conducted different studies to try to find the same link, but their results didn't back up (validate) the theory.
- In the 1940s a study was published linking smoking and lung cancer. After this many more studies were conducted all over the world that validated the conclusion of the first study.

Tip: Once an experimental method is found that gives good evidence it becomes a <u>protocol</u> — an accepted method to test that particular thing that all scientists can use.

5. The theory is rejected, or accepted

If multiple experiments show a theory to be incorrect then scientists either have to modify the theory or develop a new one, and start the testing again. If all the experiments in all the world provide good evidence to back a theory up, the theory is thought of as scientific 'fact' (for now) — see Figure 3. But it will never become totally indisputable fact. Scientific breakthroughs or advances could provide new ways to question and test the theory, which could lead to new evidence that conflicts with the current evidence. Then the testing starts all over again... And this, my friend, is the tentative nature of scientific knowledge — it's always changing and evolving.

Tip: 'Good evidence' means reliable evidence — see the next page.

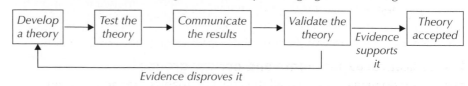

Figure 3: Flow diagram summarising the scientific process.

2. Scientific Evidence

So scientists need good evidence to back up their theories. A lot of scientific evidence comes from laboratory experiments, but there are things you can't investigate in a lab (e.g. whether stress causes heart attacks) — so you have to do a study instead. Good evidence basically means reliable evidence...

Reliable evidence

Scientific evidence needs to be **reliable**. This means that it can be consistently reproduced in independent experiments.

┌─ **Example** ───
Experiment 1 result = 15 ⎫ Reliable   Experiment 1 result = 15 ⎫ Unreliable
Experiment 2 result = 16 ⎬ evidence   Experiment 2 result = 200 ⎬ evidence
Experiment 3 result = 15 ⎭   Experiment 3 result = 79 ⎭
└──

If the results are reproducible they're more likely to be true. If the data isn't reliable for whatever reason you can't draw a valid conclusion.

The results of an experiment also need to be as **accurate** and **precise** as possible. Accurate results are those that are really close to the true answer. Precise results are those taken using sensitive instruments that measure in small increments, e.g. using a ruler with a millimetre scale gives more precise data than using a ruler with a scale in centimetres.

Getting reliable evidence

To get reliable evidence you need to do the following things:

1. Control the variables

A **variable** is a quantity that has the potential to change, e.g. weight, temperature, concentration. In an experiment you usually change one variable and measure its effect on another variable:

- The variable you change is called the **independent variable**.
- The variable that you measure is called the **dependent variable**.

Every other variable that could affect the results has to be kept the same (controlled) throughout the experiment. These variables are called **control variables**. If all the variables that could possibly affect the result are controlled then the investigation is said to be a **fair test**.

┌─ **Example** ───
For an investigation into how light intensity affects the rate of photosynthesis in plants:
- The independent variable is light intensity (as it's the one you change).
- The dependent variable is the rate of photosynthesis (the thing you measure).
- The control variables are the type of plants you use, the temperature, the carbon dioxide concentration, etc. (as these could all affect the result if they aren't kept the same throughout).
└──

It's usually straightforward to control all the variables in a lab experiment, but it can be quite tricky when doing studies. You often can't control all the variables, but the more you do control the more reliable the results will be.

2. Use control experiments and control groups

Even if you do manage to keep all the control variables the same, it's still possible that something else you're doing could affect the results. Scientists use control experiments and control groups to eliminate this possibility.

Tip: Evidence is the same thing as data or results.

Exam Tip
Make sure you really understand what reliable means — it crops up in loads of exam questions.

Tip: It's possible to be precise without being accurate. E.g. you could use a pH meter to measure pH of a solution to five decimal places (which would be very precise) — but if you hadn't calibrated the pH meter properly, it wouldn't be an accurate measurement.

Tip: Control variables are also sometimes called confounding variables.

Tip: In a study with human participants, you should try to keep the variables of all the participants the same, e.g. they should all be the same age, sex, etc.

Figure 1: *Well-designed lab experiments where all the variables are controlled give reliable results.*

In lab experiments, controls or **control experiments** are used.

┌─ **Example** ──

You want to investigate how temperature affects the rate of respiration in yeast. You decide to incubate the yeast at five different temperatures in beakers of liquid growth medium. You then measure the rate at which carbon dioxide is produced at each temperature. The faster the yeast produce CO_2, the greater their rate of respiration.

For each temperature, you'll need to measure the rate of CO_2 production in a beaker of liquid growth medium that doesn't contain any yeast. This will act as a **negative control** and make sure that any changes in the rate of CO_2 production are down to the effect of temperature on the yeast and not the effect of temperature on the liquid growth medium.

───

In studies, **control groups** are used. The subjects in the study are split into two groups — the experimental group and the control group. The control group is treated in exactly the same way as the experimental group, except for the factor you're investigating.

┌─ **Example** ──

Say you're investigating the effect of eating a low sodium (salt) diet on blood pressure. You'd have two groups. One group would be the experimental group and be given a diet low in sodium. The other group would be a control group, who would be given a diet in which sodium wasn't reduced. This is done so that you can tell that any decrease in blood pressure is due to the low sodium diet and nothing else.

───

When testing new drugs to see if they work, control groups should always be used. The control group is treated in exactly the same way as the experimental group, except they're given a thing called a **placebo** instead of the drug. A placebo is a dummy pill or injection that looks exactly like the real drug, but doesn't contain the drug. It's used to make sure that people don't improve just because they think they're being treated.

Drug trials also should be **double-blind trials**. This means that the doctor involved doesn't know whether the patient is getting the drug or the placebo, and neither does the patient. This is done to remove **bias**, e.g. doctors who expect the patients on the drugs to get better might report a greater improvement than there was.

3. Use a large sample size

Sample size is the number of samples in the investigation, e.g. the number of people in a drug trial. The general rule is the larger the sample size, the more reliable the data is. This is because it reduces the chance of getting a freak result (e.g. if you get the same result twice it might be because of chance, but if you get it 100 times it's much more likely that it's not due to chance).

Annoyingly, there are no rules about how big the sample size has to be to be for the investigation to be considered as 'reliable' — all you need to know is that bigger is always better.

4. Collect data carefully

The method used to collect the data can affect how reliable it is. For example, people aren't always truthful when answering questionnaires, which reduces the reliability of the data. Also, if you're using control groups, it's important that subjects are split into the two groups at **random**. This helps to avoid bias, and so makes the data more reliable.

Tip: A negative control is not expected to have any effect on the experiment.

Exam Tip
If you get an exam question asking why a control group is important in a particular experiment make sure your answer is specific to that experiment (not just generally about why control groups are good).

Figure 2: *The placebo (left) should look identical to the real drug (right).*

Tip: A large data set is the same thing as a large sample size.

Tip: Scientists can use statistical tests to figure out if a result is likely to be due to chance or not (see page 234 for more).

Tip: Bias is when someone intentionally, or unintentionally, favours a particular result.

5. Repeat the measurements

The reliability of a single experiment can be improved by repeating the measurements and calculating the mean. Also, the larger the number of repeats the easier it is to spot **anomalous data** (measurements that fall outside the range of values you'd expect or any pattern you already have).

Drawing conclusions from data

Conclusions need to be **valid**. A conclusion can only be considered as valid if it answers the original question and uses reliable data. It's quite tricky to draw conclusions from data — so scientists need to look out for a couple of things:

Correlations and causal relationships

The results of investigations often show a relationship between two variables, e.g. between smoking and lung cancer. A relationship between two variables is called a **correlation**. There are two types of correlation — **positive correlations** and **negative correlations**.

Positive
As one variable increases the other increases.

Negative
As one variable increases the other decreases.

No correlation
There is no relationship between the variables.

Scientists have to be very careful when drawing conclusions from data like this because a correlation between two variables doesn't always mean that a change in one variable causes a change in the other.

> ### Example
> There's a correlation in the UK between a decrease in temperature and the number of adults who are treated in hospital for serious injuries — the lower the temperature, the greater the number of people who are treated. But low temperatures don't cause serious injuries — the reason for the correlation is that there's more likely to be ice and snow around during a period of cold weather. This increases the likelihood that people will slip, fall badly and injure themselves.

If there's a relationship between two variables and a change in one variable does cause a change in the other (e.g. more ice and snow around does cause an increase in serious injuries) it's called a **causal relationship**. It can be concluded that a correlation is a causal relationship if every other variable that could possibly affect the result is controlled. In reality this is very hard to do — correlations are generally accepted to be causal relationships if lots of studies have found the same thing, and scientists have figured out exactly how one factor causes the other.

Drawing specific conclusions

Scientists can't make broad generalisations from data — they have to be very specific. They can only conclude what the results show and no more.

> ### Example
> The graph shows the results from a study into the effect of antibiotic X on protein synthesis in *E. coli*. The only conclusion you can draw is that as the concentration of antibiotic X increases, the rate of protein synthesis in *E. coli* decreases. You can't conclude this is true for any other antibiotic or any other species of bacteria.
>
>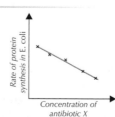

Tip: Repeating measurements in an experiment improves reliability in the same way as a large sample size — it reduces the likelihood that the results are due to chance.

Tip: All data will vary a bit, but anomalous results vary a lot from what you'd expect.

Tip: There's a statistical test called the Spearman's rank correlation test, which is a handy way of finding out whether two sets of data are correlated and how strong the correlation is. The test always gives a number between −1 and +1. A positive number means the variables are positively correlated (the closer the number to +1, the stronger the positive correlation) and a negative number means the variables are negatively correlated (the closer the number to −1, the stronger the negative correlation).

Tip: A causal relationship is sometimes called a causal link.

Tip: What conclusion is drawn might be affected by bias, e.g. if someone works for a chemical company they might be more likely to ignore data that showed their product causing environmental problems.

3. Science and Decision Making

Lots of scientific work eventually leads to important discoveries or breakthroughs that could benefit humankind. These results are used by society to make decisions.

How society uses science to make decisions

Scientific knowledge is used by society (that's you, me and everyone else) to make decisions — about the way we live, what we eat, what we drive, etc. All sections of society use scientific evidence to make decisions, e.g. politicians use it to devise policies and individuals use science to make decisions about their own lives.

┌─ Examples ─────────────────
- The maximum amount of salt people are advised to eat per day was reduced in government guidelines in 2004, due to the results of a study which showed that reducing salt intake could significantly reduce heart disease.
- Leaded petrol in cars was phased out in many countries after it was found to cause air pollution that damaged the brain.

Factors affecting decision making

Other factors can influence decisions about science or the way science is used:

Economic factors

Society has to consider the cost of implementing changes based on scientific conclusions. Sometimes it decides the cost doesn't outweigh the benefits.

┌─ Example ─────────────────
The NHS can't afford the most expensive drugs without sacrificing something else. Sometimes they decide to use a less effective, but less expensive drug, despite evidence showing there's a more effective one.

Social factors

Decisions affect people's lives — sometimes people don't want to follow advice, or are strongly against some recommendations.

┌─ Examples ─────────────────
- Scientists may suggest banning smoking and alcohol to prevent health problems, but shouldn't we be able to choose whether we want to smoke and drink or not?
- Scientists may be able to cure many diseases using stem cells, but some people are strongly against the idea of embryonic stem cell research.

Environmental factors

Some scientific research and breakthroughs might affect the environment. Not everyone thinks the benefits are worth the possible environmental damage.

┌─ Examples ─────────────────
- Scientists believe unexplored regions like remote parts of rainforests might contain untapped drug resources. But some people think we shouldn't exploit these regions because any interesting finds may lead to deforestation and reduced biodiversity in these areas.
- Scientists have developed genetically modified (GM) crops (e.g. with frost resistance, or high nutrient content), but some people think the possible environmental harm they could do outweighs their benefits.

How Science Works

1. Ecosystems

All living things are found in places where they can cope with the local conditions, like the temperature and the availability of food. It's a fairly simple concept, but you need to be able to use some fancy words to describe it...

What is an ecosystem?

An **ecosystem** is all the organisms living in a certain area and all the non-living conditions found there. It includes both **biotic** and **abiotic conditions**:

- Biotic conditions are the living features of an ecosystem, for example, the presence of predators or food.
- Abiotic conditions are the non-living features of an ecosystem, such as the temperature and soil.

Example

In a freshwater ecosystem such as a lake, the biotic conditions would include the fish and the abiotic conditions would include the temperature of the water.

The place where an organism lives within an ecosystem is known as it's **habitat** — for example, a rocky shore on the lake. Within a habitat each species has it's own **niche**.

What is a niche?

A niche is the role of a species within its habitat, for example, what it eats, and where and when it feeds. The niche a species occupies includes:

- Its biotic interactions — e.g. the organisms it eats, and those it's eaten by.
- Its abiotic interactions — e.g. the temperature range an organism can live in, the time of day when an organism is active.

Every species has its own unique niche — a niche can only be occupied by one species. It may look like two species are filling the same niche (e.g. they're both eaten by the same species), but there'll be slight differences (e.g. variations in what they eat).

Example

- **Common pipistrelle bat**
  This bat lives throughout Britain on farmland, open woodland, hedgerows and urban areas. It feeds by flying and catching insects using echolocation (high-pitched sounds) at a frequency of around 45 kHz.

- **Soprano pipistrelle bat**
  This bat lives in Britain in woodland areas, close to lakes or rivers. It feeds by flying and catching insects using echolocation, at a frequency of 55 kHz.

It may look like both species are filling the same niche (e.g. they both eat insects), but there are slight differences (e.g. they use different frequencies for their echolocation).

Learning Objective:

- Understand that within a habitat a species occupies a niche, which is determined by its adaptation to both biotic and abiotic conditions.

Specification Reference 3.4.1

Tip: You may have heard the expression "find your own niche", i.e. find the things you're good at. A species' niche is pretty similar — it's the things a species does better than any other species. H̲abitat is easier to remember — it's a species' h̲ome.

Figure 1: *The common (top) and soprano (bottom) bats are similar species but occupy different niches.*

Tip: For more on competition take a look at pages 10-11.

If two species try to occupy the same niche, they will compete with each other. One species will be more successful than the other, until only one of the species is left.

Adaptations

An adaptation is a feature that members of a species have that increases their chance of survival and reproduction. For example, giraffes have long necks to help them reach vegetation that's high up. This increases their chance of survival when food is scarce. These features can be physiological (processes inside their body), behavioural (the way an organism acts) or anatomical (structural features of their body). Organisms with better adaptations are more likely to survive, reproduce and pass on the alleles for their adaptations, so the adaptations become more common in the population. This is called natural selection.

Every species is adapted to use an ecosystem in a way that no other species can. For example, only giant anteaters can break into ant nests and reach the ants. They have claws to rip open the nest, and a long, sticky tongue which can move rapidly in and out of its mouth to pick up the ants. Organisms are adapted to both the abiotic conditions (e.g. how much water is available) and the biotic conditions (e.g. what predators there are) in their ecosystem.

Figure 2: *The webbed paw of a North American river otter is an adaptation to abiotic conditions.*

┌─ **Examples** ─────────────────────────────

Adaptations to abiotic conditions

- Otters have webbed paws (see Figure 2) — this means they can both walk on land and swim effectively. This increases their chance of survival because they can live and hunt both on land and in water.

- Whales have a thick layer of blubber (fat) — this helps to keep them warm in the coldest seas. This increases their chance of survival because they can live in places where food is plentiful.

- Brown bears hibernate — they lower their metabolism (all the chemical reactions taking place in their body) over winter. This increases their chance of survival because they can conserve energy during the coldest months.

Adaptations to biotic conditions

- Chimpanzees use twigs to fish termites out of termite mounds (see Figure 3). This increases their chance of survival because it gives them access to another source of food.

- Scorpions dance before mating — this makes sure they attract a mate of the same species. This increases their chance of reproduction by making successful mating more likely.

- Some bacteria produce antibiotics — these kill other species of bacteria in the same area. This increases their chance of survival because there's less competition for resources.

Figure 3: *The use of twigs by chimpanzees to get termites out of termite holes is an adaptation to biotic conditions.*

Practice Questions — Application

Q1   The kangaroo rat is found in deserts. Its kidneys produce extremely concentrated urine.

   a)   Is the production of concentrated urine an adaptation to biotic or abiotic conditions?

   b)   Suggest how this adaptation helps the kangaroo rat to survive.

Q2 The length of probosci was studied in bees in a mountain habitat in Colorado. The bees were found to be dominated by three species: one with a long proboscis, one with a medium-sized proboscis and one with a short proboscis. The bees use their probosci to get nectar from the corolla of flowers. One such flower is shown below.

Tip: Probosci is the plural of proboscis — a long, straw-like sucking mouth part.

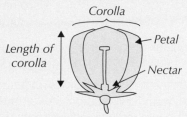

Tip: All the petals of a flower form a corolla.

Flowers with a variety of corolla lengths were observed on the mountain.

a) Give one adaptation of the bees to a biotic condition in their habitat.

b) Suggest what would happen if another species of bee with a long proboscis was introduced to the mountain habitat.

Q3 An investigation looked at the length of beaks in two closely related species of bird living in the same habitat. The birds eat seeds of similar plant species. The results are shown below.

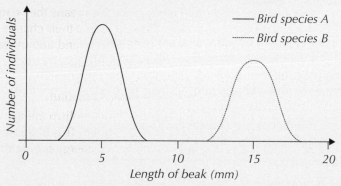

a) Describe the data shown by the graph.

b) Suggest why the two bird species are able to share the same habitat.

Practice Questions — Fact Recall

Q1 What is an ecosystem?

Q2 What is a habitat?

Q3 What is a niche?

Q4 Give two examples of:

a) the biotic interactions of a species within its niche,

b) the abiotic interactions of a species within its niche.

Q5 What is an adaptation?

Q6 a) Describe the process in which adaptations become more common in a population.

b) What is the name given to this process?

Learning Objectives:

- Know that a population is all the organisms of one species in a habitat.
- Know that populations of different species form a community.
- Understand that population size may vary as a result of the effect of abiotic factors.
- Understand that population size may vary as a result of interactions between organisms, including:
  - interspecific competition,
  - intraspecific competition,
  - predation.

Specification Reference 3.4.1

Exam Tip
Make sure you know what the terms 'population', 'community' and 'population size' mean.

Tip: Remember — abiotic factors are the non-living features of the ecosystem.

Tip: Remember — biotic factors are the living features of the ecosystem.

2. Variation in Population Size

The size of a population changes all the time for lots of different reasons. But to understand why a population grows and shrinks, first you need to know exactly what a population is...

Populations

A **population** is all the organisms of one species in a habitat. Populations of different species in a habitat make up a **community**.

> **Example**
>
> All the foxes in a wood form a population. All of the species in the wood, like the foxes, squirrels, crab apple trees and so on, form a community.

Population size is the total number of organisms of one species in a habitat. This number changes over time because of the effect of various factors.

Abiotic factors and population size

The population size of any species varies because of abiotic factors, e.g. the amount of light, water or space available, the temperature of their surroundings or the chemical composition of their surroundings. When abiotic conditions are ideal for a species, organisms can grow fast and reproduce successfully.

> **Example**
>
> When the temperature of a mammal's surroundings is the ideal temperature for metabolic reactions to take place, they don't have to use up as much energy maintaining their body temperature. This means more energy can be used for growth and reproduction, so their population size will increase.

When abiotic conditions aren't ideal for a species, organisms can't grow as fast or reproduce as successfully.

> **Example**
>
> When the temperature of a mammal's surroundings is significantly lower or higher than their optimum body temperature, they have to use a lot of energy to maintain the right body temperature. This means less energy will be available for growth and reproduction, so their population size will decrease.

Biotic factors and population size

Population size can also vary because of biotic factors. These factors include interspecific competition, intraspecific competition and predation.

1. Interspecific competition

Interspecific competition is when organisms of different species compete with each other for the same resources. This can mean that the resources available to both populations are reduced, e.g. if they share the same source of food, there will be less available to both of them. This means both populations will be limited by a lower amount of food. They'll have less energy for growth and reproduction, so the population sizes will be lower for both species. If two species are competing but one is better adapted to its surroundings than the other, the less well adapted species is likely to be out-competed — it won't be able to exist alongside the better adapted species.

Example

Grey squirrels were introduced to the UK. They now compete with the native red squirrels for the same food sources and habitats. As they share the same source of food, there is less available to both of them. So in areas where both red and grey squirrels live, both populations are smaller than they would be if there was only one species there.

Since the introduction of the grey squirrel to the UK, the native red squirrel has disappeared from large areas. The grey squirrel has a better chance of survival because it's larger and can store more fat over winter. It can also eat a wider range of food than the red squirrel.

Figure 1: Interspecific competition between red (top) and grey (bottom) squirrels has caused a decline in the population of red squirrels in the UK.

2. Intraspecific competition

Intraspecific competition is when organisms of the same species compete with each other for the same resources. It can cause a cyclical change in population size, where the population grows, shrinks, grows again and so on (see Figure 2). This is because the population of a species increases when resources are plentiful. As the population increases, there'll be more organisms competing for the same amount of space and food. Eventually, resources such as food and space become limiting — there isn't enough for all the organisms. The population then begins to decline. A smaller population then means that there's less competition for space and food, which is better for growth and reproduction — so the population starts to grow again. This cyclical pattern then continues...

Example

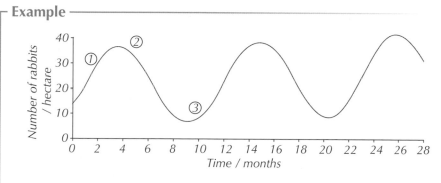

Figure 2: Intraspecific competition in a rabbit population.

1. There were lots of resources available so the population of rabbits grew.
2. The population grew so large that the resources became limiting. As there weren't enough resources, the rabbit population fell.
3. A smaller population of rabbits meant there was less competition, so the population of rabbits began to grow again.

Tip: Don't get inter- and intra-specific competition mixed up. If you're struggling, just remember — int**er** means diff**er**ent species, whereas intr**a** means the s**a**me species.

3. Predation

Predation is where an organism (the predator) kills and eats another organism (the prey), e.g. lions kill and eat (predate on) buffalo. The population sizes of predators and prey are interlinked — as the population of one changes, it causes the other population to change (see Figure 4 on the next page).

As the prey population increases, there's more food for predators, so the predator population grows. As the predator population increases, more prey is eaten so the prey population then begins to fall. This means there's less food for the predators, so their population decreases, and so on.

Example

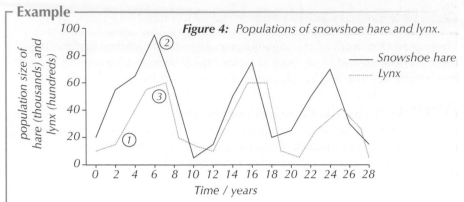

Figure 4: *Populations of snowshoe hare and lynx.*

1. In the graph above, the lynx population grew after the snowshoe hare population increased. This is because there was more food available for the lynx.

2. Greater numbers of lynx ate lots of snowshoe hares, so the population of hares fell.

3. Reduced snowshoe hare numbers meant there was less food for the lynx, so the population of lynx fell.

Predator-prey relationships are usually more complicated than this though because there are other factors involved, like availability of food for the prey. E.g. it's thought that the population of snowshoe hare initially begins to decline because there's too many of them for the amount of food available. This is then accelerated by predation from the lynx.

Practice Questions — Application

Tip: In the exam, if you're given a graph with two y-axes like the one on the right, make sure you read the key carefully so you know which line relates to which axis.

A team investigated changes in the size of a population of owls and a population of mice over twenty years. They also monitored changes in temperature. Their results are shown on the graph below.

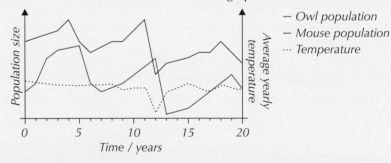

— Owl population
— Mouse population
··· Temperature

Q1   Give one factor affecting the population of owls which is biotic.

Tip: With 'suggest' questions, like in Q2 on the right, you probably won't have learned the exact answer — you need to use the information you're given and apply your own knowledge to answer the question.

Q2   Describe how the fall in temperature between years 11 and 12 affected the mouse population size, and suggest a reason for the change in population size.

Q3   Explain how variation in the mouse population size over the twenty year period could have caused changes in the owl population size.

Practice Questions — Fact Recall

Q1   What is: a) a population?   b) a community?

Q2   Define interspecific competition and intraspecific competition.

3. Investigating Populations

There are lots of ways of investigating populations. Whichever method you use, you need to make sure your samples are random, you've carried out a risk assessment and you've thought about the ethics involved.

Abundance and distribution

Investigating populations of organisms involves looking at the abundance and distribution of species in a particular area.

Abundance

Abundance is the number of individuals of one species in a particular area. The abundance of mobile organisms and plants can be estimated by simply counting the number of individuals in samples taken. There are other measures of abundance that can be used too:

▪ Frequency — the number of samples a species is recorded in, e.g. 70% of samples.

▪ Percentage cover (for plants only) — how much of the area you're investigating is covered by a species (see p.14).

Distribution

Distribution is where a particular species is within the area you're investigating.

Sampling

Most of the time it would be too time-consuming to measure the number of individuals and the distribution of every species in the entire area you're investigating, so instead you take samples:

1. Choose an area to sample — a small area within the area being investigated.

2. Samples should be random to avoid bias, e.g. by randomly selecting coordinates from a grid (see below).

3. Use an appropriate technique to take a sample of the population (see pages 14-16).

4. Repeat the process, taking as many samples as possible in the time you have available. This gives a more reliable estimate for the whole area.

5. The number of individuals for the whole area can then be estimated by taking an average of the data collected in each sample and multiplying it by the size of the whole area. The percentage cover for the whole area can be estimated by taking the average of all the samples.

Random number generators

If you were investigating populations in a field, you could pick random sample sites by dividing the field into a grid and using a random number generator and a random letter generator to select coordinates. This will give you coordinates at random, e.g. B7, E5, etc (see Figure 1). Then you just take your samples from these coordinates.

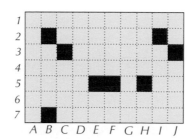

Figure 1: *Randomly selected squares in a field.*

Learning Objectives:

▪ Know how to use percentage cover and frequency as measures of abundance.

▪ Know how to carry out experiments and investigations into populations.

▪ Understand and have a critical appreciation of some of the ways in which the numbers and distribution of organisms may be investigated.

▪ Know how to take random samples with quadrats and count along transects to obtain quantitative data.

▪ Know how to use mark-release-recapture methods to estimate population sizes of mobile species.

▪ Know how to carry out appropriate risk management for practical work.

▪ Understand the ethical issues related to organisms and their environment which are raised when carrying out fieldwork.

Specification Reference 3.4.1

Exam Tip
Make sure you know what the terms 'abundance' and 'distribution' mean.

Tip: Drawing numbers out of a hat is another way of generating random numbers.

Running means

It's important that you take enough samples to give a reliable estimate. One way of doing this is to take a running mean — this is where you work out the mean of all the data each time you collect a new sample. Once the mean no longer changes by a large amount, you should have data that gives a reliable estimate for the whole area.

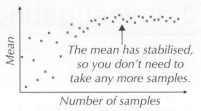

The mean has stabilised, so you don't need to take any more samples.

Number of samples

Mean

Figure 2: *A running mean, plotted on a graph.*

Methods for investigating populations

There are lots of different methods for studying populations of organisms, but you need to choose the most suitable one to use — the method will depend on the type of organism and its habitat. Quadrats and transects are used for studying plants, whereas pitfall traps, pooters and beating trays are used for studying insects. However, all of these methods have their own little drawbacks...

Quadrats

A quadrat is a square frame divided into a grid of 100 smaller squares by strings attached across the frame — see Figure 3.

Figure 3: *A 0.25 m² quadrat.*

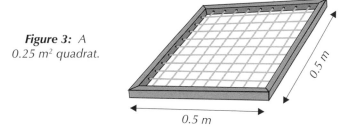

0.5 m

0.5 m

Quadrats are placed on the ground at different points within the area you're investigating. The species frequency or the number of individuals of each species is recorded in each quadrat.

The percentage cover of a species can also be measured by counting how much of the quadrat is covered by the species — you count a square if it's more than half-covered (see Figure 4). Percentage cover is a quick way to investigate populations and you don't have to count all the individual plants.

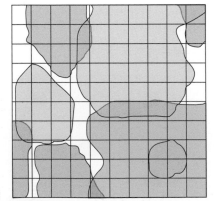

Figure 4: *Measuring percentage cover using a quadrat.*

Species A: 42 squares = 42%

Species B: 12 squares = 12%

Species C: 47 squares = 47%

Figure 5: *Quadrats can be used to measure the abundance of plant species in a field.*

Quadrats are useful for quickly investigating areas with plant species that fit within a small quadrat — areas with larger plants and trees need very large quadrats.

Transects

You can use lines called transects to help find out how plants are distributed across an area, e.g. how species change from a hedge towards the middle of a field. There are three types:

1. **Line transects** — a tape measure is placed along the transect and the species that touch the tape measure are recorded.

2. **Belt transects** — quadrats are placed next to each other along the transect to work out species frequency and percentage cover along the transect.

3. **Interrupted transects** — instead of investigating the whole transect of either a line or a belt, you can take measurements at intervals.

Tip: Line transects are quick to carry out but a belt transect will give more data (as it covers a wider area). An interrupted belt transect is a good compromise between the two — it's quicker than a belt transect and gives more information than a line transect.

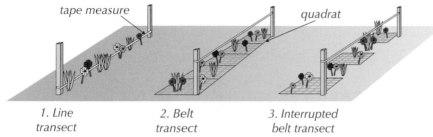

tape measure *quadrat*

1. Line transect *2. Belt transect* *3. Interrupted belt transect*

Figure 6: *Diagram to show the different types of transect.*

Pitfall traps

Pitfall traps are steep-sided containers that are sunk in a hole in the ground. The top is partially open so insects fall into the container and can't get out again (see Figure 7). Trapped insects are protected from rain and some predators by a raised lid.

The sample can be affected by predators small enough to fall into the pitfall trap though — they may eat other insects, affecting the results.

raised lid

walking insects fall in and are trapped

flowerpot or similar container

stone to raise lid

Figure 7: *Diagram to show how an insect gets caught in a pitfall trap.*

Figure 8: *A pitfall trap with a cover to protect insects from rain and predators.*

Pooters

Pooters are jars that have rubber bungs sealing the top, and two tubes stuck through the bung (see Figure 9). The shorter tube has mesh over the end that's in the jar whereas the longer tube is open at both ends. When you inhale through the shorter tube, air is drawn through the longer tube. If you place the end of the longer tube over an insect it'll be sucked into the jar.

The problem with pooters is that it can take a long time (or lots of people) to get a large sample. Also, some species may be missed if the sample isn't large enough.

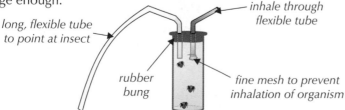

inhale through flexible tube

long, flexible tube to point at insect

rubber bung

fine mesh to prevent inhalation of organism

Figure 9: *Diagram to show insects being caught using a pooter.*

Figure 10: *A pooter being used to collect insects from a tree.*

Figure 11: *A scientist using a beating sheet fastened between trees.*

Tip: Beating trays are usually white so that you can see the insects.

Figure 13: *A turtle being marked with a spot of yellow paint before being released.*

Exam Tip
Make sure you know the equation for estimating the total population size — don't rely on being given it in the exam.

Tip: The answer is rounded down to 38... so that you don't end up with a third of a woodlouse.

Beating trays

A beating tray is a tray or sheet held under a plant or tree. The plant or tree is shaken and a sample of insects falls onto the beating tray (see Figure 12). Beating trays can be useful because you can use them to take large samples, giving good estimates of the abundance of each species.

However, the sample may not be random as most of it will be made up of insects that fall easily when the vegetation is shaken.

Figure 12: *Diagram to show insects caught on a beating tray.*

Mark-release-recapture

Mark-release-recapture is a method used to measure the abundance of more mobile species. Here's how it's done:

1. Capture a sample of a species using an appropriate technique, e.g. you could use pitfall traps to capture mobile ground insects (see page 15), and count them.

2. Mark them in a harmless way, e.g. by putting a spot of paint on them (see Figure 13), or by removing a tuft of fur.

3. Release them back into their habitat.

4. Wait a week, then take a second sample from the same population.

5. Count how many of the second sample are marked.

6. You can then use this equation to estimate the total population size:

$$\text{Total population size} = \frac{\text{Number caught in 1st sample} \times \text{Number caught in 2nd sample}}{\text{Number marked in 2nd sample}}$$

Example

A pitfall trap was used to capture a sample of woodlice in a garden. The first sample contained 15 woodlice. The woodlice were marked and then released. A week later, a second sample of woodlice was collected from the same pitfall trap. There were 23 woodlice in the second sample, and 9 of them were marked.

$$\text{Total population size} = \frac{\text{Number caught in 1st sample} \times \text{Number caught in 2nd sample}}{\text{Number marked in 2nd sample}}$$

$$= \frac{15 \times 23}{9} = 38.3$$

So the mark-release-recapture method gives an estimated total population size of 38 woodlice.

The accuracy of the mark-release-recapture method depends on a few assumptions:

- The marked sample has had enough time and opportunity to mix back in with the population.
- The marking hasn't affected the individuals' chances of survival, and is still visible.
- Changes in population size due to births, deaths and migration are small during the period of the study.

Tip: 'Accuracy' means how free of errors something is — see page 3 for more.

Practice Questions — Application

Q1 A student is investigating the abundance of daisies in a field.

a) She decides to use a quadrat to measure the percentage cover of daisies in the field. Describe how she could do this.

b) Describe how the student could take random samples using a quadrat.

Q2 A team of scientists is investigating the abundance of ladybirds in bushes along a footpath. They use beating trays to take samples.

a) Describe how a beating tray could be used to collect a sample of ladybirds from one of the bushes.

b) The team found it difficult to count the ladybirds on the beating trays. Suggest why.

c) Describe another suitable piece of equipment that the team could use to collect a sample of ladybirds.

Tip: Remember, the method you use to investigate the organism depends on the organism itself.

Q3 The mark-release-recapture method was used to estimate the size of a black beetle population in two different locations. On day one, the beetles were marked using white paint and then released. A second sample was captured the following day. The results are shown in the table below.

Location	Size of first sample	Size of second sample	Number of marked beetles in second sample
A	19	14	3
B	17	21	6

a) Use the data in the table to estimate the total population size of beetles at:

i)   location A,

ii) location B.

b) Are the estimates for these locations accurate? Explain your answer.

Risk assessments

When you're carrying out fieldwork to investigate populations you expose yourself to risks — things that could potentially cause you harm. You need to think about what risks you'll be exposed to during fieldwork, so you can plan ways to reduce the chance of them happening — this is called a risk assessment. Risk assessments are always carried out to ensure that fieldwork's done in the safest way possible. Here are some examples of the fieldwork risks when investigating populations and the ways to reduce the risks:

Figure 14: You can minimise the risk of slipping on boggy ground, e.g. by wearing appropriate footwear.

Tip: The table on the right shows common risks and ways to reduce them. You could get asked about other risks in your exam that aren't listed here — if so, just use your common sense.

Falls and slips	Wear suitable footwear for the terrain, e.g. wellies on wet or boggy ground, and take care on rough terrain. Make sure the study area isn't near any cliffs or on steep ground.
Bad weather	Check the weather forecast beforehand and take precautions, e.g. wear warm or waterproof clothing on cold or wet days. If the weather is too bad, do the fieldwork another day.
Stings and bites	Wear insect repellent or, if you have an allergy, take medication with you.

Ethical issues

All fieldwork affects the environment where it's carried out, e.g. lots of people walking around may cause soil erosion. Some people don't think it's right to damage the environment when doing fieldwork, so investigations should be planned to have the smallest impact possible, for example, people should restrict where they walk to the area being studied.

Some fieldwork affects the organisms being studied, e.g. capturing an organism for study may cause it stress. Some people don't think it's right to distress organisms at all when doing fieldwork, so investigations should be planned so that organisms are treated with great care, and are kept and handled as little as possible. They should also be released as soon as possible after they have been captured.

Figure 15: Birds that are caught can be marked by placing a ring around a foot — but this can raise ethical issues as capture can cause stress to some birds.

Tip: A protected species is a species which is in protected by law because it is endanger of becoming extinct.

Practice Questions —Application

Q1 An investigation is being conducted into the population size of dragonflies along the bank of a river. The bank is steep and there has been a high level of rainfall in the area.

    a) Give one risk posed by the investigation, and suggest how this risk can be reduced.

    Previous studies have suggested that a population of water voles, which are a protected species, may live in burrows on the river bank.

    b) Explain why conducting fieldwork along the river might raise ethical issues.

Practice Questions — Fact Recall

Q1 What is meant by the terms: a) abundance,   b) distribution?

Q2 Name and describe two measures of abundance.

Q3 What is: a) a quadrat,   b) a pooter,   c) a pitfall trap?

Q4 Give the equation for estimating total population size using data collected by the mark-release-recapture method.

4. Analysing and Interpreting Distribution Data

Learning Objectives:

- Be able to analyse and interpret data relating to the distribution of organisms, and recognise correlations and causal relationships.

- Appreciate the tentative nature of conclusions that may be drawn from data relating to the distribution of organisms.

Specification Reference 3.4.1

Once you've got your data on organisms, you can analyse and interpret it...

Analysing data on organism distribution

In the exam, you could be asked to interpret data on the distribution of organisms. You need to be able to identify correlations and causal relationships — but often, identifying what has caused a change in the distribution of an organism is really tricky. For example, over the last fifty years the distribution of bumblebees in England has become much less widespread. This could be due to competition, predation, pesticides, climate change or the loss of meadows... but it isn't clear which is the most important factor. Sometimes there are so many factors affecting the distribution of an organism that you can only draw a tentative conclusion.

(HOW SCIENCE WORKS)

Tip: For more on correlations and causal relationships, see page 5.

┌ Example ─────

A group of students investigated how the distribution of plant species changed with distance from a path. They used an interrupted belt transect (see p. 15) and measured percentage cover of plant species in each quadrat. The students also carried out a survey at the same location to record how many people strayed away from the path, and how far they strayed. Here's a table and graph showing their results:

Distance from footpath / m	Percentage cover
0	0
2	12
4	18
6	32
8	41
10	64
12	76
14	88
16	93
18	96
20	100

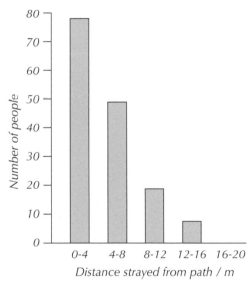

Figure 1: Table comparing the percentage cover of plants with distance from the footpath.

Figure 2: Graph showing the number of people who strayed from the footpath and the distance they strayed.

You might have to...

1. Describe the data

- The table shows low percentage cover of plants near the path, e.g. 2 m from the path it was 12%, but higher percentage cover away from the path, e.g. 20 m from the path it was 100% (88% more).

- The graph shows lots of walkers near the path, e.g. 0-4 m from the path there were 79 walkers, but fewer walkers away from the path, e.g. 16-20 m from the path there were none.

Tip: If you're given more than one set of data and asked a 'describe' question in the exam, make sure you know which data set the question is on about — it could be asking you to describe just one data set or both of them.

2. Draw conclusions

- There's a positive correlation between distance from the path and percentage cover of plants — as distance from the path increases, the percentage cover of plants increases.

- There's a negative correlation between distance from the path and the number of people that walk there — as distance from the path increases, the number of people that walk there decreases.

- There's a negative correlation between the number of walkers and the percentage cover of plants — the higher the number of people that walk over an area, the lower the percentage cover of plants.

You can't conclude that the lower percentage cover of plants near the path is caused by the higher number of people walking there. There could be other factors involved that affect the percentage cover of plants, e.g. the path may be covered by stones or gravel, so plants won't grow on or near the path regardless of how many people walk on it.

3. Suggest explanations for your conclusions:

As you move away from the path the number of people that trample the ground decreases because people tend to follow the path. As you move away from the path the percentage cover of plants increases because plants grow and survive better where they're trodden on less.

Tip: See pages 232-234 for more on interpreting data.

Tip: A kite diagram shows the distribution and abundance of organisms along a transect. The thickness of the kite shape shows the abundance — the thicker the kite shape, the more organisms there are.

Practice Questions — Application

A scientist has been investigating the effect of salt spray from a road adjacent to an inland field. Her results are shown below.

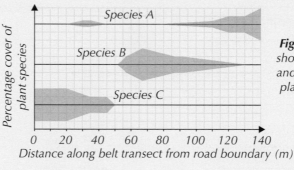

Figure 3: Kite diagram showing the distribution and abundance of three plant species in a field.

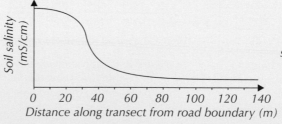

Figure 4: Graph showing the change in soil salinity in a field.

Q1 Describe the data shown in the kite diagram and the graph.

Q2 One of the plant species is normally found in coastal areas. Which species is this likely to be, A, B or C? Explain your answer.

Q3 The scientist is unable to prove that salt spray from the road is responsible for the absence of species B between 0 and 20 m from the road using the data shown above. Explain why.

5. Human Populations

Data about human populations can be presented in different ways — for example, as a growth curve or an age-population pyramid. These curves and pyramids can help scientists to analyse trends in populations and how they change over time. You need to know all about them...

Birth and death rates

Human population sizes constantly change. Whether they're growing or shrinking (and by how much) depends on the population's **birth rate** and **death rate**.

- The birth rate is the number of live births each year for every 1000 people in the population.
- The death rate is the number of people that die each year for every 1000 people in the population.

┌─ Examples ───

- A birth rate of 10/1000 would mean that in one year there were 10 live births for every 1000 people.
- A death rate of 10/1000 would mean that in one year there were 10 deaths for every 1000 people.

You can work out how fast the population's changing by calculating the **population growth rate**. Population growth rate is how much the population size increases or decreases in a year. You can work it out using the birth and death rate:

$$\text{population growth rate (per 1000 people per year)} = \text{birth rate} - \text{death rate}$$

This gives you the overall (net) number of people that the population grows or shrinks by in a year for every 1000 people.

┌─ Examples ───

Country A: The birth rate is 13/1000 and the death rate is 10/1000.

Population growth rate = birth rate – death rate

= 13/1000 – 10/1000

= 3/1000

So the population will grow by 3 people for every 1000 people each year.

The population growth rate is normally given as a percentage:

$$\frac{3}{1000} \times 100 = 0.3\%$$

Country B: The birth rate is 8.2/1000 and the death rate is 10.7/1000.

Population growth rate = birth rate – death rate

= 8.2/1000 – 10.7/1000

= -2.5/1000

So the population will fall by 2.5 people for every 1000 people each year.

Or, as a percentage: $\frac{-2.5}{1000} \times 100 = -0.25\%$

Learning Objectives:

- Be able to calculate population growth rates from data on birth rate and death rate.
- Be able to relate changes in the size and structure of human populations to different stages in demographic transition.
- Understand population size and structure, population growth rate, age-population pyramids, survival rates and life expectancy.
- Be able to interpret growth curves, survival curves and age-population pyramids.

Specification Reference 3.4.1

Tip: If you're asked to calculate a population growth rate and it comes out as a negative number, don't be surprised (although it's always a good idea to double-check any calculations for mistakes). Some countries, like Germany, have death rates that are higher than their birth rates. These countries are usually in Demographic Stage 5 — see page 22.

The Demographic Transition Model

The Demographic Transition Model (DTM) is a graph that shows changes in birth rate, death rate and total population size for a human population over a long period of time. It's divided into five stages:

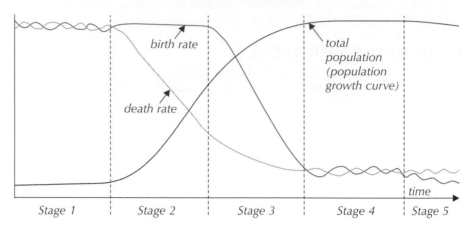

Figure 1: The Demographic Transition Model

Figure 2: India is at stage 3 of the demographic transition model.

Stage 1

The birth rate and death rate fluctuate at a high level, so the population stays low. The birth rate is high because there's no birth control or family planning and education is poor. Lots of children die young (there's high infant mortality), so parents have more children so that enough survive to work on farms, as well as look after them in later life. The death rate is high because there's poor health care, sanitation and diet, leading to disease and starvation.

Stage 2

The death rate falls while the birth rate remains high, so the population increases rapidly. The death rate falls because health care, sanitation and diet improve. The birth rate remains high because there's still little birth control or family planning.

Stage 3

The birth rate falls rapidly while the death rate falls more slowly. This causes the population to increase at a slower rate. The birth rate falls rapidly because of the increased use of birth control and family planning. Also, the economy becomes more heavily based on manufacturing rather than agriculture, so fewer children are needed to work on farms.

Stage 4

The birth rate and death rate fluctuate at a low level, so the population remains stable but high. The birth rate stays low because there's an increased demand for luxuries and material possessions, so less money is available to raise children. They're not needed to work to provide income, so parents have fewer children.

Stage 5

The birth rate begins to fall while the death rate remains stable. This means the population begins to decrease. The birth rate falls because children are expensive to raise and people often have dependent elderly relatives. The death rate remains steady despite continued health care advances as larger generations of elderly people die.

Plotting human population data

Data on human populations can be plotted in different ways to show how the size of a population changes over time, a population's survival rate and the number of people in different age groups in a population.

1. Population growth curves

Population change can be shown by a population growth curve (the DTM has one, see page 22). They're made by plotting data for population size against time — see Figure 3.

Growth curves show whether the population was increasing or decreasing by the direction of the curve (up or down). The steepness of the curve shows how fast the population was changing (the steeper the curve, the faster it was changing). You can use the curve to calculate the rate of change.

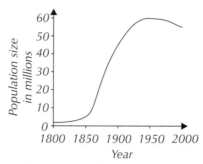

Figure 3: *Population growth curve.*

Example

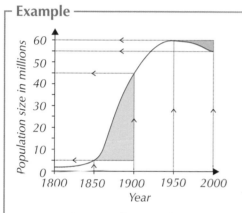

Between 1850 and 1900, the population increased from 5 to 45 million people.

45 000 000 – 5 000 000
= 40 000 000 people

$$\frac{40\ 000\ 000}{50\ \text{years}} = 800\ 000 \text{ people per year}$$

So between 1850 and 1900, the population increased at a rate of 800 000 people per year.

Between 1950 and 2000, the population decreased from 60 to 55 million people.

55 000 000 – 60 000 000 = -5 000 000 people

$$\frac{5\ 000\ 000}{50\ \text{years}} = 100\ 000 \text{ people per year}$$

So between 1950 and 2000, the population decreased at a rate of 100 000 people per year.

Tip: Make sure you're confident at reading values off a graph. If you're not that great at it, get practising — it's a skill you're definitely gonna need in your exam.

2. Survival curves

Survival curves show the percentage of all the individuals that were born in a population that are still alive at any given age — see Figure 4.

- Population 1 — few people die at a young age, lots of people survive to an old age.
- Population 2 — many people die at a young age, but some survive to an old age.
- Population 3 — most people die at a young age, very few survive to an old age.

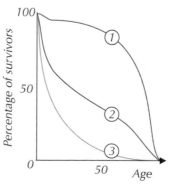

Figure 4: *Survival curves for three populations.*

Tip: In the exam, you could get asked to explain the shape of a survival curve. For example, if it shows a high death rate, you'll need to think about the factors that could cause this — like a high rate of disease, lack of food and poor medical care (see page 22).

Survival curves can be used to work out the survival rate for any given age. To do this, you read off the percentage of people who are alive at a given age.

Example

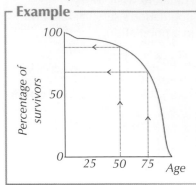

In this survival curve:

- Around 90% of people survive to the age of 50.

- Around 70% of people survive to the age of 75.

Figure 5: *Survival curve for a single population.*

Life expectancy is the age that a person born into a population is expected to live to — it's worked out by calculating the average age that people die. You can work it out using a survival curve by looking at the age at which 50% of the population are still alive.

Exam Tip
You might think it's a bit odd getting a mathsy type question in a biology exam, but often the maths itself isn't too tricky — its working out what the question wants that takes a bit of work. If you get stumped, just read the question through carefully and think about how you can use the information you're given.

Example

Figure 6 shows survival curves for two countries, A and B.

To work out the life expectancy for each country, all you need to do is read off the graph the age at which 50% of the population are still alive.

So,

- Country A has a life expectancy of 22.5 years.

- Country B has a life expectancy of 70 years — 47.5 years greater than Country A.

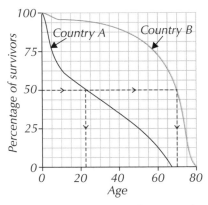

Figure 6: *Survival curve for a population whose maximum age is 80 years.*

3. Age-population pyramids

Population structure can be shown using age-population pyramids. These show how many males and females there are in different age groups within a population.

Examples

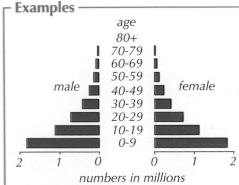

Figure 7 shows a population that has a lot of young people with very few surviving to old age — there's a low life expectancy.

Figure 7: *Age-population pyramid showing a country in DTM stage 1.*

Figure 8 shows a population that has a lot of young people with more surviving to old age — life expectancy is higher.

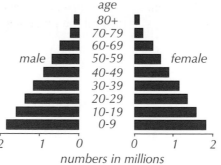

Figure 8: *Age-population pyramid showing a country in DTM stage 2.*

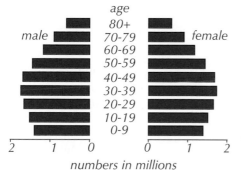

Figure 10 shows a population that has fewer young people with a lot of older people — life expectancy is high.

Figure 10: *Age-population pyramid showing a country in DTM stage 5.*

Figure 9: *Nepal is at DTM stage 2 and has a large number of young people.*

Figure 11: *Countries in DTM stage 5, like Japan, have a large number of older people.*

Practice Questions — Application

Q1 The diagrams below show the age structures of the population of Country Z in 1980 and in 2010.

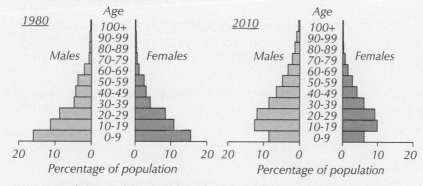

a) Describe two demographic changes which have taken place in Country Z between 1980 and 2010. For each change, suggest a reason why it might have happened.

b) The table below shows the birth and death rates for Country Z.

Year	Birth Rate (per 1000 people)	Death Rate (per 1000 people)
1980	35.4	36.2
2010	21.3	14.7

Calculate the rate of population growth as a percentage in Country Z in: i) 1980,   ii) 2010.

c) In 1980 Country Z was believed to be in the first stage of the DTM.

   i) What is the DTM?

   ii) In what stage of the DTM is Country Z most likely to be in 2010? Explain your answer.

Q2 The graph on the right shows a population growth curve for Country X.

a) Describe the trend shown by the graph.

b) Calculate the population growth rate between 1850 and 1875.

c) Between which years was the death rate greater than the birth rate? Explain your answer.

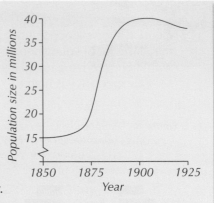

Section Summary

Make sure you know:

- That biotic conditions are all the living features of an ecosystem and that abiotic features are all the non-living features of an ecosystem.
- That a habitat is where a species lives and that a niche is the role of a species within its habitat, which is determined by it's biotic and abiotic interactions.
- That species have adaptations to biotic and abiotic conditions which increase their chance of survival and reproduction.
- That a population is all the organisms of one species within a habitat, and that all the populations of different species in a habitat form a community.
- That the size of a population varies because of the effect of abiotic factors, such as the temperature of the surroundings.
- That the size of a population varies because of the effect of biotic factors, which include interspecific competition (competition between two different species), intraspecific competition (competition between members of the same species) and predation (which is where one organism kills and eats another).
- That species abundance can be measured using frequency (the number of samples a species is recorded in) and percentage cover (how much of an area is covered by the species).
- The importance of taking samples at random to avoid bias.
- How to use quadrats, transects, pitfall traps, pooters and beating trays when conducting investigations on populations.
- How to calculate the size of a mobile population using the mark-release-recapture method.
- How to carry out an appropriate risk assessment for your investigation and consider any ethical issues raised by it.
- How to analyse data on the distribution of organisms.
- That the birth rate is the number of live births each year for every 1000 people in the population and the death rate is the number of people that die each year for every 1000 people.
- How to calculate a population growth rate (by subtracting the death rate from the birth rate), and how to convert the population growth rate into a percentage.
- The shape of the Demographic Transition Model (DTM) and what it shows.
- How the birth rate, death rate and population size change over each of the five stages of the DTM.
- That population data plotted on a population growth curve shows the changes in population size.
- That survival curves show the percentage of all individuals that were born in a population who are still alive at any given age.
- That age-population pyramids show the age structure and gender of a population.

1   An investigation has been conducted on two species of grasshopper, species
A and species B, normally found in grassy fields. Both species of grasshopper
have long hind legs with strong muscles which allow them to jump long distances.
Their colour provides camouflage in the grass. Their exoskeletons have thin waxy
coats to prevent dehydration under hot, dry conditions and their eggs can delay
development during winter to ensure they hatch when temperatures are warmer.

1 (a)   Give two adaptations of the grasshoppers to biotic conditions and explain how
these features increase their chances of survival and reproduction.

(2 marks)

1 (b)   The diets of the two species of grasshopper were studied.
The results are shown below.

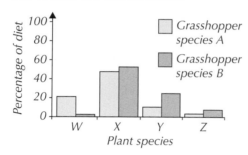

Explain what the information
provided in the graph suggests
about grasshopper species A and B.

(3 marks)

1 (c)   The graph below shows changes in population size of grasshopper species A
and B.

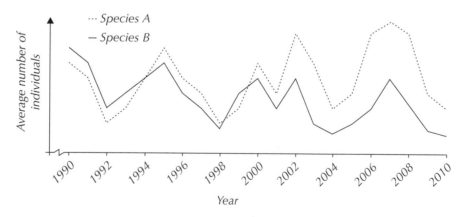

Describe and explain the trend shown by the graph, with reference to the type
of competition it shows.

(3 marks)

1 (d)   The team collected their data on the grasshoppers by catching samples of them
in cages over the vegetation.

Give one advantage and one disadvantage of the method used by the team.

(2 marks)

2 A team of scientists are investigating the distribution of marsh marigolds across a field that is directly next to a stream.

2 (a) (i) Suggest and describe a method the scientists could use to investigate the distribution of marsh marigolds.

(2 marks)

2 (a) (ii) The team decide they want to record the percentage cover of marsh marigolds. Describe how they could measure the percentage cover and give two advantages of measuring species abundance this way.

(3 marks)

2 (b) Abiotic factors were investigated at the same places as the data on marsh marigolds was recorded. Explain what is meant by the term 'abiotic conditions'.

(1 mark)

The results of the investigation are recorded in the graphs below.

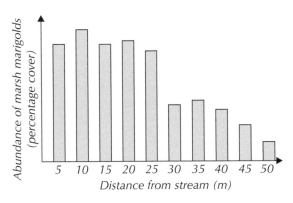
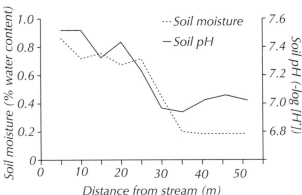

2 (c) The team conclude that marsh marigolds grow better in waterlogged ground.

Do you agree with their conclusion? Use data from the two graphs to explain your answer.

(5 marks)

2 (d) The stream is prone to flooding and the land around it is often boggy.

Describe two risks that the scientists should be aware of and suggest the appropriate course of action they should take to reduce their risk.

(2 marks)

3 A student is investigating the population of snails in his garden. He decides to use the mark-release-recapture method.

3 (a) Describe how the student could use the mark-release-recapture method to estimate the population size of snails in his garden.

(5 marks)

3 (b) The student caught 10 snails in the first sample and 15 snails in the second sample. Eight of the snails in the second sample were marked.

Calculate the size of the population of snails.

(1 mark)

1. Storing and Releasing Energy

Energy is required for all life processes. This means that being able to store and release energy is really important for plants and animals.

Why is energy important?

Plant and animal cells need energy for biological processes to occur.

Examples

- Plants need energy for things like photosynthesis, active transport (e.g. to take in minerals via their roots), DNA replication, cell division and protein synthesis.
- Animals need energy for things like muscle contraction, maintenance of body temperature, active transport, DNA replication, cell division and protein synthesis.

Photosynthesis and energy

Photosynthesis is the process where energy from light is used to make glucose from water (H_2O) and carbon dioxide (CO_2). (The light energy is converted to chemical energy in the form of glucose — $C_6H_{12}O_6$.) The overall equation is:

$$6CO_2 + 6H_2O + \text{Energy} \longrightarrow C_6H_{12}O_6 + 6O_2$$

Energy is stored in the glucose until the plants release it by respiration. Animals obtain glucose by eating plants (or other animals), then respire the glucose to release energy.

Photosynthesis is an example of a **metabolic pathway** — the process occurs in a series of small reactions controlled by enzymes.

Respiration and energy

Plant and animal cells release energy from glucose — this process is called respiration. This energy is used to power all the biological processes in a cell. There are two types of respiration:

- **Aerobic respiration** — respiration using oxygen.
- **Anaerobic respiration** — respiration without oxygen.

Aerobic respiration produces carbon dioxide and water, and releases energy. The overall equation is:

$$C_6H_{12}O_6 + 6O_2 \longrightarrow 6CO_2 + 6H_2O + \text{Energy}$$

Respiration is another example of a metabolic pathway.

ATP

ATP (adenosine triphosphate) is the immediate source of energy in a cell. A cell can't get its energy directly from glucose. So, in respiration, the energy released from glucose is used to make ATP. ATP is made from the nucleotide base adenine, combined with a ribose sugar and three phosphate groups, (see Figure 1). It carries energy around the cell to where it's needed.

Learning Objectives:

- Understand that ATP provides the immediate source of energy for biological processes.
- Know that ATP is synthesised from ADP and phosphate.

Specification Reference 3.4.2

Tip: Without energy, the biological processes described above would stop and the plant or animal would die.

Tip: Energy is never created or destroyed. It's always converted from one form to another. For example, in photosynthesis light energy is converted to chemical energy (glucose). This energy is then used to fuel biological processes.

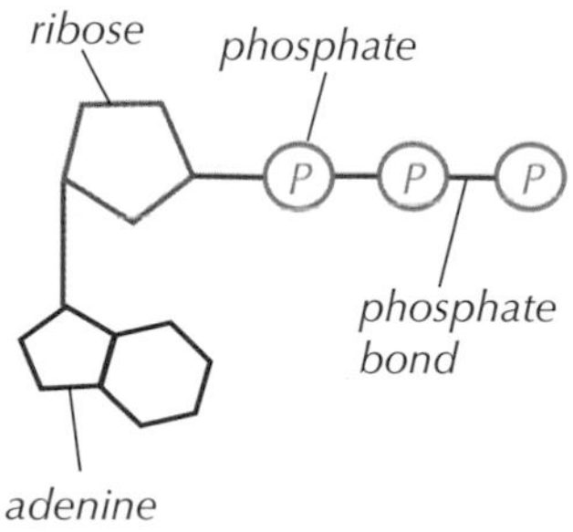

Figure 1: *The structure of adenosine triphosphate (ATP). It consists of adenine, ribose and three phosphate groups.*

Tip: Inorganic phosphate (P_i) is just the fancy name for a single phosphate.

Tip: Adenosine diphosphate has two phosphates. Adenosine triphosphate has three phosphates.

Tip: In a cell there's a constant cycle between ADP and P_i, and ATP. This allows energy to be stored and released as it's needed.

Tip: It's important to remember that ATP isn't energy — it's a store of energy. Energy is used to make ATP, then it's released when ATP is hydrolysed to ADP and P_i.

ATP is synthesised from ADP (adenosine diphosphate) and inorganic phosphate (P_i) using energy from an energy-releasing reaction, e.g. the breakdown of glucose in respiration. The energy is stored as chemical energy in the phosphate bond (see Figure 2). The enzyme **ATP synthase** catalyses this reaction.

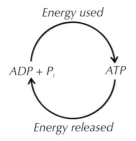

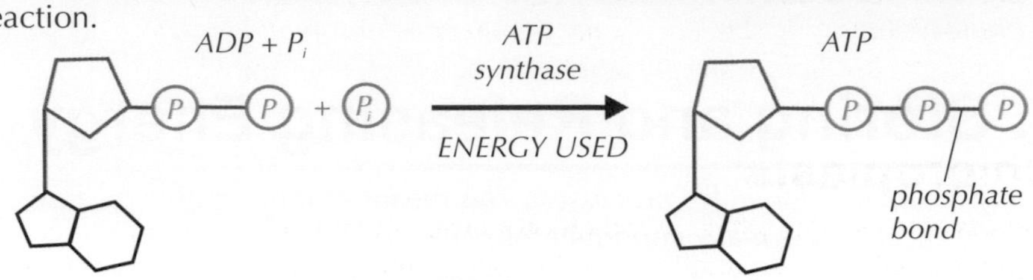

Figure 2: *The synthesis of ATP.*

This process is known as **phosphorylation** — adding phosphate to a molecule. ADP is phosphorylated to ATP.

ATP then diffuses to the part of the cell that needs energy. Here, it's broken down back into ADP and inorganic phosphate (P_i). Chemical energy is released from the phosphate bond and used by the cell. **ATPase** catalyses this reaction.

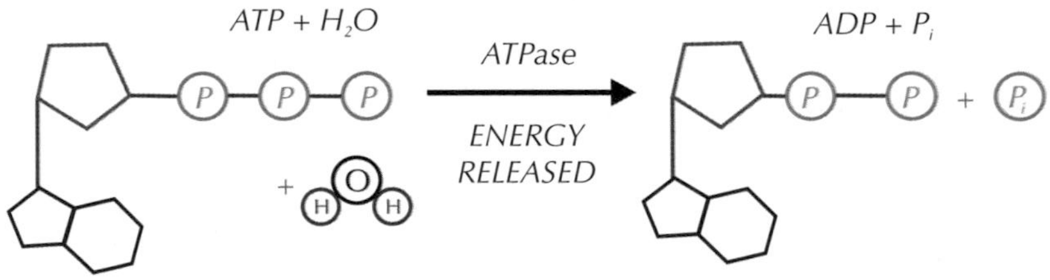

Figure 3: *The breakdown of ATP.*

This process is known as **hydrolysis**. It's the splitting (lysis) of a molecule using water (hydro).

ATP's properties

ATP has specific properties that make it a good energy source.

- ATP stores or releases only a small, manageable amount of energy at a time, so no energy is wasted.
- It's a small, soluble molecule so it can be easily transported around the cell.
- It's easily broken down, so energy can be easily released.
- It can transfer energy to another molecule by transferring one of its phosphate groups.
- ATP can't pass out of the cell, so the cell always has an immediate supply of energy.

Practice Questions — Fact Recall

Q1 Name three biological processes in plants that need energy.

Q2 Describe the structure of a molecule of ATP.

Q3 a) What is ATP broken down into by ATPase?

b) By what process is ATP broken down?

Q4 Give three properties of ATP and explain how they make it a good energy source.

2. Photosynthesis and the Light-dependent Reaction

In photosynthesis, light energy is used to make glucose. It involves a series of reactions, but before we get stuck into it you need to know a bit of background information...

Chloroplasts

Photosynthesis takes place in the chloroplasts of plant cells. Chloroplasts are small, flattened organelles found in plant cells (see Figure 1). They have a double membrane called the chloroplast envelope. **Thylakoids** (fluid-filled sacs) are stacked up in the chloroplast into structures called **grana** (singular = granum). The grana are linked together by bits of thylakoid membrane called **lamellae** (singular = lamella).

Chloroplasts contain **photosynthetic pigments** (e.g. chlorophyll a, chlorophyll b and carotene). These are coloured substances that absorb the light energy needed for photosynthesis. The pigments are found in the thylakoid membranes — they're attached to proteins. The protein and pigment is called a **photosystem**. There are two photosystems used by plants to capture light energy. Photosystem I (or PSI) absorbs light best at a wavelength of 700 nm and photosystem II (PSII) absorbs light best at 680 nm.

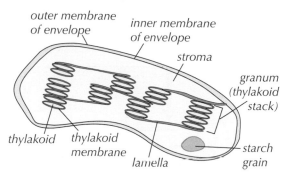

Figure 1: *The structure of a chloroplast.*

Contained within the inner membrane of the chloroplast and surrounding the thylakoids is a gel-like substance called the **stroma** — see Figure 1. It contains enzymes, sugars and organic acids. Carbohydrates produced by photosynthesis and not used straight away are stored as starch grains in the stroma.

Redox reactions

Redox reactions are reactions that involve **oxidation** and **reduction**. They occur in photosynthesis (and in respiration) so it's really important that you get your head round them:

- If something is reduced it has gained electrons (e⁻), and may have gained hydrogen or lost oxygen.
- If something is oxidised it has lost electrons, and may have lost hydrogen or gained oxygen.
- Oxidation of one molecule always involves reduction of another molecule.

Coenzymes

A coenzyme is a molecule that aids the function of an enzyme. They work by transferring a chemical group from one molecule to another. A coenzyme used in photosynthesis is **NADP**. NADP transfers hydrogen from one molecule to another — this means it can reduce (give hydrogen to) or oxidise (take hydrogen from) a molecule.

Learning Objectives:

- Know that photosynthesis in a typical C3 plant includes the light-dependent and light-independent reactions.

- Understand the light-dependent reaction including that:

  - light energy excites electrons in chlorophyll and that energy from these excited electrons generates ATP and reduced NADP,

  - the production of ATP involves electron transfer associated with the electron transfer chain in chloroplast membranes,

  - the photolysis of water produces protons, electrons and oxygen.

Specification Reference 3.4.3

Tip: Don't worry about the 'C3 plant' mentioned in the learning objectives — it's just a type of plant, you don't need to know exactly what this means.

Tip: One way to remember electron and hydrogen movement is OILRIG. **O**xidation **I**s **L**oss, **R**eduction **I**s **G**ain.

Tip: When hydrogen is transferred between molecules, electrons are transferred too.

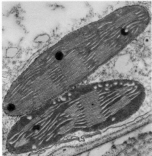

Figure 2: A cross-sectional image of two chloroplasts.

Tip: Reduced NADP is also written as NADPH — it's NADP that's gained a hydrogen. Remember OILRIG (see previous page) — reduction is gain.

Tip: See pages 36-37 for loads more information on the Calvin cycle.

Tip: The light-independent reaction can take place in the dark. However, it needs the products of the light-dependent reaction, (ATP and reduced NADP) so in reality it only continues for a little while after it gets dark.

The stages of photosynthesis

There are actually two stages that make up photosynthesis — the light-dependent reaction and the light-independent reaction. The next few pages are all about the light-dependent reaction, but before we get into all that you need to know how the two stages link together.

1. The light-dependent reaction

As the name suggests, this reaction needs light energy — see Figure 3. It takes place in the thylakoid membranes of the chloroplasts. Here, light energy is absorbed by photosynthetic pigments in the photosystems and converted to chemical energy. The light energy is used to add a phosphate group to ADP to form ATP, and to reduce NADP to form reduced NADP. ATP transfers energy and reduced NADP transfers hydrogen to the light-independent reaction. During the process water (H_2O) is oxidised to oxygen (O_2).

2. The light-independent reaction (the Calvin cycle)

As the name suggests, this reaction doesn't use light energy directly. (But it does rely on the products of the light-dependent reaction.) It takes place in the stroma of the chloroplast — see Figure 3. Here, the ATP and reduced NADP from the light-dependent reaction supply the energy and hydrogen to make glucose from CO_2.

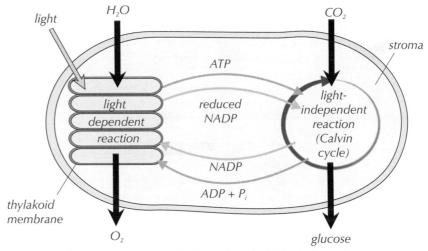

Figure 3: How the light-dependent and light-independent reactions link together in a chloroplast.

The light-dependent reaction

In the light-dependent reaction, the light energy absorbed by the photosystems is used for three things:

1. Making ATP from ADP and inorganic phosphate. This is called **photophosphorylation** — it's the process of adding phosphate to a molecule using light.
2. Making reduced NADP from NADP.
3. Splitting water into protons (H⁺ ions), electrons and oxygen. This is called **photolysis** — it's the splitting (lysis) of a molecule using light (photo) energy.

The light-dependent reaction actually includes two types of photophosphorylation — non-cyclic and cyclic. Each of these processes has different products and is explained on the next couple of pages.

Photosynthesis Map

The light-dependent reaction

You are here

The light-independent reaction

Non-cyclic photophosphorylation

Non-cyclic photophosphorylation produces ATP, reduced NADP and oxygen (O_2). To understand the process you need to know that the photosystems (in the thylakoid membranes) are linked by **electron carriers**. Electron carriers are proteins that transfer electrons. The photosystems and electron carriers form an **electron transport chain** — a chain of proteins through which excited electrons flow. There are several processes going on all at once in non-cyclic photophosphorylation — they're shown in the diagrams below.

1. Light energy excites electrons in chlorophyll

Light energy is absorbed by PSII. The light energy excites electrons in chlorophyll. The electrons move to a higher energy level (i.e. they have more energy — see Figure 4). These high-energy electrons move along the electron transport chain to PSI.

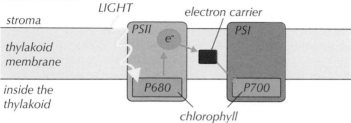

2. Photolysis of water produces protons, electrons and oxygen

As the excited electrons from chlorophyll leave PSII to move along the electron transport chain, they must be replaced. Light energy splits water into protons (H^+ ions), electrons and oxygen. (So the oxygen in photosynthesis comes from water.) The reaction is: $H_2O \longrightarrow 2H^+ + \frac{1}{2}O_2$

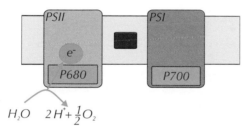

3. Energy from the excited electrons makes ATP

The excited electrons lose energy as they move along the electron transport chain (see Figure 5). This energy is used to transport protons (H^+ ions) into the thylakoid so that the thylakoid has a higher concentration of protons than the stroma. This forms a proton gradient across the membrane. Protons move down their concentration gradient, into the stroma, via an enzyme called ATP synthase. The energy from this movement combines ADP and inorganic phosphate (Pi) to form ATP.

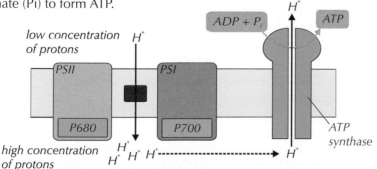

Tip: To remind yourself what photosystems are, take a look back at page 31.

Tip: Not all of the electron carriers are shown in these diagrams.

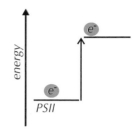

Figure 4: *Light energy excites electrons in PSII, moving them to a higher energy level.*

Tip: The O_2 produced from the photolysis of water is really important. It diffuses out of the chloroplast and eventually into the atmosphere for us to breathe. Good old plants.

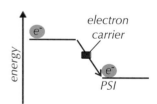

Figure 5: *The excited electrons lose energy as they pass down the electron transport chain.*

Tip: Chemiosmosis is the name of the process where the movement of protons (H^+ ions) across a membrane generates ATP. This process also occurs in respiration (see p. 47).

4. Energy from the excited electrons generates reduced NADP.

Light energy is absorbed by PSI, which excites the electrons again to an even higher energy level. Finally, the electrons are transferred to NADP, along with a proton from the stroma, to form reduced NADP.

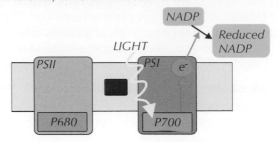

Tip: Remember a 'proton' is just another word for a hydrogen ion (H⁺).

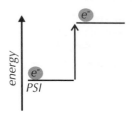

Figure 6: *Light energy excites electrons in PSI to an even higher energy level.*

Tip: The ATP and reduced NADP made here in the light-dependent reaction are really important for use later on in the light-independent reaction (see page 36).

Tip: ATP is formed in the same way in cyclic photophosphorylation as in non-cyclic photophosphorylation — by the movement of protons across the thylakoid membrane.

Tip: Tempting as it is, you need to be able to answer this question without looking back at the last couple of pages.

Cyclic photophosphorylation

Cyclic photophosphorylation produces ATP and only uses PSI. It's called 'cyclic' because the electrons from the chlorophyll molecule aren't passed onto NADP, but are passed back to PSI via electron carriers. This means the electrons are recycled and can repeatedly flow through PSI. This process doesn't produce any reduced NADP or oxygen — it only produces small amounts of ATP.

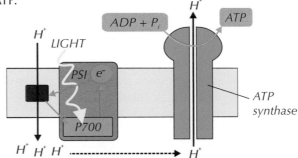

Practice Questions — Application

Q1 This diagram on the right shows a process in the light-dependent reaction.

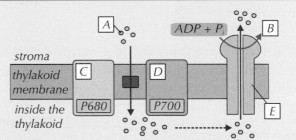

a) The object labelled A in the diagram is transported across the thylakoid membrane, so that its concentration is higher in the thylakoid than in the stroma.
   i) What is the name of object A?
   ii) Explain why it is important that the concentration of object A is higher inside the thylakoid than in the stroma.
b) What is the name of structure C?
c) Which structure, C or D, is involved in cyclic photophosphorylation?
d) What does cyclic photophosphorylation produce?

Q2 The diagram below shows the energy levels of electrons at different stages of the light-dependent reaction of photosynthesis.

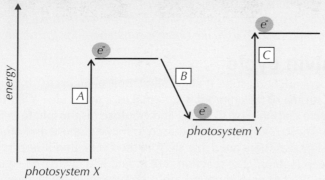

a) What are the correct names of photosystems X and Y?

b) Explain what is happening at stage A on the diagram.

c) Electrons lose energy at stage B in the diagram. What is this energy used for?

d) At point C in the diagram, electrons reach their highest energy level. What happens to the electrons after this point in non-cyclic photophosphorylation?

Practice Questions — Fact Recall

Q1 a) What are photosynthetic pigments?

b) Give one example of a photosynthetic pigment.

Q2 NADP is a coenzyme used in photosynthesis. What chemical group does it transfer between molecules?

Q3 Where in the chloroplast does the light-dependent reaction take place?

Q4 Which products of the light-dependent reaction are needed in the light-independent reaction?

Q5 What is photophosphorylation?

Q6 What is the electron transport chain?

Q7 a) Name the products of the photolysis of water.

b) What is the purpose of photolysis in the light-dependent reaction?

Q8 Excited electrons lose energy as they move along the electron transport chain. Explain how this leads to ATP synthesis.

Q9 Name the photosystem(s) involved in:

a) non-cyclic photophosphorylation,

b) cyclic photophosphorylation.

Q10 Name the products of:

a) non-cyclic photophosphorylation,

b) cyclic photophosphorylation.

Tip: Make sure you get your head round what happens in cyclic and non-cyclic phosphorylation (see pages 33-34) — don't get them mixed up.

3. Light-independent Reaction

The light-independent reaction is the second (and final, phew) stage of photosynthesis. It uses the products of the light-dependent reaction (ATP and reduced NADP) to make organic substances for the plant.

The Calvin cycle

The light-independent reaction is also called the Calvin cycle. It takes place in the stroma of the chloroplasts. It makes a molecule called **triose phosphate** from carbon dioxide (CO_2) and **ribulose bisphosphate** (a 5-carbon compound). Triose phosphate can be used to make glucose and other useful organic substances. There are a few steps in the cycle, and it needs ATP and H^+ ions to keep it going. The reactions are linked in a cycle (see Figure 1), which means the starting compound, ribulose bisphosphate, is regenerated.

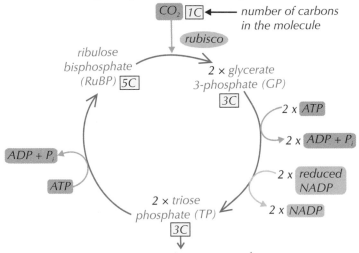

Figure 1: One turn of the Calvin cycle.

Here's what happens at each stage in the cycle:

1. Formation of glycerate 3-phosphate

Carbon dioxide enters the leaf through the stomata and diffuses into the stroma of the chloroplast. Here, it's combined with ribulose bisphosphate (RuBP), a 5-carbon compound. This gives an unstable 6-carbon compound, which quickly breaks down into two molecules of a 3-carbon compound called **glycerate 3-phosphate** (GP). **Ribulose bisphosphate carboxylase** (rubisco) catalyses the reaction between carbon dioxide and RuBP.

$$RuBP\ (5C) + CO_2 \xrightarrow{rubisco} unstable\ 6C\ compound \longrightarrow 2 \times GP\ (3C)$$

2. Formation of triose phosphate

The 3-carbon compound GP is reduced to a different 3-carbon compound called triose phosphate (TP). ATP (from the light-dependent reaction) provides the energy to do this. The H^+ ions come from reduced NADP (also from the light-dependent reaction). Reduced NADP is recycled to NADP. Triose phosphate is then converted into many useful organic compounds, e.g. glucose (see pages 38-39).

$$2 \times GP\ (3C) \xrightarrow[2 \times ATP \quad 2 \times ADP + Pi]{\quad 2 \times reduced\ NADP \quad 2 \times NADP \quad} 2 \times TP\ (3C)$$

3. Regeneration of ribulose bisphosphate

Five out of every six molecules of TP produced in the cycle aren't used to make useful organic compounds, but to regenerate RuBP. Regenerating RuBP uses the rest of the ATP produced by the light-dependent reaction.

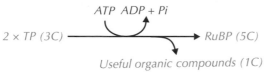

Hexose sugars

A hexose sugar is a monosaccharide that has six carbon atoms, e.g. glucose (see Figure 2). One hexose sugar is made by joining two molecules of triose phosphate (TP) together. Hexose sugars can be used to make larger carbohydrates (see page 38).

The Calvin cycle needs to turn six times to make one hexose sugar. The reason for this is that three turns of the cycle produces six molecules of triose phosphate (because two molecules of TP are made for every one CO_2 molecule used). Five out of six of these TP molecules are used to regenerate ribulose bisphosphate (RuBP). This means that for three turns of the cycle only one TP is produced that's used to make a hexose sugar.

As a hexose sugar has six carbons, two TP molecules are needed to form one hexose sugar. This means the cycle must turn six times to produce two molecules of TP that can be used to make one hexose sugar — see Figure 3. Six turns of the cycle need 18 ATP and 12 reduced NADP from the light-dependent reaction.

This might seem a bit inefficient, but it keeps the cycle going and makes sure there's always enough RuBP ready to combine with carbon dioxide taken in from the atmosphere.

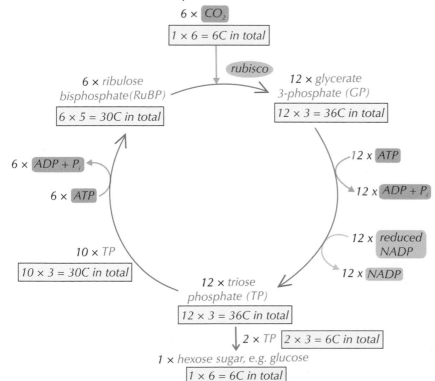

Figure 3: Six turns of the Calvin cycle.

Tip: Useful organic compounds have more than one carbon atom, e.g. glucose has six carbon atoms. This means the cycle has to turn more than once to make them — see below.

Tip: It's really important that RuBP is regenerated. If it wasn't then glycerate 3-phosphate wouldn't be formed, the Calvin cycle would stop and photosynthesis would be unable to continue.

Figure 2: The structure of glucose, a hexose sugar.

Exam Tip
If you're asked in the exam to work out how many turns of the Calvin cycle are needed to produce a certain number of hexose sugars you need to remember that five out of every six TP molecules are used to regenerate RuBP.

Tip: Six turns of the Calvin cycle produce 12 GP molecules because one turn produces 2 GP, so $6 \times 2 = 12$ GP.

Carbohydrates, lipids and proteins

The Calvin cycle is the starting point for making all the organic substances a plant needs. Triose phosphate (TP) and glycerate 3-phosphate (GP) molecules are used to make carbohydrates, lipids and proteins:

- **Carbohydrates** — hexose sugars are made from two triose phosphate molecules (see the previous page) and larger carbohydrates (e.g. sucrose, starch, cellulose — see Figure 4) are made by joining hexose sugars together in different ways.

- **Lipids** — these are made using glycerol, which is synthesised from triose phosphate, and fatty acids, which are synthesised from glycerate 3-phosphate.

- **Proteins** — some amino acids are made from glycerate 3-phosphate, which are joined together to make proteins.

Figure 4: *Cellulose strands in a plant cell wall made from hexose sugars.*

Tip: Rubisco is one of the slowest-working enzymes in the natural world.

Tip: The Calvin cycle can be summarised as follows:

Inputs

CO_2
ATP
Reduced NADP

↓

Outputs

Organic substances
RuBP

Practice Questions — Application

Q1 Rubisco is an enzyme that catalyses the first reaction in the Calvin cycle. Some scientists are trying to genetically modify rubisco to try to increase the speed at which it works. They believe if they can make rubisco work faster then plants will be able to produce organic substances, such as glucose, more quickly. Use your knowledge of photosynthesis to explain how increasing the speed of rubisco could increase the speed of glucose production.

Q2 Phosphoribulokinase is an enzyme involved in the regeneration of ribulose bisphosphate. If this enzyme stopped working properly, suggest what effect it would have on the light-independent reaction of photosynthesis in a plant. Explain your answer.

Practice Questions — Fact Recall

Q1 a) What is the name of the 5-carbon compound that combines with carbon dioxide to form an unstable 6-carbon compound in the first reaction of the Calvin cycle?

b) The 6-carbon compound produced only exists fleetingly before it breaks down into two molecules of a 3-carbon compound. What is the name of this 3-carbon compound?

Q2 a) Write out a word equation to show the formation of two molecules of triose phosphate.

b) Is this reaction an oxidation or reduction reaction?

Q3 Describe the role of ATP in the Calvin cycle.

Q4 If six molecules of triose phosphate (TP) are produced by the Calvin cycle, how many of these will be used to regenerate ribulose bisphosphate?

Q5 To make one hexose sugar:

a) How many turns of the Calvin cycle are needed?

b) How many molecules of ATP are needed?

c) How many molecules of reduced NADP are needed?

Q6 Describe how the products of the Calvin cycle are used to make the following organic substances:
a) large carbohydrates, b) lipids, c) proteins.

4. Limiting Factors in Photosynthesis

Learning Objectives:
- Be able to understand the principle of limiting factors and how the limiting factors of temperature, carbon dioxide concentration and light intensity affect the rate of photosynthesis.
- Be able to explain how growers apply a knowledge of limiting factors in enhancing temperature, carbon dioxide concentration and light intensity in commercial glasshouses. Also, be able to evaluate such applications using appropriate data.

Specification Reference 3.4.3

Plants have optimum conditions for photosynthesis. If you're a budding gardener then these pages are for you...

Optimum conditions for photosynthesis

The ideal conditions for photosynthesis vary from one plant species to another, but the conditions below would be ideal for most plant species in temperate climates like the UK.

1. High light intensity of a certain wavelength

Light is needed to provide the energy for the light-dependent reaction — the higher the intensity of the light, the more energy it provides. Only certain wavelengths of light are used for photosynthesis. The photosynthetic pigments chlorophyll a, chlorophyll b and carotene only absorb the red and blue light in sunlight (see Figure 1).

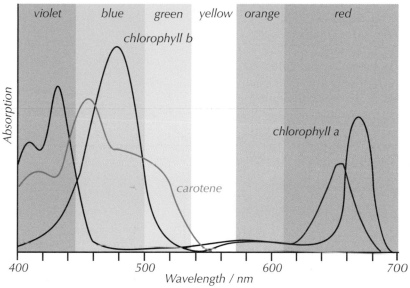

Figure 1: The wavelengths of light absorbed by chlorophylls a and b, and carotene.

Tip: Green light is reflected, which is why plants look green.

2. Temperature around 25 °C

Photosynthesis involves enzymes (e.g. ATP synthase, rubisco). If the temperature falls below 10 °C the enzymes become inactive, but if the temperature is more than 45 °C they may start to **denature**. Also, at high temperatures stomata close to avoid losing too much water. This causes photosynthesis to slow down because less carbon dioxide enters the leaf when the stomata are closed.

Tip: When an enzyme becomes denatured the bonds holding it together break. It loses its shape so the active site won't fit the substrate. The enzyme can no longer function as a catalyst.

3. Carbon dioxide at 0.4%

Carbon dioxide makes up 0.04% of the gases in the atmosphere. Increasing this to 0.4% gives a higher rate of photosynthesis, but any higher and the stomata start to close.

4. Water

Plants also need a constant supply of water — too little and photosynthesis has to stop but too much and the soil becomes waterlogged (reducing the uptake of minerals such as magnesium, which is needed to make chlorophyll a).

Tip: At AS you learnt that stomata are pores in the epidermis of a plant leaf which allow gas exchange.

Limiting factors of photosynthesis

Light, temperature and carbon dioxide can all limit photosynthesis. All three of these things need to be at the right level to allow a plant to photosynthesise as quickly as possible. If any one of these factors is too low or too high, it will limit photosynthesis (slow it down). Even if the other two factors are at the perfect level, it won't make any difference to the speed of photosynthesis as long as that factor is at the wrong level.

Tip: A limiting factor is a variable that can slow down the rate of a reaction.

Figure 2: As night falls, light intensity begins to limit the rate of photosynthesis.

Examples

- On a warm, sunny, windless day, it's usually carbon dioxide that's the limiting factor.
- At night it's usually the light intensity that's the limiting factor.

However, any of these factors could become the limiting factor, depending on the environmental conditions. The graphs below show the effect of each limiting factor on the rate of photosynthesis:

Examples

Light intensity

Between points A and B, the rate of photosynthesis is limited by the light intensity. So as the light intensity increases, so can the rate of photosynthesis. Point B is the **saturation point** — increasing light intensity after this point makes no difference, because something else has become the limiting factor. The graph now levels off.

Tip: The saturation point is where a factor is no longer limiting the reaction — something else has become the limiting factor.

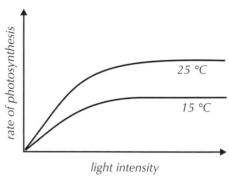

Temperature

Both these graphs level off when light intensity is no longer the limiting factor. The graph at 25 °C levels off at a higher point than the one at 15 °C, showing that temperature must have been a limiting factor at 15 °C.

Tip: As each of the graphs level off, it doesn't mean that photosynthesis has stopped — it means that the rate of photosynthesis is not increasing anymore.

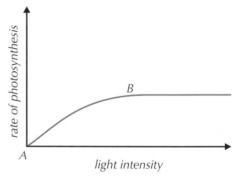

Carbon dioxide concentration

Both these graphs level off when light intensity is no longer the limiting factor. The graph at 0.4% carbon dioxide (CO_2) levels off at a higher point than the one at 0.04%, so carbon dioxide concentration must have been a limiting factor at 0.04% carbon dioxide. The limiting factor here isn't temperature because it's the same for both graphs (25 °C).

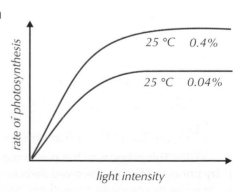

Increasing plant growth

Commercial growers (e.g. farmers) know the factors that limit photosynthesis and therefore limit plant growth. This means they can create an environment where plants get the right amount of everything that they need, which increases growth and so increases yield. Growers create optimum conditions in **glasshouses**, in the following ways:

Limiting Factor	Management in Glasshouse
Carbon dioxide concentration	Carbon dioxide is added to the air, e.g. by burning a small amount of propane in a carbon dioxide generator.
Light	Light can get in through the glass. Lamps provide light at night time.
Temperature	Glasshouses trap heat energy from sunlight, which warms the air. Heaters and cooling systems can also be used to keep a constant optimum temperature, and air circulation systems make sure the temperature is even throughout the glasshouse.

Interpreting data on limiting factors

(HOW SCIENCE WORKS)

You need to be able to interpret data on limiting factors.
Here are some examples of the kind of data you might get in the exam:

Examples

Carbon dioxide

The graph below shows the effect on plant growth of adding carbon dioxide to a greenhouse.

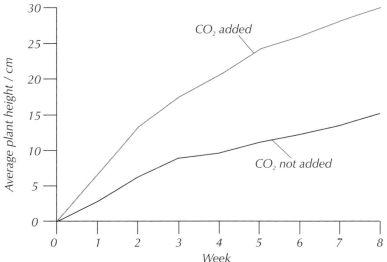

In the greenhouse with added carbon dioxide plant growth was faster (the line is steeper) and on average the plants were larger after 8 weeks than they were in the control greenhouse (30 cm compared to only 15 cm in the greenhouse where no carbon dioxide was added).

This is because the plants use carbon dioxide to produce glucose by photosynthesis. The more carbon dioxide they have, the more glucose they can produce, meaning they can respire more and so have more ATP for DNA replication, cell division and protein synthesis.

Tip: A greenhouse is the same thing as a glasshouse.

***Figure 3:** Lamps in greenhouses provide light at night.*

Tip: Remember the wavelength of light is also important. Commercial growers will often use red or blue lights to maximise photosynthesis. If they used green light it would be reflected by the plant. — see page 39.

Exam Tip
In the exam you might be given a graph like the one on the right and asked questions on it. Make sure you read all the information in the question carefully — it's always there for a reason.

Tip: In this study, the control was growing plants in a greenhouse where CO_2 wasn't added. Using this control would have made sure that no other factors, apart from the level of CO_2, were affecting the results. For more information on controls see page 3-4.

Light intensity

The graph below shows the effect of light intensity on plant growth, and the effect of two different types of heater:

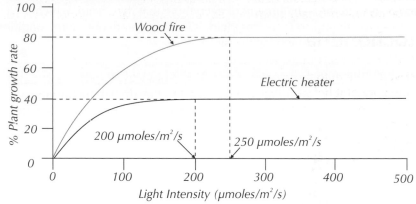

Exam Tip
μmoles/m²/s is a unit when measuring light intensity. Don't panic if you see unfamiliar units like this in the exam — just focus on what the axis is showing you, e.g. here it's light intensity.

- At the start of the graph, the greater the light intensity the greater the plant growth.

- At 200 μmoles/m²/s of light the bottom graph flattens out, showing that carbon dioxide concentration or temperature is limiting growth in these plants.

- At 250 μmoles/m²/s of light the top graph flattens out. The difference between the two graphs could be because the wood fire increases the temperature more than the electric heater or because it's increasing the concentration of carbon dioxide in the air (an electric heater doesn't release carbon dioxide).

Tip: If you were conducting this experiment you would have to measure the temperature and the carbon dioxide concentration in each situation to be able to decide which was actually the factor limiting photosynthesis.

Practice Questions — Application

Q1   A farmer grows two tomato crops — one in a greenhouse and the other outside.
He records the average plant height each week for seven weeks.
The results are shown on the right.

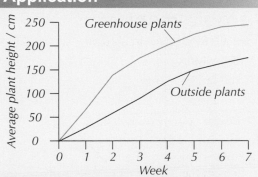

a) For each tomato crop, calculate the percentage difference in the average plant height between week two and week five.

b) Describe three ways in which the farmer may have created ideal conditions in the greenhouse in order to increase photosynthesis.

Q2   a) Jen has two house plants. She puts plant A under a light with a wavelength of 520 nm and plant B under a light with a wavelength of 480 nm. All other conditions the two plants are kept in are the same. After 4 weeks she measures the height of both plants. Which plant do you think was tallest? Explain your answer.

b) Jen keeps another house plant in her conservatory, which gets sun throughout the day and can reach temperatures of 40°C. She regularly waters the plant but it's beginning to die. Suggest why this might be and explain your answer.

Tip: Have a look back at the graph on page 39 to see which colours different wavelengths of light correspond to.

5. Respiration

Respiration is the process that allows cells to produce ATP from glucose. It can be done aerobically (with oxygen) or anaerobically (without oxygen).

Mitochondria

Most of the reactions in respiration take place in the mitochondria. You covered the mitochondrial structure at AS, but you might want to refresh your memory of it before you start this section — see Figure 1. The folds (cristae) in the inner membrane of the mitochondrion provide a large surface area to maximise respiration.

 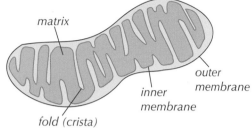

matrix

outer membrane

inner membrane

fold (crista)

Figure 1: *A mitochondrion in a nerve cell (left) and mitochondrial structure (right).*

Coenzymes

As you saw in photosynthesis, a coenzyme is a molecule that aids the function of an enzyme by transferring a chemical group from one molecule to another. Coenzymes used in respiration include **NAD**, **coenzyme A** and **FAD**. NAD and FAD transfer hydrogen from one molecule to another. This means they can reduce (give hydrogen to) or oxidise (take hydrogen from) a molecule. Coenzyme A transfers acetate between molecules (see pages 45-46).

Aerobic respiration

There are four stages in aerobic respiration:

1. Glycolysis.
2. The link reaction.
3. The Krebs cycle.
4. Oxidative phosphorylation.

The first three stages are a series of reactions. The products from these reactions are used in the final stage to produce loads of ATP. The first stage happens in the cytoplasm of cells and the other three stages take place in the mitochondria.

     Anaerobic respiration doesn't involve the link reaction, the Krebs cycle or oxidative phosphorylation. The products of glycolysis are converted to ethanol or lactate instead (see page 49 for more).

     All cells use glucose to respire, but organisms can also break down other complex organic molecules (e.g. fatty acids, amino acids), which can then be respired.

Stage 1 — Glycolysis

Glycolysis makes **pyruvate** from glucose. Glycolysis involves splitting one molecule of glucose (with 6 carbons — 6C) into two smaller molecules of pyruvate (3C). The process happens in the cytoplasm of cells. Glycolysis is the first stage of both aerobic and anaerobic respiration and doesn't need oxygen to take place — so it's an anaerobic process.

Learning Objectives:

- Understand aerobic respiration in such detail as to show that:
  - glycolysis takes place in the cytoplasm and involves the oxidation of glucose to pyruvate with a net gain of ATP and reduced NAD,
  - pyruvate combines with coenzyme A in the link reaction to produce acetyl coenzyme A,
  - acetyl coenzyme A is effectively a 2-carbon molecule that combines with a 4-carbon molecule to produce a 6-carbon molecule which enters the Krebs cycle,
  - in a series of oxidation-reduction reactions the Krebs cycle generates reduced coenzymes and ATP by substrate-level phosphorylation, and CO_2 is lost,
  - the synthesis of ATP by oxidative phosphorylation is associated with the transfer of electrons down the electron transport chain and passage of protons across the mitochondrial membrane.
- Know that in anaerobic respiration glycolysis is followed by the production of ethanol or lactate and the regeneration of NAD.

Specification Reference 3.4.4

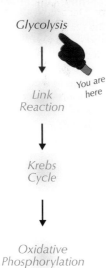

Tip: Remember the first part of OILRIG, (page 31) — oxidation is loss, so when triose phosphate is oxidised it loses hydrogen.

Tip: Glycolysis takes place in the cytoplasm of cells because glucose can't cross the outer mitochondrial membrane. Pyruvate can cross this membrane, so the rest of the reactions in respiration occur within the mitochondria.

Stages in glycolysis

There are two stages in glycolysis — phosphorylation and oxidation. First, ATP is used to phosphorylate glucose to triose phosphate. Phosphorylation is the process of adding phosphate to a molecule. Then triose phosphate is oxidised, releasing ATP. Overall there's a net gain of 2 ATP.

1. Phosphorylation

Glucose is phosphorylated by adding 2 phosphates from 2 molecules of ATP. This creates 2 molecules of triose phosphate and 2 molecules of ADP.

2. Oxidation

Triose phosphate is oxidised (loses hydrogen), forming 2 molecules of pyruvate. NAD collects the hydrogen ions, forming 2 reduced NAD. 4 ATP are produced, but 2 were used up in stage one, so there's a net gain of 2 ATP.

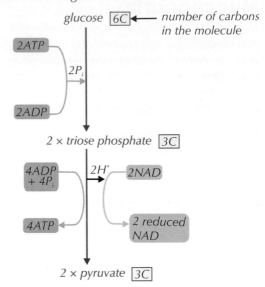

The products of glycolysis

Here's what happens to all the products of glycolysis...

Products from glycolysis	Where it goes
2 reduced NAD	To oxidative phosphorylation
2 pyruvate	To the link reaction
2 ATP (net gain)	Used for energy

Practice Questions — Application

Use the following diagram to answer Q1 to 3.

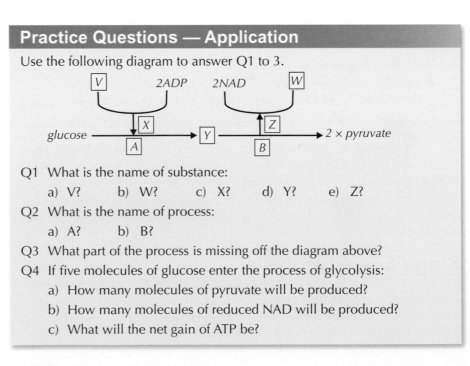

Q1 What is the name of substance:
   a) V?   b) W?   c) X?   d) Y?   e) Z?

Q2 What is the name of process:
   a) A?   b) B?

Q3 What part of the process is missing off the diagram above?

Q4 If five molecules of glucose enter the process of glycolysis:
   a) How many molecules of pyruvate will be produced?
   b) How many molecules of reduced NAD will be produced?
   c) What will the net gain of ATP be?

Stage 2 — The link reaction

The link reaction converts pyruvate to acetyl coenzyme A. Pyruvate is **decarboxylated**, so one carbon atom is removed from pyruvate in the form of carbon dioxide. NAD is reduced — it collects hydrogen from pyruvate, changing pyruvate into acetate. Acetate is combined with coenzyme A (CoA) to form acetyl coenzyme A (acetyl CoA). No ATP is produced in this reaction.

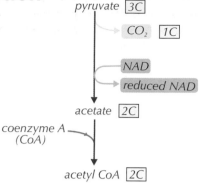

Tip: Decarboxylation is the removal of carbon dioxide from a molecule.

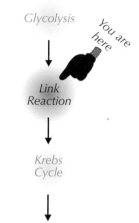
Respiration Map

How many times does the link reaction occur per glucose molecule?

Two pyruvate molecules are made for every glucose molecule that enters glycolysis. This means the link reaction and the third stage (the Krebs cycle) happen twice for every glucose molecule.

The products of the link reaction

Here's what happens to the products of two link reactions (i.e. for one glucose molecule):

Products from two link reactions	Where it goes
2 acetyl coenzyme A	To the Krebs cycle
2 carbon dioxide	Released as a waste product
2 reduced NAD	To oxidative phosphorylation

Stage 3 — The Krebs cycle

The Krebs cycle produces reduced coenzymes and ATP. It involves a series of oxidation-reduction reactions, which take place in the matrix of the mitochondria. The cycle happens once for every pyruvate molecule, so it goes round twice for every glucose molecule.

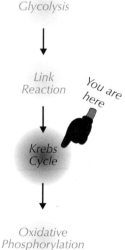
Respiration Map

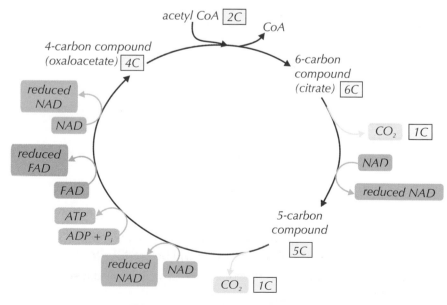

Figure 2: One turn of the Krebs cycle.

Tip: In respiration carbon dioxide is produced in the link reaction and the Krebs cycle.

Here's what happens at each stage in the Krebs cycle:

1. Formation of citrate

Tip: Coenzyme A transfers acetate between molecules (see page 43 for a reminder on coenzymes).

Acetyl CoA from the link reaction combines with oxaloacetate to form citrate. Coenzyme A goes back to the link reaction to be used again.

$$oxaloacetate\ (4C) + acetyl\ CoA\ (2C) \longrightarrow citrate\ (6C)$$

2. Formation of a 5-carbon compound

The 6C citrate molecule is converted to a 5C molecule. Decarboxylation occurs, where carbon dioxide is removed. **Dehydrogenation** also occurs. The hydrogen is used to produce reduced NAD from NAD.

Tip: Dehydrogenation is the removal of hydrogen from a molecule.

$$citrate\ (6C) \longrightarrow 5\text{-}carbon\ compound$$

with CO_2, NAD, reduced NAD

3. Regeneration of oxaloacetate

Tip: See page 45 if you can't remember what decarboxylation is.

The 5C molecule is then converted to a 4C molecule. (There are some intermediate compounds formed during this conversion, but you don't need to know about them.) Decarboxylation and dehydrogenation occur, producing one molecule of reduced FAD and two of reduced NAD. ATP is produced by the direct transfer of a phosphate group from an intermediate compound to ADP. When a phosphate group is directly transferred from one molecule to another it's called **substrate-level phosphorylation**. Citrate has now been converted into oxaloacetate.

Tip: Reduced NAD and reduced FAD may also be written as NADH and FADH$_2$. Don't worry, they still mean the same thing.

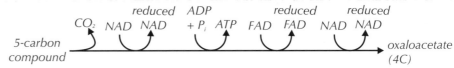

5-carbon compound → CO_2, NAD, reduced NAD, $ADP + P_i$, ATP, FAD, reduced FAD, NAD, reduced NAD → oxaloacetate (4C)

The products of the Krebs cycle

Some products of the Krebs cycle are reused, some are released and others are used for the next stage of respiration — oxidative phosphorylation.

Tip: The table only shows the products of <u>one</u> turn of the Krebs cycle. The cycle turns <u>twice</u> for one glucose molecule, so one glucose molecule produces twice as much as what's shown in the table.

Product from one Krebs cycle	Where it goes
1 coenzyme A	Reused in the next link reaction
Oxaloacetate	Regenerated for use in the next Krebs cycle
2 carbon dioixde	Released as a waste product
1 ATP	Used for energy
3 reduced NAD	To oxidative phosphorylation
1 reduced FAD	To oxidative phosphorylation

Tip: Remember that the Krebs cycle is just that... a cycle — some of its products need to be recycled for the process to continue.

Practice Questions — Application

Q1 The diagram below shows part of the Krebs cycle:

oxaloacetate ⟶ citrate ⟶ 5C-intermediate

a) How many carbon atoms do oxaloacetate and citrate each have?

b) What happens to turn the 5C-intermediate back into oxaloacetate?

Q2 If six molecules of glucose were respired, how many molecules of CO_2 would be produced from the Krebs cycle?

Q3 Fats can be broken down and converted into acetyl coenzyme A. Explain how this allows fats to be respired.

Stage 4 — Oxidative Phosphorylation

Oxidative phosphorylation is the process where the energy carried by electrons, from reduced coenzymes (reduced NAD and reduced FAD), is used to make ATP. (The whole point of the previous stages is to make reduced NAD and reduced FAD for the final stage.) Oxidative phosphorylation involves two processes — the **electron transport chain** and **chemiosmosis**.

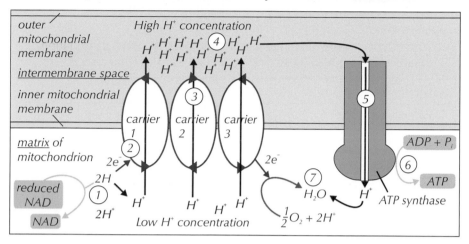

Respiration Map

Glycolysis

↓

Link Reaction

↓

Krebs Cycle *You are here*

↓

Oxidative Phosphorylation

The numbers of the steps below correspond to the circled numbers in the diagram above.

1. Hydrogen atoms are released from reduced NAD and reduced FAD as they're oxidised to NAD and FAD. The hydrogen atoms split into protons (H^+) and electrons (e^-).

2. The electrons move along the electron transport chain (made up of three electron carriers), losing energy at each carrier, (see Figure 2).

3. This energy is used by the electron carriers to pump protons from the mitochondrial matrix into the intermembrane space (the space between the inner and outer mitochondrial membranes).

4. The concentration of protons is now higher in the intermembrane space than in the mitochondrial matrix — this forms an electrochemical gradient (a concentration gradient of ions).

5. Protons move down the electrochemical gradient, back into the mitochondrial matrix, via ATP synthase.

6. This movement drives the synthesis of ATP from ADP and inorganic phosphate (P_i). The movement of H^+ ions across a membrane, which generates ATP, is called chemiosmosis.

7. In the mitochondrial matrix, at the end of the transport chain, the protons, electrons and oxygen (from the blood) combine to form water. Oxygen is said to be the **final electron acceptor**.

Tip: The regenerated coenzymes from the electron transport chain are reused in the Krebs cycle.

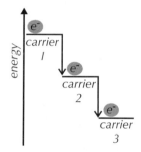

Figure 2: *As electrons move along the electron transport chain, they lose energy.*

Exam Tip
Don't write that protons move into or out of the inner mitochondrial membrane — they move across it.

Practice Question — Application

Q1 Antimycin A inhibits carrier 2 in the electron transport chain of oxidative phosphorylation.

   a) If antimycin A was added to isolated mitochondria, what state (oxidised or reduced) would carriers 1 and 3 be in after its addition? Explain your answers.

   b) Suggest why antimycin A can be used as a fish poison.

Tip: The job of a carrier is to transfer electrons. When a carrier receives electrons it's reduced and when it passes on electrons it becomes oxidised again.

Aerobic respiration and ATP

Tip: The number of ATP produced per reduced NAD or reduced FAD was thought to be 3 and 2, but new research has shown that the figures are nearer 2.5 and 1.5.

As you know, oxidative phosphorylation makes ATP using energy from the reduced coenzymes — 2.5 ATP are made from each reduced NAD and 1.5 ATP are made from each reduced FAD.

The table below shows that a cell can make 32 ATP from one molecule of glucose in aerobic respiration. (Remember, one molecule of glucose produces 2 pyruvate, so the link reaction and Krebs cycle happen twice.)

Tip: For each molecule of glucose, 28 molecules of ATP are produced by oxidative phoshorylation (i.e. that's the ATP made from reduced NAD and reduced FAD).

Stage of respiration	Molecules produced	Number of ATP molecules
Glycolysis	2 ATP	**2**
Glycolysis	2 reduced NAD	2 × 2.5 = **5**
Link Reaction (×2)	2 reduced NAD	2 × 2.5 = **5**
Krebs cycle (×2)	2 ATP	**2**
Krebs cycle (×2)	6 reduced NAD	6 × 2.5 = **15**
Krebs cycle (×2)	2 reduced FAD	2 × 1.5 = **3**
		Total ATP = **32**

Aerobic respiration summary

Glycolysis, the link reaction and the Krebs cycle are basically a series of reactions which produce ATP, reduced NAD, reduced FAD and CO_2. The reduced coenzymes (NAD and FAD) are then used in oxidative phosphorylation, to produce loads more ATP. The overall process is shown below:

Tip: Don't forget oxygen's role in respiration. It's the final electron acceptor in the electron transport chain in oxidative phosphorylation (see page 47).

Tip: Remember that the whole purpose of respiration is to produce ATP to fuel biological processes. That's why it's happening continuously in plant and animal cells.

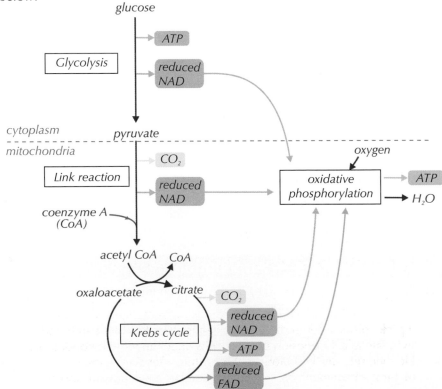

Anaerobic Respiration

As you know, in aerobic respiration (where there's lots of oxygen) pyruvate goes on to the third stage of respiration, the Krebs cycle (via the link reaction). In the Krebs cycle, more ATP is made and NAD is reduced (see page 45-46).

However, in anaerobic respiration (where there's no oxygen) the process stops at glycolysis. Pyruvate is converted into ethanol (alcoholic fermentation) or lactate (lactate fermentation).

Alcoholic fermentation

This occurs in plants and yeast.

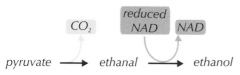

Lactate fermentation

This occurs in animal cells and some bacteria.

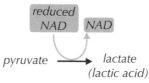

The production of lactate or ethanol regenerates NAD. This means glycolysis can continue even when there isn't much oxygen around, so a small amount of ATP can still be produced to keep some biological process going... clever.

Tip: Anaerobic respiration only produces 2 ATP per glucose molecule — this is the amount of ATP produced in glycolysis.

Practice Questions — Application

Q1 Kate is competing in a 100 m sprint. Towards the end of the race her body cannot supply oxygen to the muscle cells in her legs quickly enough.

a) Will Kate's muscle cells begin respiring aerobically or anaerobically towards the end of the race?

b) How many molecules of ATP are produced per molecule of glucose by this type of respiration?

c) Write out the word equation for this reaction.

Q2 The diagram below shows the two fates of glucose in anaerobic conditions.

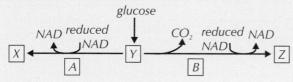

a) What is the name of substance:

   i) X?   ii) Y?   iii) Z?

b) Which process, A or B:

   i) is lactate fermentation?

   ii) happens in plant cells?

   iii) can happen in bacterial cells?

c) How many molecules of ATP are made by each of these processes?

Q3 Janus Green B is an artificial hydrogen acceptor. It is a useful redox reaction indicator as it is a blue colour when oxidised and turns to a pink colour when reduced. A scientist adds Janus Green B and pyruvate to a suspension of yeast cells under anaerobic conditions. He then records the colour of the mixture after 5 minutes. Suggest what colour the mixture should be. Explain your answer.

Tip: Artificial hydrogen acceptors can accept hydrogen and become reduced. This means they can be used to model the function of some coenzymes, e.g. NAD.

Q1 What is ATP used for in glycolysis?

Q2 What role does the coenzyme NAD play in glycolysis?

Q3 a) In the link reaction, pyruvate is converted into acetate. Describe how this happens.

b) The second stage of the link reaction relies on coenzyme A. What is the role of coenzyme A in the link reaction?

c) State what happens to the products of the link reaction.

Q4 In one turn of the Krebs cycle:

a) how many molecules of CO_2 are released, and where are they released from?

b) how many molecules of reduced FAD are made?

Q5 During the Krebs cycle ATP is produced by the direct transfer of a phosphate group from an intermediate compound to ADP. What name is given to this process?

Q6 After each turn of the Krebs cycle, what happens to:

a) coenzyme A?

b) oxaloacetate?

Q7 During oxidative phosphorylation, what happens to electrons as they move down the electron transport chain?

Q8 What is said to be the final electron acceptor in oxidative phosphorylation?

Q9 Give one example of a decarboxylation reaction in respiration.

Q10 Draw out the table below and fill it in with crosses to show where the following substances are made in respiration.

Substance	Glycolysis	Link reaction	Krebs cycle	Oxidative phosphorylation
ATP				
reduced NAD				
reduced FAD				
CO_2				

Section Summary

Make sure you know...

- That ATP is the immediate source of energy in a cell. It is used to carry out biological processes.

- That ATP is synthesised from ADP and phosphate by ATP synthase. It is hydrolysed by ATPase.

- That photosynthesis (where plants use light energy to make glucose) has two stages — the light-dependent reaction and the light-independent reaction.

- That the light-dependent reaction includes non-cyclic photophosphorylation and cyclic photophosphorylation. In both processes, light energy is absorbed by the chlorophyll in photosystems and used to excite electrons. As the electrons move down the electron transport chain they lose energy, which is used to generate a proton gradient across the thylakoid membrane. The subsequent movement of protons down their concentration gradient is used to produce ATP. In non-cyclic photophosphorylation reduced NADP is also produced.

- That the photolysis of water is the splitting of water using light and that it produces protons, electrons and water. It happens in non-cyclic photophosphorylation.

- That in the light-independent reaction carbon dioxide (CO_2) enters the Calvin cycle, where it is combined with ribulose bisphosphate (RuBP) to form two molecules of glycerate 3-phosphate (GP). These two molecules of GP are then reduced to two molecules of triose phosphate (TP), using ATP and reduced NADP from the light-dependent reaction. Five out of every six molecules of TP are used to regenerate RuBP, (allowing the Calvin cycle to continue), while the remaining TP is used to produce organic substrates such as carbohydrates, lipids and proteins.

- That a limiting factor is a variable that can slow down the rate of a reaction. The limiting factors of photosynthesis are light intensity, temperature and carbon dioxide concentration.

- That commercial growers create ideal conditions of light intensity, carbon dioxide concentration and temperature in glasshouses, so that these factors are less likely to limit photosynthesis and that crop yield is increased.

- How to interpret data on limiting factors in photosynthesis.

- The four stages of aerobic respiration — glycolysis (which happens in the cytoplasm), the link reaction, the Krebs cycle and oxidative phosphorylation (the last three stages happen in the mitochondria).

- That in glycolysis, ATP is used to phosphorylate glucose to triose phosphate. Triose phosphate is then oxidised to pyruvate. There is a net gain of two ATP and two reduced NAD, per molecule of glucose.

- That in the link reaction, pyruvate is converted to acetate (via decarboxylation and the reduction of NAD). Then acetate is combined with coenzyme A to form acetyl coenzyme A.

- That acetyl coenzyme A (a 2C molecule) combines with oxaloacetate (4C) to produced citrate (6C) in the first reaction of the Krebs cycle. This is followed by a series of oxidation-reduction reactions to produce reduced NAD, reduced FAD, ATP and CO_2. The reduced coenzymes are used in oxidative phosphorylation.

- That ATP is produced in the Krebs cycle by substrate-level phosphorylation — a phosphate group is directly transferred from an intermediate molecule to ADP.

- That oxidative phosphorylation uses electrons from reduced NAD and reduced FAD to make ATP. Electrons travel down the electron transport chain, losing energy as they go. This energy is used to form a proton gradient across the inner mitochondrial membrane, which is used to make ATP by chemiosmosis. Water is also produced in this process.

- That in anaerobic respiration pyruvate (from glycolysis) is converted to ethanol or lactate. Only two ATP per molecule of glucose can be produced by this method and NAD is regenerated.

Exam-style Questions

1   A scientist carried out an
    experiment on respiration
    in yeast cells. She put
    some yeast into a test tube
    containing glucose solution
    and added a layer of oil.
    The rest of the apparatus
    was set up as shown on
    the right.

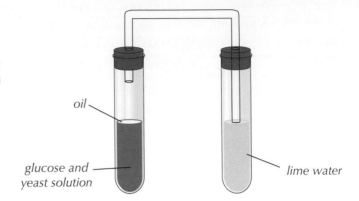

oil

*glucose and
yeast solution*

lime water

1 (a)   After 20 minutes bubbles appeared in the second test tube
        and the lime water turned cloudy. Explain these results.

                                                                    (2 marks)

1 (b)   The scientist removes the bung from the first test tube.
        State what smell you think she will observe.

                                                                    (1 mark)

1 (c) (i)   Oil prevents oxygen from entering the solution.
            Explain how respiration can continue in the absence of oxygen.

                                                                    (2 marks)

1 (c) (ii) Describe how this type of respiration is carried out in animal cells.

                                                                    (2 marks)

1 (d)   The scientist carried out a second experiment. She set up another test tube with the
        same amount of yeast and glucose in it, but without adding a layer of paraffin. The
        test tube also had no bung. Will more ATP have been produced by the yeast cells in
        the first or the second experiment? Explain your answer.

                                                                    (1 mark)

2   In oxidative phosphorylation hydrogen atoms are released from
    reduced NAD and reduced FAD.

2 (a) (i)   Describe the reactions in respiration in which these reduced coenzymes
            are produced.

                                                                    (5 marks)

2 (a) (ii) The hydrogen atoms split up into hydrogen ions and electrons.
            Describe the movement of electrons in oxidative phosphorylation.

                                                                    (3 marks)

2 (b)   DNP is an uncoupler. This means it carries H^+ ions from the intermembrane space
        back into the matrix of mitochondria during oxidative phosphorylation. Describe and
        explain the effect that DNP would have on the production of ATP in animal cells.

                                                                    (4 marks)

3 DNIP is an artificial hydrogen acceptor that can be used to measure the rate of photosynthesis. When DNIP is reduced it turns from blue to colourless. In the presence of NADP, DNIP is reduced first. A scientist used DNIP to investigate the rate of photosynthesis in plant chloroplasts under three different conditions. The results are shown below.

Tube	Condition	Colour after 24 hours
A	Unboiled chloroplasts kept in the dark	blue
B	Unboiled chloroplasts kept in the light	colourless
C	Boiled chloroplasts kept in the light	blue

3 (a) Explain the result for tube B

(3 marks)

3 (b) Explain the results for tubes A and C.

(2 marks)

3 (c) Describe the role of reduced NADP in the light-independent reaction of photosynthesis.

(2 marks)

4 A student carried out a study into the effect of different factors on the rate of photosynthesis in a certain species of plant. He calculated the rate of photosynthesis by measuring how much oxygen was released by the plants over a period of time.

4 (a) Is this an accurate way of calculating the rate of photosynthesis? Explain your answer.

(1 mark)

4 (b) The student carried out three experiments in his study — the results of which are shown in the graph on the right. In each experiment the plants had an adequate supply of water.

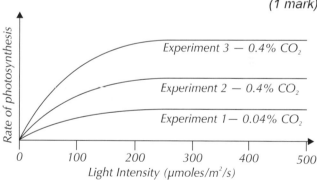

4 (b) (i) Describe and explain the results of experiment 1.

(3 marks)

4 (b) (ii) What is the limiting factor of photosynthesis in experiment 2? Explain your answer.

(2 marks)

4 (c) The student extended experiment 2 by measuring the amount of RuBP and TP produced by the plant over time. After 5 minutes, the student lowered the CO_2 concentration of the plants to 0.04%. Describe and explain what effect the lowering of CO_2 concentration had on the levels of RuBP and TP in the plants.

(3 marks)

Tip: The producers are at the bottom of the food chain and energy moves up through the food chain as it passes between trophic levels.

Tip: Remember, the <u>primary</u> consumer is the <u>first</u> consumer in a food chain, the <u>secondary</u> consumer is the <u>second</u> consumer in the food chain, and the <u>tertiary</u> consumer is the <u>third</u> consumer.

1. Energy Transfer and Energy Loss

Plants get their energy from the sun, and animals get their energy by eating plants or other animals. But some energy is always lost as it moves between organisms — and you can show this using some nifty equations and diagrams.

Ecosystems and energy

An ecosystem includes all the organisms living in a particular area and all the non-living (abiotic) conditions. The main route by which energy enters an ecosystem is **photosynthesis** (e.g. by plants, see p. 29). (Some energy enters sea ecosystems when bacteria respire chemicals from deep sea vents.)

During photosynthesis plants convert sunlight energy into a form that can be used by other organisms — plants are called **producers** (even though they're only converting the energy, not producing it). Energy is transferred through the living organisms of an ecosystem when organisms eat other organisms, e.g. producers are eaten by organisms called **primary consumers**. Primary consumers are then eaten by **secondary consumers** and secondary consumers are eaten by **tertiary consumers**. Each of the stages (e.g. producers, primary consumers) is called a **trophic level**.

Food chains and **food webs** show how energy is transferred through an ecosystem. Food chains show simple lines of energy transfer. Food webs show lots of food chains in an ecosystem and how they overlap.

─ **Example** ─

The example below shows a food chain (red box) and a food web (blue box).

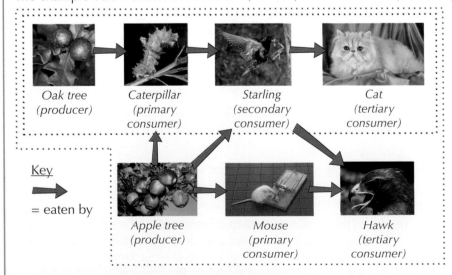

Oak tree (producer) → Caterpillar (primary consumer) → Starling (secondary consumer) → Cat (tertiary consumer)

Key
→ = eaten by

Apple tree (producer) → Mouse (primary consumer) → Hawk (tertiary consumer)

Energy locked up in the things that can't be eaten (e.g. bones, faeces) gets recycled back into the ecosystem by microorganisms called **decomposers** — they break down dead or undigested material (see page 62).

Calculating energy transfer

Not all the energy (e.g. from sunlight or food) that's available to the organisms in a trophic level is transferred to the next trophic level — around 90% of the total available energy is lost in various ways. Some of the available energy (60%) is never taken in by the organisms in the first place (see Figure 1). Reasons for this include:

- Plants can't use all the light energy that reaches their leaves (e.g. some is the wrong wavelength).

- Some parts of food, e.g. roots or bones, aren't eaten by organisms so the energy isn't taken in.

- Some parts of food are indigestible so pass through organisms and come out as waste, e.g. faeces.

      The rest of the available energy (40%) is absorbed by the body — this is called the **gross productivity** (see Figure 1). But not all of this is available to the next trophic level either. 30% of the total energy available (75% of the gross productivity) is lost to the environment when organisms use energy produced from respiration for movement or body heat. This is called **respiratory loss**.

      This means that only 10% of the total energy available (25% of the gross productivity) becomes biomass (e.g. it's stored or used for growth) — this is called the **net productivity** (Figure 1). Net productivity is the amount of energy that's available to the next trophic level. Here's how net productivity is calculated:

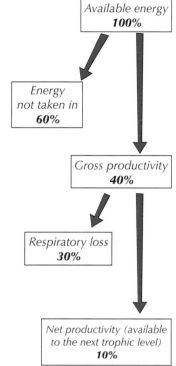

Figure 1: Diagram showing energy transfer in a typical food chain.

Tip: When light energy from the sun is 'lost', this doesn't mean it disappears — it's just converted into different forms of energy.

Tip: The photosynthetic pigments in plants only absorb the blue and red wavelengths of light in sunlight, see p.39.

Figure 2: Respiratory loss from a rabbit.

Exam Tip
You need to know the equation for net productivity for the exam, so learn it off by heart.

Tip: The unit kJm⁻² yr⁻¹ just means kilojoules per square metre per year.

Tip: In this example, the rabbits take in 8000 kJm⁻² yr⁻¹ of energy.

$$\text{net productivity} = \text{gross productivity} - \text{respiratory loss}$$

Example

Rabbits feed on grass which contains 20 000 kJm⁻² yr⁻¹ of energy. However, they don't take in 12 000 kJm⁻² yr⁻¹ of the energy available to them. You can use this information to work out the rabbits' gross productivity.

$$\text{gross productivity} = \text{energy available} - \text{energy not taken in}$$
$$= 20\ 000 - 12\ 000$$
$$= 8000 \text{ kJm}^{-2}\text{yr}^{-1}$$

The rabbits lose 6000 kJm⁻² yr⁻¹ using energy from respiration. You can use this to calculate the net productivity of the rabbits:

$$\text{net productivity} = \text{gross productivity} - \text{respiratory loss}$$
$$= 8000 - 6000$$
$$= 2000 \text{ kJm}^{-2}\text{yr}^{-1}$$

So 2000 kJm⁻² yr⁻¹ is available to the next trophic level.

Efficiency of energy transfer

To find out how efficient the transfer of energy is between two trophic levels you need to work out the **percentage efficiency of energy transfer**. If you know the amount of energy available to a trophic level (net productivity of the previous trophic level) and the net productivity of that trophic level, you can work it out using this equation:

$$\frac{\%\ \text{efficiency of}}{\text{energy transfer}} = \frac{\text{net productivity of trophic level}}{\text{net productivity of previous trophic level}} \times 100$$

┌─ **Example** ─────────────────────────────

Following on from the example on page 55, the rabbits receive 20 000 kJm⁻² yr⁻¹ from the grass, and their net productivity is 2000 kJm⁻² yr⁻¹.

So the percentage efficiency of energy transfer is:

$$(2000 \div 20\ 000) \times 100 = 10\%$$

The efficiency of energy transfer is not the same throughout a food chain — as you move up a food chain energy transfer becomes more efficient. Different amounts of energy are lost at different stages for different reasons, as shown in the table below:

Stage of food chain	Efficiency of energy transfer	Reason
Sun to producer	Low, around 2-3%	Not all the light energy that plants receive can be absorbed (see page 39) and some energy that is absorbed is then lost during photosynthesis.
Producer to consumer	5-10%	Energy transfer is less efficient from producer to consumer (i.e. to herbivores) than from consumer to consumer (i.e. to carnivores) because plants contain a greater proportion of indigestible material (see p. 55) than animals.
Consumer to consumer	High, around 15-20%	

The efficiency of energy transfer also varies between types of organisms. For example, energy transfer is less efficient in warm-blooded organisms than in cold-blooded organisms. This is because warm-blooded organisms use a lot of energy from respiration to keep their body temperature constant, whereas other animals, such as insects, don't need to do this.

Pyramid diagrams

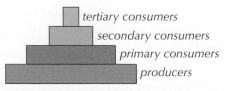

tertiary consumers
secondary consumers
primary consumers
producers

Food chains can be shown by drawing pyramids with each block representing a trophic level. Producers are always on the bottom, then primary consumers are above them, followed by secondary consumers then tertiary consumers. The area of each block tells you about the size of the trophic level. There are three types of pyramid — pyramids of number, biomass and energy — see the next page.

Tip: This just shows that 10% of the energy available in the grass is passed on to the rabbit.

Exam Tip
Don't forget — the efficiency of energy transfer underlines with increasing trophic level.

Tip: Remember, energy that's used for growth and reproduction isn't lost — it becomes biomass in an organism.

Pyramids of numbers

Pyramids of numbers show the number of organisms in each trophic level.

Example 1

grass → grasshoppers → pheasants → fox

The pyramid of numbers on the right corresponds to the food chain shown above and in Figure 3.

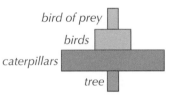

fox
pheasants
grasshoppers
grass

They're not always pyramid shaped though — small numbers of big organisms (like trees) or large numbers of small organisms (like parasites) change the shape.

Examples 2 and 3

The pyramid of numbers below shows that one tree is supporting the whole food chain.

bird of prey
birds
caterpillars
tree

The pyramid of numbers below shows that there are lots of fleas (a type of parasite) on each fox.

fleas
fox
rabbits
grass

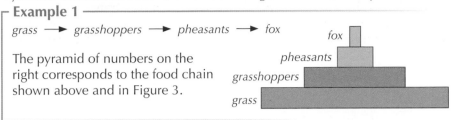

Figure 3: This food chain is shown as a pyramid of numbers in Example 1.

Pyramids of biomass

Pyramids of biomass show the amount of biomass in each trophic level — the dry mass of the organisms in kgm^{-2} (kilograms per square metre) at a single moment in time. They nearly always come out pyramid-shaped.

Example 1

tree → caterpillars → insectivorous → bird
                      birds   of prey

The pyramid of biomass on the right corresponds to the food chain above.

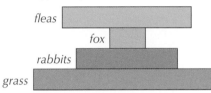

bird of prey
insectivorous birds
caterpillars
tree

Tip: Pyramids of biomass are usually pyramid shaped because biomass is a store of energy and energy is lost between trophic levels (see p. 55).

An exception is when they're based on plant plankton (microorganisms that photosynthesise) — the amount of plant plankton is quite small at any given moment, but because they have a short life span and reproduce very quickly there's a lot around over a period of time (see Figure 4).

Tip: Pyramids of biomass are based on dry biomass. The organisms are dried out before being weighed to remove all the water.

Example 2

The pyramid of biomass on the right shows there is a small amount of plant plankton at a single moment in time, resulting in a relatively small amount of biomass.

large fish
small fish
animal plankton
plant plankton

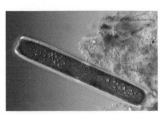

Figure 4: A diatom, a type of plant plankton.

Pyramids of energy

Pyramids of energy show the amount of energy available in each trophic level in kilojoules per square metre per year ($kJm^{-2}yr^{-1}$) — the net productivity of each trophic level (see page 55). Pyramids of energy are always pyramid shaped.

Example

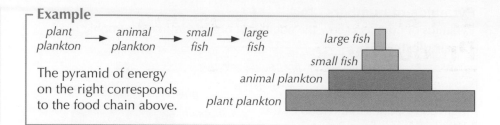

plant plankton → animal plankton → small fish → large fish

The pyramid of energy on the right corresponds to the food chain above.

large fish

small fish

animal plankton

plant plankton

Practice Questions — Application

Q1 In a food chain mussels have a gross productivity of 22 861 $kJm^{-2}yr^{-1}$ and a respiratory loss of 17 000 $kJm^{-2}yr^{-1}$.
a) Calculate the net productivity of the mussels.

The mussels provide food for crayfish which have a net productivity of 627 $kJm^{-2}yr^{-1}$.
b) Calculate the efficiency of energy transfer between the mussels and the crayfish.

Q2 The diagram below shows the net productivity in a food chain. Use the diagram to answer the following questions.

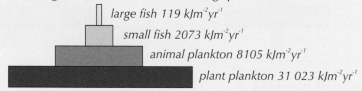

large fish 119 $kJm^{-2}yr^{-1}$

small fish 2073 $kJm^{-2}yr^{-1}$

animal plankton 8105 $kJm^{-2}yr^{-1}$

plant plankton 31 023 $kJm^{-2}yr^{-1}$

a) What type of pyramid is shown in the diagram above?
b) The gross productivity of the small fish is 8072 $kJm^{-2}yr^{-1}$. Calculate the respiratory loss of the small fish.
c) The respiratory loss of the large fish is 450 $kJm^{-2}yr^{-1}$. Calculate the gross productivity of the large fish.
d) Give one reason why the gross productivity of the large fish is less than the net productivity of the small fish.
e) Calculate the percentage efficiency of energy transfer between each stage of the food chain.

Practice Questions — Fact Recall

Q1 What is the main route by which energy enters an ecosystem?
Q2 Name the type of diagram that shows lots of food chains in an ecosystem and how they overlap.
Q3 What is the name given to the amount of energy taken in by an organism?
Q4 What is respiratory loss?
Q5 a) What is net productivity?
    b) State the equation for net productivity.
Q6 What do pyramids of numbers show?
Q7 What do pyramids of biomass show?
Q8 Explain why some pyramids of number and biomass may not be pyramid shaped, whereas pyramids of energy are always pyramid shaped.

2. Farming Practices and Productivity

Knowing about the efficiency of energy transfer in food chains can help farmers maximise the amount of energy in the food they produce.

Intensive farming and productivity

A **natural ecosystem** is an ecosystem that hasn't been changed by human activity. The energy input of a natural ecosystem is the amount of sunlight captured by the producers in the ecosystem.

Intensive farming involves changing an ecosystem by controlling the **biotic** or **abiotic** conditions, e.g. the presence of pests or the amount of nutrients available, to make it more favourable for crops or livestock. This means intensively farmed crops or livestock can have greater net productivity (a greater amount of biomass) than organisms in natural ecosystems. The energy input might be greater in an intensively farmed area than in a natural ecosystem, e.g. cattle may be given food that's higher in energy than their natural food. Or it might be the same as a natural ecosystem, e.g. a field of crops still receives the same amount of sunlight as a natural field.

Intensive farming methods increase productivity in different ways:
- They can increase the efficiency of energy conversion — more of the energy organisms have is used for growth and less is used for other activities, e.g. recovering from disease or movement.
- They can remove growth limiting factors — more of the energy available can be used for growth.
- They can increase energy input — more energy is added to the ecosystem so there's more energy for growth.

The three main intensive farming methods involve killing pest species, using fertilisers and rearing livestock intensively.

Rearing livestock intensively

Rearing livestock intensively involves controlling the conditions they live in and when they're slaughtered, so more of their energy is used for growth and less is used for other activities. This means the efficiency of energy conversion is increased so more biomass is produced and productivity is increased.

┌ **Examples** ─────────────────────────────
- Animals may be kept in warm, indoor pens where their movement is restricted. Less energy is wasted moving around and heat loss is reduced.
- Animals may be given feed that's higher in energy and lower in indigestible material than their natural food. This increases the energy input, so more energy is available for growth.
- Animals may be slaughtered before they reach adulthood. Young animals use a greater amount of their energy for growth, so this means more energy is transferred to their biomass.

The benefits are that more food can be produced in a shorter space of time, often at lower cost. However, enhancing productivity by intensive rearing raises ethical issues. For example, some people think the conditions intensively reared animals are kept in cause the animals pain, distress or restricts their natural behaviour, so it shouldn't be done.

Learning Objectives:
- Be able to compare natural ecosystems to those based on modern intensive farming in terms of energy input and productivity.
- Know the ways in which productivity is affected by farming practices that increase the efficiency of energy conversion. These include:
  - intensive rearing of domestic livestock,
  - the use of chemical pesticides, biological agents and integrated systems in controlling pests on agricultural crops,
  - the use of natural and artificial fertilisers.
- Be able to apply your understanding of biological principles to present scientific arguments that explain how these and other farming practices affect productivity.
- Be able to evaluate economic and environmental issues involved with farming practices that increase productivity.
- Consider ethical issues arising from enhancement of productivity.

Specification Reference 3.4.5

Tip: Restricting an animal's movement means they respire less, which lowers their respiratory loss.

Killing pest species

Pests are organisms that reduce the productivity of crops by reducing the amount of energy available for growth. This means the crops are less efficient at converting energy. Here are three ways that farmers reduce pest numbers:

1. Using chemical pesticides

There are different types of chemical pesticides:

- **Herbicides** kill weeds that compete with agricultural crops for energy. Reducing competition means crops receive more energy, so they grow faster and become larger, increasing productivity.

- **Fungicides** kill fungal infections that damage agricultural crops. The crops use more energy for growth and less for fighting infection, so they grow faster and become larger, increasing productivity.

- **Insecticides** kill insect pests that eat and damage crops. Killing insect pests means less biomass is lost from crops, so they grow to be larger, which means productivity is greater.

Using chemical pesticides raises environmental and economic issues:

Environmental issues	Economic issues
- They may directly affect (damage or kill) other non-pest species, e.g. butterflies. - They may indirectly affect other non-pest species, e.g. eating a lot of primary consumers that each contain a small amount of chemical pesticide can be enough to poison a secondary consumer.	- Chemical pesticides can be expensive. It may not be profitable for some farmers to use chemical pesticides — their cost may be greater than the extra money made from increased productivity.

2. Using biological agents

Biological agents reduce the numbers of pests, so crops lose less energy and biomass, increasing productivity. There are different types of biological agents:

- **Natural predators** introduced to the ecosystem eat the pest species, e.g. ladybirds eat greenfly.

- **Parasites** live in or lay their eggs on a pest insect. Parasites either kill the insect or reduce its ability to function, e.g. some species of wasps lay their eggs inside caterpillars — the eggs hatch and kill the caterpillars.

- **Pathogenic** (disease-causing) **bacteria** and **viruses** are used to kill pests, e.g. the bacterium *Bacillus thuringiensis* produces a toxin that kills a wide range of caterpillars.

Using biological agents raises environmental and economic issues:

Environmental issues	Economic issues
- Natural predators introduced to an ecosystem may become a pest species themselves. - Biological agents can affect (damage or kill) other non-pest species.	- Biological agents may be less cost-effective than chemical pesticides, i.e. they may increase productivity less in the short term for the same amount of money invested.

3. Using integrated systems

Integrated systems use both chemical pesticides (e.g. insecticides) and biological agents (e.g. parasites). The combined effect of using both can reduce pest numbers even more than either method alone, meaning productivity is increased even more.

Figure 1: *Braconoid wasps lay their eggs in sphinx moth caterpillars.*

Tip: Biological agents don't increase productivity as much as chemical pesticides in the short-term because it takes time for them to become established and able to reduce pest numbers.

Integrated systems can reduce costs if one method is particularly expensive — the expensive method can be used less because the two methods are used together. Integrated systems can reduce the environmental impact of things like pesticides, because less is used.

Using fertilisers

Fertilisers are chemicals that provide crops with minerals needed for growth, e.g. nitrates. Crops use up minerals in the soil as they grow, so their growth is limited when there aren't enough minerals. Adding fertiliser replaces the lost minerals, so more energy from the ecosystem can be used to grow, increasing the efficiency of energy conversion.

There are two different types of fertiliser:

- **Natural fertilisers** are organic matter — they include manure and sewage sludge (that's "muck" to you and me).
- **Artificial fertilisers** are inorganic — they contain pure chemicals (e.g. ammonium nitrate) as powders or pellets.

Using fertilisers raises environmental and economic issues:

Figure 2: Fertilisers are spread on fields to provide minerals for plant growth, helping to increase crop productivity.

Environmental issues	Economic issues
- Fertiliser can be washed into rivers and ponds, killing fish and plant life because of eutrophication. - Using fertilisers changes the balance of nutrients in the soil — too much of a particular nutrient can cause crops and other plants to die.	- Farmers need to get the amount of fertiliser they apply just right. Too much and money is wasted as excess fertiliser is washed away (causing eutrophication). Too little and productivity won't be increased, so less money can be made from selling the crop.

Tip: There's more about eutrophication on page 71.

Practice Questions — Application

Q1 A farmer is intensively farming chickens — they're shown in the photo on the right. Use evidence from the photo and your own knowledge to describe and explain how the farmer is increasing productivity.

Q2 A farmer is having problems with aphids on his sweet potato crop. He uses a neonicotinoid pesticide to destroy the aphids' nervous system. Explain how using this pesticide will increase productivity.

Practice Questions — Fact Recall

Q1 Give three ways in which intensive farming methods can increase productivity.

Q2 a) Describe the different types of biological agents that can be used to kill pest species.

   b) Give one economic issue with using biological agents.

Q3 What is an integrated system?

Q4 Explain the difference between natural and artificial fertilisers.

Q5 Describe an economic issue with using fertilisers.

Q6 Give one example of an ethical argument against rearing livestock intensively.

Exam Tip
Livestock means a population of <u>animals</u> kept by humans for a commercial purpose — so if you get a question about livestock, don't talk about plants.

Learning Objectives:

- Understand the role of microorganisms in the carbon cycle in sufficient detail to illustrate the process of saprobiontic nutrition. (The names of individual species are not required.)

- Understand the importance of respiration, photosynthesis and human activity in giving rise to short-term fluctuation and long-term change in global carbon dioxide concentration.

- Understand the roles of carbon dioxide and methane in enhancing the greenhouse effect and bringing about global warming.

Specification Reference 3.4.6

Tip: CO_2 diffuses into the air spaces within a leaf (via stomata), and then into the plant cells — they don't absorb carbon compounds through their roots.

***Figure 1**: Fungi (the white areas) have begun decomposing these slices of bread.*

Tip: Microorganisms that carry out saprobiontic nutrition are called saprobionts.

3. The Carbon Cycle and Global Warming

Photosynthesis is the main way that energy enters an ecosystem — it's how energy from sunlight is used to make carbon compounds, and so it's where the carbon cycle begins...

The carbon cycle

All organisms need carbon to make essential compounds, e.g. plants use CO_2 (carbon dioxide) in photosynthesis to make glucose. The carbon cycle is how carbon moves through living organisms and the non-living environment. It involves four processes — photosynthesis, respiration, decomposition and combustion:

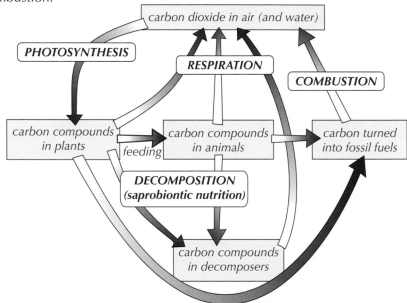

Photosynthesis

Carbon (in the form of CO_2 from air and water) is absorbed by plants when they carry out photosynthesis — it becomes carbon compounds in plant tissues. Carbon is passed on to primary consumers when they eat the plants. It's passed on to secondary and tertiary consumers when they eat other consumers.

Decomposition

All living organisms die and are broken down by microorganisms called **decomposers**, e.g. bacteria and fungi. Decomposers secrete enzymes which break down the carbon compounds (e.g. starch) in dead organic material. The decomposers then absorb the products of digestion (e.g. maltose) for use in respiration. Feeding on dead organic matter is called **saprobiontic nutrition** (see Figure 1).

Respiration

Carbon is returned to the air (and water) as all living organisms (including the decomposers) carry out respiration, which produces CO_2.

Combustion

If dead organic matter ends up in places where there aren't any decomposers, e.g. deep oceans or bogs, its carbon compounds can be turned into fossil fuels over millions of years (by heat and pressure). The carbon in fossil fuels is released when they're burnt — this is called combustion.

Fluctuations in CO₂ concentration

Respiration (which is carried out by all organisms) adds CO_2 to the atmosphere. Photosynthesis removes CO_2 from the atmosphere. The amount of respiration and photosynthesis going on varies on a daily and a yearly basis, so the amount of atmospheric CO_2 changes.

Daily change in CO₂ concentration

Respiration is carried out constantly through the day and night whereas photosynthesis only takes place during the daylight hours. CO_2 concentration falls during the day because it's being removed by plants as they carry out photosynthesis. In bright light, the rate of photosynthesis is greater than the rate of respiration by plants, so they use more CO_2 than they produce.

CO_2 concentration increases at night because it's no longer being removed (no photosynthesis is happening), but all organisms are still respiring and adding CO_2 to the atmosphere.

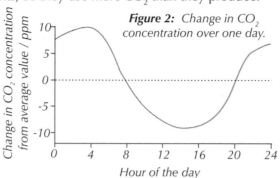

Figure 2: Change in CO_2 concentration over one day.

Yearly change in CO₂ concentration

Most plant life exists in the northern hemisphere because that's where most land is. Most plant growth occurs in the summer (June-Aug in the northern hemisphere) because that's when the light intensity is greatest — more photosynthesis can occur, which means there's more energy to grow. CO_2 concentration falls during the summer (see Figure 3) because more is being removed from the atmosphere as more plants are photosynthesising. CO_2 concentration increases throughout autumn and winter (Sep-April in the northern hemisphere) because less is being removed from the atmosphere, as fewer plants are photosynthesising.

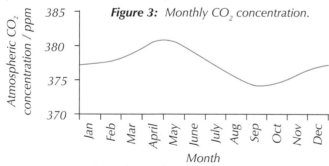

Figure 3: Monthly CO_2 concentration.

Practice Questions — Application

Q1 A scientist records the concentration of CO_2 in the air above a field of poppies over a 24 hour period in the summer. She found that the CO_2 concentration was highest during the night and lowest at midday. Use your knowledge of photosynthesis to explain these results.

Q2 The scientist expands her study to record the concentration of CO_2 above the same field in the UK over the course of a year. Predict what her findings will be and explain your answer.

Exam Tip
When writing about how respiration increases CO_2 concentration, you need to be precise and say 'respiration by plants/ animals/all organisms' (depending on the context) to get the full marks.

Exam Tip
It's really important to remember that respiration occurs during the day and night, but photosynthesis happens during the day only.

Tip: CO_2 can change with area too. E.g. in a forest, CO_2 concentration is greatest at ground level and then decreases with height. This is because there are fewer leaves at ground level and less light for photosynthesis. Also, there are more animals at ground level which are releasing CO_2 by respiration.

Exam Tip
You could be asked about the changes in CO_2 concentration for any type of context, e.g. over a forest or a roundabout. Don't be thrown by the context, just remember to think about whether it will effect the level of CO_2. For example, there may be a higher level of CO_2 at a roundabout due to traffic.

Figure 7: An increase in cattle rearing has increased the amount of methane released into the atmosphere.

Global warming

Global warming is the term for the increase in average global temperature over the last century (see Figure 4). There's a scientific consensus that this increase has been caused by human activity. (It can't be explained by natural causes, which happen more slowly.)

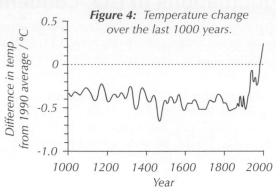

Figure 4: Temperature change over the last 1000 years.

Human activity has caused global warming by enhancing the **greenhouse effect** — the effect of **greenhouse gases** absorbing outgoing energy, so that less is lost to space. The greenhouse effect is essential to keep the planet warm, but too much greenhouse gas in the atmosphere means the planet warms up.

Two of the main greenhouse gases are CO_2 and methane. An increase in human activities like burning fossil fuels (for industry and in cars), farming and deforestation has increased atmospheric concentrations of CO_2 and methane. This has enhanced the greenhouse effect and caused a rise in average global temperature — global warming.

Carbon dioxide (CO_2)

Atmospheric CO_2 concentration has increased rapidly since the mid-19th century from 280 ppm (parts per million) to nearly 380 ppm (see Figure 5). The concentration had been stable for the previous 10 000 years.

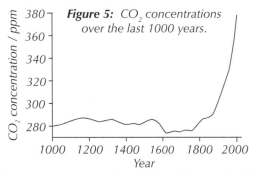

Figure 5: CO_2 concentrations over the last 1000 years.

CO_2 concentration is increasing as more fossil fuels like coal, oil, natural gas and petrol are burnt, e.g. in power stations or in cars. Burning fossil fuels releases CO_2. CO_2 concentration is also increased by the destruction of natural **sinks** (things that keep CO_2 out of the atmosphere by storing carbon). E.g. trees are a big CO_2 sink — they store the carbon as organic compounds. CO_2 is released when trees are burnt, or when decomposers break down the organic compounds and respire.

Methane

Atmospheric methane concentration has increased rapidly since the mid-19th century from 700 ppb (parts per billion) to 1700 ppb in 2000 — see Figure 6. The level had been stable for the previous 850 years.

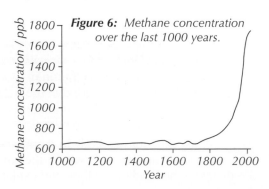

Figure 6: Methane concentration over the last 1000 years.

Methane concentration is increasing because more methane is being released into the atmosphere, e.g. because more fossil fuels are being extracted, there's more decaying waste and there are more cattle which give off methane as a waste gas. Methane can also be released from natural stores, e.g. frozen ground (permafrost). As temperatures increase it's thought these stores will thaw and release large amounts of methane into the atmosphere.

Tip: Incomplete combustion of fossil fuels gives off methane and so does decaying waste.

Practice Questions — Application

The graph below shows the average atmospheric concentrations of CO_2 and methane above two areas of forest, X and Y, over 11 years.

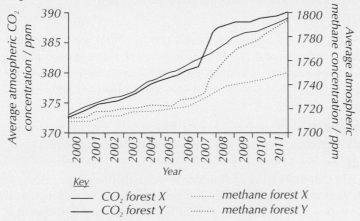

Key
— CO_2 forest X .... methane forest X
— CO_2 forest Y .... methane forest Y

Tip: Make sure you read the graph carefully — there's a lot going on with both the axes and all the lines, so it's easy to make a mistake if you rush.

Q1 Does this graph provide evidence for a global change in CO_2 concentration over the past century? Explain your answer.

Q2 One of the forests was cleared of its trees.

    a) In which forest was deforestation carried out and what year did it start? Explain your answers.

    b) Use evidence from the graph to suggest a way in which this cleared land was used.

    c) Explain how deforestation can contribute to global warming.

Practice Questions — Fact Recall

Q1 Describe the movement of carbon through the carbon cycle.

Q2 What is the process of feeding on dead organic matter called?

Q3 Explain why CO_2 concentration is greater at night than during the day.

Q4 What is global warming?

Q5 Explain the link between an increase in CO_2 concentration in the atmosphere and global warming.

Q6 Describe one human activity that is:

    a) increasing atmospheric CO_2 concentration.

    b) increasing atmospheric methane concentration.

Tip: Remember, there are four main processes involved in the carbon cycle.

■ Be able to analyse,
interpret and evaluate
data relating to
evidence of global
warming and its
effects on:
  ■ the yield of crop
    plants,
  ■ the life-cycles and
    numbers of insect
    pests,
  ■ the distribution
    and numbers of wild
    animals and plants.
**Specification
Reference 3.4.6**

Tip: A limiting factor
for photosynthesis is
something that can stop
it from happening any
faster, e.g. temperature,
CO_2 concentration and
light intensity (see p.40).

Tip: Global warming
could also cause a
decrease in crop yield,
e.g. by causing severe
weather that could
damage or limit plant
growth, or by affecting
soil fertility and water
availability.

Tip: Don't forget that
changing temperature
can also indirectly affect
an animal's distribution.
For example, warmer
temperatures might
allow the spread of
plants eaten by an
animal species — and
the spread of food
sources might be
more important than
changing temperatures
in the expansion of the
animal's range.

4. The Effects of Global Warming

*Global warming is a rise in average global temperature over the last century,
but its effects are more complicated than us just feeling a bit warmer...*

Effects of global warming on organisms

Increasing CO_2 concentration is causing global warming (see p. 64), which is
leading to other climate changes, e.g. different rainfall patterns and changes
to seasonal weather patterns.   All organisms could be affected by this, but
different organisms could be affected in different ways.

Crop yield

The increasing CO_2 concentration that's causing global warming could also
be causing an increase in crop yields (the amount of crops produced from an
area). CO_2 concentration is a limiting factor for photosynthesis, so increasing
global CO_2 concentration could mean crops grow faster, increasing
crop yields.

Insect pests

Climate change may affect the life cycle of some insect species.

> **Example**
>
> It's thought that increasing global temperature means some insects go
> through their larval stage quicker and emerge as adults earlier, e.g. some
> butterflies may spend 10 fewer days as larvae for every 1 °C rise in
> temperature.

Climate change may also affect the numbers of some insect species. Some
species are becoming more abundant, whilst other species are becoming less
abundant.

> **Examples**
>
> ■ Warmer and wetter summers in some places have led to an increase in
>   the number of mosquitoes.
> ■ Some tropical insect species can only thrive in specific temperature
>   ranges, so if it gets too hot fewer insects may be able to reproduce
>   successfully.

Wild animals and plants

Climate change could affect the distribution of many wild animal and plant
species. Some species may become more widely distributed, e.g. species that
need warmer temperatures may spread further as the conditions they thrive in
exist over a wider area. Other species may become less widely distributed,
e.g. species that need cooler temperatures may have smaller ranges as the
conditions they thrive in exist over a smaller area.

Climate change could also affect the number of wild animals and
plants. Some species are becoming more abundant and other species are
becoming less abundant.

> **Examples**
>
> ■ Boarfish are increasing in number in parts of the Atlantic Ocean where
>   sea temperature is rising.
> ■ Polar bears need frozen sea ice to hunt and global warming is causing
>   more sea ice to melt. It's thought that the number of polar bears is
>   decreasing because there isn't enough sea ice for them to hunt on.

Analysing data on the effects of global warming

Analysing data's pretty important when looking at the effects of global warming. Here are a few examples:

Example 1 — Temperature and Crop Yield

A study was carried out to investigate whether rising growing season temperature is affecting crop yields. Some of the data from the study is shown in Figure 1.

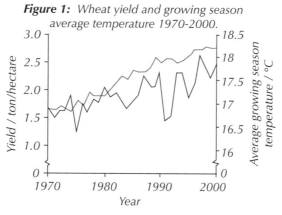

Figure 1: *Wheat yield and growing season average temperature 1970-2000.*

KEY
— wheat yield
— temperature

Tip: The unit 'ton/hectare' means the number of tons of crop per hectare of field.

You might be asked to:

Describe the data:

The temperature fluctuated between 1970 and 2000, but the general trend was a steady increase from just under 17 °C to just under 18 °C. The wheat yield also showed a trend of increasing from around 1.6 tons per hectare in 1970 to around 2.7 tons per hectare in 2000.

Exam Tip
If you're asked to describe a graph it's a good idea to include figures from the graph in your answer.

Draw a conclusion:

The graph shows a positive correlation between temperature and wheat yield. The increasing growing season temperature could be linked to the increasing wheat yields.

Even though the graph shows a correlation, you can't conclude that the increase in temperature caused the increase in wheat yield — there could have been other factors involved. This study actually found that the rising growing season temperature had a negative effect on wheat yields, but improvements in technology during the same period meant that crop yields increased overall.

Tip: Remember, just because there's a correlation between two sets of data doesn't always mean there's a causal relationship. See page 5 for more on drawing conclusions.

Example 2 — Temperature and Insect Numbers

A study counted the number of greenfly in an area from 1960 to 2000. A separate study collected data on global temperature at the same time. The results are shown in Figure 2.

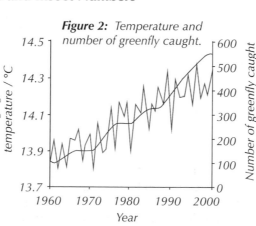

Figure 2: *Temperature and number of greenfly caught.*

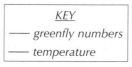

KEY
— greenfly numbers
— temperature

You might be asked to:

Describe the data:
The temperature fluctuated between 1960 and 2000, but the general trend was a steady increase from just over 13.8 °C to just over 14.4 °C.
The number of greenfly also fluctuated with a generally increasing trend from around 110 in 1960 to just around 480 in 2000.

Draw a conclusion:
There's a positive correlation between temperature and numbers of greenfly. The increasing global temperature could be linked to the increasing greenfly numbers.

Suggest an explanation for your conclusion:
Greenfly numbers could be increasing because higher temperatures may increase their food supply, e.g. the rate of photosynthesis may increase at higher temperatures, allowing plants to grow faster and become larger.

Example 3 — Temperature and the Distribution of Organisms

A study was carried out to investigate the effect of temperature on the changing distribution of subtropical plankton species in the north Atlantic. Data collected on global sea surface temperature is shown in Figure 3 and the results of the plankton distribution study are shown in Figure 4.

Figure 3: Global sea temperature change.

 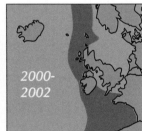

Figure 4: Subtropical plankton distribution.

■ subtropical plankton

You might be asked to:

Describe the data:
Sea surface temperature fluctuated around the average between 1950 and 1978, then there was a steady increase between 1978 and 2000, up to just over 0.3 °C greater than the average.

Subtropical plankton species were found in the sea south of the UK in 1958-1981. By 2000-2002 their distribution had moved further north along the west coast of the UK and Ireland to the Arctic Ocean.

Draw a conclusion:
There's a link between rising global sea surface temperature and the northward change in distribution of subtropical plankton.

The data shows a link, but you can't say that the increase in temperature caused the change in distribution — there could have been other factors involved, e.g. overfishing could have removed plankton predator species.

Practice Questions — Application

Q1 A study recorded the abundance of aphids (a pest species) in an area from 1960 to 2000. The same study recorded the mean April temperature of the area. The results are shown on the graph below.

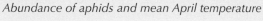

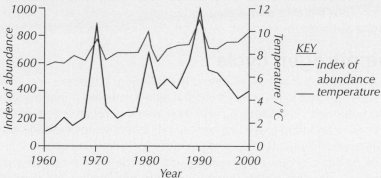

Tip: The index of abundance is just an estimate of the size of a population of organisms.

a) Describe in detail the data shown on the graph.

b) Draw a conclusion from the data shown on the graph.

c) The study concludes that warmer spring temperatures have encouraged the hatching of aphid eggs, which in turn has caused the population spikes. Is this conclusion valid? Explain your answer.

Q2 A farmer is concerned by reports that a rise in temperature may cause a species of aphid to begin breeding earlier in the year, and the effect this would have on his crops. He reads an agricultural magazine which has collected laboratory data to produce the graph below:

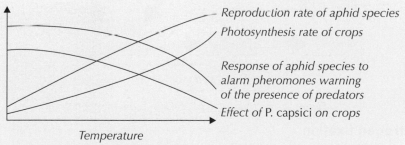

Tip: There are lots of different species of aphid.

Tip: Pheromones are chemicals that allow communication between members of the same species.

The magazine used this graph to conclude that global warming may be beneficial for crop growth.

a) Suggest why the magazine reached this conclusion.

b) The farmer believes that the magazine's conclusions are not valid and remains concerned for his crops. Explain why he is right.

Tip: *P. capsici* is a pathogen which affects some crops.

Practice Questions — Fact Recall

Q1 Explain why an increasing global CO_2 concentration could cause an increase in crop yields.

Q2 Give two ways that climate change is affecting insect pest species.

Q3 Suggest why climate change may cause some species to become more widely distributed and other species to become less widely distributed.

- Understand the role of microorganisms in the nitrogen cycle in sufficient detail to illustrate the processes of nitrogen fixation, ammonification, nitrification and denitrification. (The names of individual species are not required.)

- Know the environmental issues arising from the use of fertilisers.

- Understand the processes of leaching and eutrophication.

- Be able to analyse, interpret and evaluate data relating to eutrophication.

Specification Reference 3.4.6

Figure 1: *Pink nodules of* Rhizobium *on plant roots.*

Tip: There's more about what reduction means on page 31.

Tip: Don't worry — you <u>don't</u> need to learn the names of the microorganisms.

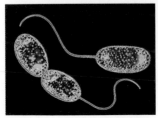

Figure 3: *Nitrobacter* *bacteria.*

5. The Nitrogen Cycle and Eutrophication

Plants and animals need nitrogen to make proteins and nucleic acids for growth. There are natural processes that make nitrogen available to plants, but for crops this isn't always enough. Farmers can add extra nitrogen to soil by using fertilisers, but this can cause environmental problems.

The nitrogen cycle

The atmosphere's made up of about 78% nitrogen, but plants and animals can't use it in that form — they need bacteria to convert it into nitrogen compounds first. The nitrogen cycle shows how nitrogen is converted into a usable form and then passed on between different living organisms and the non-living environment. The nitrogen cycle includes food chains (nitrogen is passed on when organisms are eaten), and four different processes that involve bacteria — nitrogen fixation, ammonification, nitrification and denitrification:

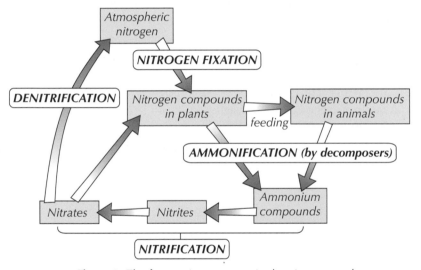

Figure 2: *The four main processes in the nitrogen cycle.*

Nitrogen fixation

Nitrogen fixation is when nitrogen gas in the atmosphere is reduced to ammonia by bacteria called *Rhizobium*. The ammonia can then be used by plants.

Rhizobium are found inside root nodules (growths on the roots — see Figure 1) of leguminous plants (e.g. peas, beans and clover). They form a **mutualistic relationship** with the plants — they provide the plant with nitrogen compounds and the plant provides them with carbohydrates.

Ammonification

Ammonification is when nitrogen compounds from dead organisms are turned into ammonium compounds by **decomposers** (see p. 62).

Animal waste (urine and faeces) also contains nitrogen compounds. These are also turned into ammonium compounds by decomposers.

Nitrification

Nitrification is when ammonium compounds in the soil are changed into nitrogen compounds that can then be used by plants. First **nitrifying bacteria** (e.g. *Nitrosomonas*) change ammonium compounds into nitrites. Then other nitrifying bacteria called *Nitrobacter* (see Figure 3) change nitrites into nitrates.

Denitrification

Denitrification is when nitrates in the soil are converted into nitrogen gas by **denitrifying bacteria** (see Figure 4) — they use nitrates in the soil to carry out respiration and produce nitrogen gas. This happens under anaerobic conditions (where there's no oxygen), e.g. in waterlogged soils.

Nitrogen fertilisers and eutrophication

Parts of the nitrogen cycle can also be carried out artificially and on an industrial scale. The **Haber process** produces ammonia from atmospheric nitrogen — it's used to make things like fertilisers.

Nitrogen fertilisers are sprayed onto fields of crops by farmers, so that the crops have enough nitrogen for maximum growth. However, nitrogen fertilisers can be **leached** into waterways (e.g. when too much is applied to a field). Leaching is when water-soluble compounds in the soil are washed away, e.g. by rain or irrigation systems. They're often washed into nearby ponds and rivers. The leaching of nitrogen fertilisers can cause **eutrophication** — this is explained below and in Figure 5.

1. Nitrates leached from fertilised fields stimulate the growth of algae in ponds and rivers.
2. Large amounts of algae block light from reaching the plants below.
3. Eventually the plants die because they're unable to photosynthesise enough.
4. Bacteria feed on the dead plant matter. The increased numbers of bacteria reduce the oxygen concentration in the water by carrying out aerobic respiration.
5. Fish and other aquatic organisms die because there isn't enough dissolved oxygen.

Figure 4: Pseudomonas aeruginosa *are a type of denitrifying bacteria.*

Tip: Less denitrification happens in soils that contain more oxygen (e.g. sandy soils), than in waterlogged soils (e.g. clay soils) — because denitrifying bacteria work in anaerobic conditions.

Tip: Eutrophication is where too many nitrates in the water cause a sequence of "mega-growth, mega-death and mega-decay" involving most of the plant and animal life in the water.

Tip: There's more about fertilisers and why they're used on page 61.

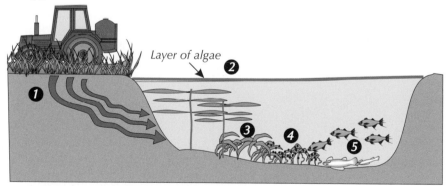

Layer of algae

Figure 5: *The process of eutrophication.*

Practice Questions — Fact Recall

Q1 What is nitrogen fixation?

Q2 What type of organisms carry out ammonification?

Q3 Describe the process of nitrification.

Q4 Name the process by which nitrates in the soil are converted into nitrogen gas by bacteria.

Q5 By what process do nitrogen fertilisers get into waterways?

Q6 During eutrophication large numbers of bacteria feed on dead plant matter. Explain how this can lead to the death of fish and other aquatic organisms.

Interpreting data on eutrophication

You've got to know how to analyse data, so here's an example of the kind of thing you might get in your exam:

Tip: There's more information about controls on pages 3-4.

Figure 6: Algae growing on the Thames estuary.

Example

A study was conducted to investigate the effect, on a nearby river, of adding fertiliser to farmland.

The oxygen and algal content of a river that runs past a field where nitrate fertiliser had been applied, was measured at the field and up to a distance of 180 m away. A similar control river next to an unfertilised field was also studied. The results are shown in Figures 7 and 8.

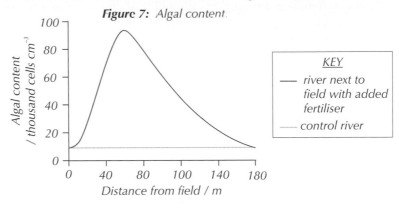

Figure 7: Algal content.

KEY
— river next to field with added fertiliser
······ control river

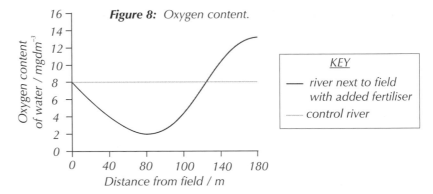

Figure 8: Oxygen content.

KEY
— river next to field with added fertiliser
······ control river

Describe the data:

The algal content of the water increases sharply from 10 000 cells cm^{-3} at the field to 95 000 cells cm^{-3} at a distance of 60 m from the field. Algal content then decreases beyond 60 m to 10 000 cells cm^{-3} at 180 m.

The oxygen content of the water decreases from 8 $mgdm^{-3}$ at the field to 2 $mgdm^{-3}$ at a distance of 80 m from the field. The oxygen content then increases beyond 80 m up to 13 $mgdm^{-3}$ at 180 m, where it begins to level off.

The control river showed a steady algal content of 10 000 cells cm^{-3} at all distances, as well as a steady oxygen content of 8 $mgdm^{-3}$ at all distances.

Draw a conclusion:

There's a negative correlation between the algal content and the oxygen content of the water — as the algal content increases, the oxygen content decreases, and vice versa.

Evaluate the methodology:

A control river was used which helps to control the effect of some variables, e.g. water temperature. But it doesn't remove the effect of all variables, e.g. different organisms may live in the control river, which could affect the algal or oxygen content.

The experiment only looked at two rivers, which means the sample size was small. Studying other rivers may have produced different results and a different conclusion. More experiments and results would be needed to make the data more reliable.

Suggest an explanation for your conclusion:

The results suggest leaching of the fertiliser and eutrophication have occurred. Nitrate fertilisers from the field could have leached into the river and caused the algal content of the river to increase by stimulating algal growth. The increased algal content could have prevented light from reaching plants below, causing them to die and be decomposed by bacteria. The bacteria use up the oxygen in the river when carrying out aerobic respiration, resulting in decreased dissolved oxygen levels.

Tip: When evaluating the methodology you need to think about what the people behind the experiment are trying to do and whether the experiment achieves this. Look at the sample size used, if there was a control and whether or not all of the other variables have been controlled.

Practice Questions — Application

A study was conducted to investigate the changes in nitrate concentration and algal content down a stretch of river with two farms along it (river A). In the same study, the nitrate concentration and algal content of a river without farmland along it (control river) was also recorded. The results are shown in the graph below:

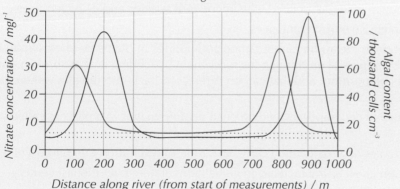

Nitrate concentration and algal content of two rivers

KEY

—— river A nitrate concentration   ····· control river nitrate concentration
—— river A algal content   ····· control river algal content

Q1 Describe the data shown by the graph for river A.

Q2 a) Suggest the distance at which the two farms are situated along river A. Explain your answer.

   b) i) Calculate the percentage increase in peak nitrate concentration between the first and second farm along the river.

   ii) Suggest a reason for this increase.

Q3 Describe the data shown by the graph for the control river.

Q4 a) Draw a conclusion from the data shown in the graph.

   b) Suggest an explanation for your conclusion.

Exam Tip
Make sure you know your way around basic maths — you could get some maths questions in the exam, and they're easy marks if you know what you're doing.

Section Summary

Make sure you know...

- That the main route by which energy enters an ecosystem is photosynthesis.
- That energy is transferred through a food chain and food web from a producer to primary consumers, then to secondary consumers and finally to tertiary consumers by feeding.
- That each of the stages within a food chain (the producers, primary consumers, secondary consumers and tertiary consumers) are called trophic levels.
- How energy is lost as it is transferred between trophic levels, e.g. some parts of food aren't eaten by organisms, so not all of the energy is taken in.
- That you can work out the total amount of energy that can be passed from one trophic level to the next using the equation: net productivity = gross productivity − respiratory loss.
- How to work out percentage efficiency of energy transfer using the equation:
  (net productivity of trophic level ÷ net productivity of previous trophic level) × 100
- That food chains can be drawn as pyramids of numbers (to show the number of organisms at each trophic level), pyramids of biomass (to show the amount of biomass at each trophic level) and pyramids of energy (to show the amount of energy at each trophic level).
- Why pyramids of number and pyramids of biomass are not always pyramid shaped, and why pyramids of energy are always pyramid shaped.
- That a natural ecosystem is an ecosystem that hasn't been changed by human activity.
- That intensive farming changes an ecosystem by altering its energy input and productivity.
- How killing pest species (by using chemical pesticides, biological agents or integrated systems), using fertilisers (natural and artificial) and rearing livestock intensively increase productivity by increasing the efficiency of energy conversion in a food chain.
- The economic and environmental issues associated with killing pest species and using fertilisers.
- The ethical issues raised by intensive farming practices.
- That in the carbon cycle, carbon in the air becomes carbon compounds in plants by photosynthesis, that these carbon compounds are passed on through the food chain by feeding and are broken down by microorganisms during decomposition, and that carbon is released back into the atmosphere by respiration and combustion.
- How some microorganisms called decomposers feed on dead organic matter in a process called saprobiontic nutrition.
- How CO_2 concentration fluctuates on a daily and yearly basis, due to respiration and photosynthesis.
- That global warming is the term given to the increase in global temperature over the last century and that human activity has caused it by enhancing the greenhouse effect.
- How increases in CO_2 concentration and methane concentration are enhancing the greenhouse effect.
- How global warming can lead to climate change, which could affect crop yield, the life cycle and numbers of insect pests, and the distribution and abundance of wild animals and plants.
- How to analyse, interpret and evaluate data about global warming and its effects on crop yield, insect pests, and wild animals and plants.
- The role of microorganisms in the four main processes of the nitrogen cycle, which are nitrogen fixation, ammonification, nitrification and denitrification.
- That leaching is when water soluble compounds in the soil are washed away, e.g by rain.
- That the leaching of nitrogen fertilisers can cause eutrophication.
- How to analyse, interpret and evaluate data on eutrophication.

Exam-style Questions

1   On the right is a diagram showing the net productivity of some organisms in a food web. All the figures are in $kJm^{-2}yr^{-1}$.

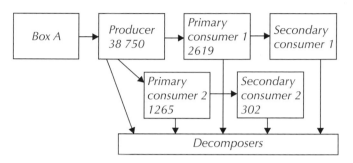

1 (a)   What source of energy is represented by Box A?

(1 mark)

1 (b)   Name the process by which energy from Box A is transferred to the producer and give one reason why this energy transfer is not 100% efficient.

(2 marks)

1 (c)   The respiratory loss of secondary consumer 1 is 1571 $kJm^{-2}yr^{-1}$ and its gross productivity is 2143 $kJm^{-2}yr^{-1}$. Calculate its net productivity.

(2 marks)

1 (d)   Give two reasons why the energy absorbed by secondary consumer 2 will not equal 1265 $kJm^{-2}yr^{-1}$.

(2 marks)

1 (e)   Calculate the difference in the percentage efficiency of energy transfer between the producer and primary consumer 1, and the producer and primary consumer 2.

(3 marks)

1 (f) (i)   Producers contain carbon compounds, e.g. cellulose. Describe how decomposers make this carbon available to other producers.

(4 marks)

1 (f) (ii)   Describe one other way in which carbon compounds in plants become carbon dioxide in the air.

(2 marks)

2   The diagram on the right shows a simplified version of the nitrogen cycle.

2 (a)   Name the process labelled Y in the diagram.

(1 mark)

2 (b)   Describe the three processes of the nitrogen cycle named on the diagram.

(6 marks)

2 (c)   Explain how the use of nitrate fertilisers can cause eutrophication.

(6 marks)

3   A study was carried out to investigate the effect of different types of pest control
on greenfly – a pest species. Three fields of potato crops, each with a greenfly
infestation, were treated with a different type of pest control — one with a pesticide,
the other with lacewing insects (a natural predator of greenfly) and the third with an
integrated system. The study included a control. The number of greenfly in each
field was recorded over time. The net productivity of each field was also measured.
The graphs below show the results.

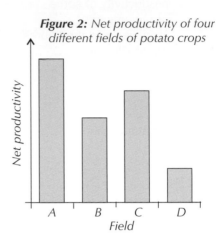

Figure 1: Number of greenfly in four different fields of potato crops over time

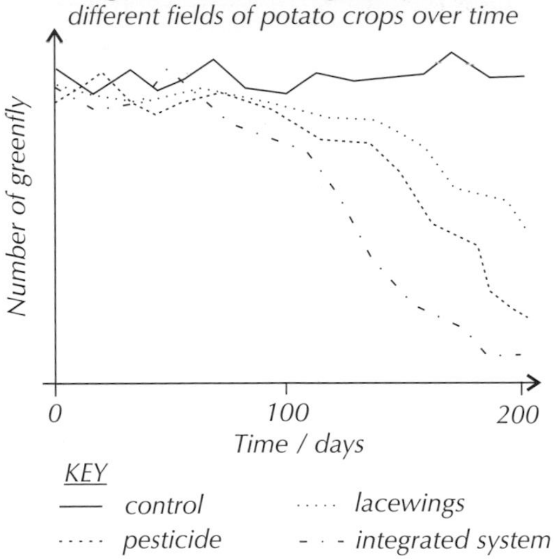

Figure 2: Net productivity of four different fields of potato crops

KEY
—— *control*   ····· *lacewings*
····· *pesticide*   - · · *integrated system*

3 (a)   Describe the control used in this study.

(1 mark)

3 (b)   Using the results of Figure 1 and your own knowledge, identify which field
in Figure 2 is the control field and which is the field treated with the
integrated system. Explain your answers.

(4 marks)

3 (c)   The table below shows the cost of using lacewings or pesticide on one field of crops
(approx. 10 acres).

Type of pest control	Price per field (£)
Lacewings	100
Pesticide	750

A farmer's crops have been affected by greenfly. He decides to control the pest
using lacewings.

3 (c) (i)   Use the graphs provided above to discuss the disadvantages of using lacewings
compared to pesticides and integrated systems.

(3 marks)

3 (c) (ii)   Using all the information provided above, suggest why the farmer decided to use
lacewings rather than other forms of pest control.

(4 marks)

1. Succession

The plants and animals in an environment gradually change over long periods of time — and the environment itself changes too. This is due to a natural process called succession.

What is succession?

Succession is the process by which an ecosystem (see page 7) changes over time. Succession happens in a series of stages. At each stage, the species in an area slowly change the environmental conditions (for example, by making the soil more fertile), making those conditions more suitable for other species. This means that the **biotic conditions** change as the **abiotic conditions** change, causing one community of organisms to be succeeded (replaced) by another. There are two main types of succession — primary succession (see below) and secondary succession (see page 79).

Primary succession

Primary succession happens on land that's been newly formed or exposed, e.g. where a volcano has erupted to form a new rock surface, or where sea level has dropped exposing a new area of land. There's no soil or organic material to start with, e.g. just bare rock.

Pioneer stage of succession

Primary succession starts when species colonise a new land surface. Seeds and spores are blown in by the wind and begin to grow. The first species to colonise the area are called **pioneer species**. The abiotic conditions are hostile (harsh) and only pioneer species can grow because they're specialised to cope with the harsh conditions.

┌─ Examples ─────────────────────────────────

Hostile abiotic conditions

- There is limited water available because there's no soil to retain water.

- There are few minerals or nutrients because there's no soil.

- There may be high light intensity, exposure to wind and rain, and fluctuating temperatures because the area is directly exposed to the Sun and the elements.

Pioneer species

- Marram grass can grow on sand dunes near the sea because it has deep roots to get water and can tolerate the salty environment (see Figure 1).

- Lichens are organisms usually made up of a fungus and an alga. They're able to survive in rocky conditions because the fungus secretes acids which erode the rock, releasing minerals.

- Shrubs of the *Calligonum* genus are pioneer species that can grow in areas that experience periodic drought.

Learning Objectives:

- Understand succession from pioneer species to climax community.

- Understand that at each stage in succession, certain species may be recognised which change the environment so that it becomes more suitable for other species.

- Understand that the changes in the abiotic environment result in a less hostile environment and changing diversity.

Specification Reference 3.4.7

Tip: Biotic conditions are the living features of an ecosystem, e.g. the plant and animal communities. Abiotic conditions are the non-living features, such as light, CO_2 and water availability.

Figure 1: *Marram grass is able to grow in hostile conditions on sand dunes.*

The pioneer species change the abiotic conditions — they die and microorganisms decompose the dead organic material (humus). This forms a basic soil. This makes conditions less hostile, e.g. the basic soil helps to retain water, which means new organisms can move in and grow. The new organisms then die and are decomposed, adding more organic material, making the soil deeper and richer in minerals such as nitrates. Nitrogen-fixing bacteria turn nitrogen from the atmosphere into ammonia, which can then be used by plants (see page 70). This means larger plants like shrubs can start to grow in the deeper soil, which retains even more water and contains more nutrients.

Tip: A community is all the populations of different species found in a habitat (see page 10).

Tip: You learnt about species diversity at AS level — it's the number of different species and the abundance of each species within a community.

Tip: Biomass is the mass of living organisms in an ecosystem.

Later stages of succession

At each stage, different plants and animals that are better adapted for the improved conditions move in, out-compete the plants and animals that are already there, and become the dominant species in the ecosystem. The dominant species are the ones which cause the most change to the abiotic environment, making it more suitable for other species.

As succession goes on, the ecosystem becomes more complex. New species move in alongside existing species, which means the species diversity increases. Plants create more habitats for animals, the abiotic conditions become less hostile and the amount of biomass increases.

Eventually these changes result in a **climax community** — the ecosystem is supporting the largest and most complex community of plants and animals it can. It won't change much more — it's in a steady state.

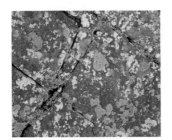

Figure 2: *Lichens (orange and white) have adaptations that allow them to live on bare rock.*

Tip: Primary succession also happens on sand dunes, salt marshes and even in lakes.

Exam Tip
You don't need to learn the exact details of this example for the exam, but you do need to understand what's going on and why.

Example — primary succession

1. Bare rock lacks soil, is exposed to strong winds and has periods of drought. Lichens (the pioneer species) are able to survive because they can grow in cracks to avoid the wind, break down rock to release minerals and are adapted to survive periods of drought.

bare rock — lichen

2. The lichens die and are decomposed helping to form a thin soil, which thickens as more organic material is formed. This means other species such as mosses can grow.

thin soil — moss

3. Larger plants that need more water can move in as the soil deepens, e.g. grasses and small flowering plants. The soil continues to deepen as the larger plants die and are decomposed.

small flowering plants — grass

4. Shrubs, ferns and small trees begin to grow, out-competing the grasses and smaller plants to become the dominant species. Diversity increases.

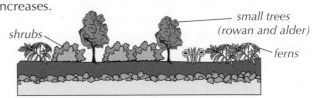
shrubs — small trees (rowan and alder) — ferns

5. Finally, the soil is deep and rich enough in nutrients to support large trees. These become the dominant species, and the climax community is formed.

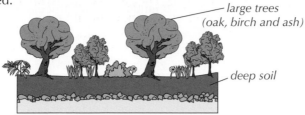

large trees (oak, birch and ash)

deep soil

Tip: Tall plants can reduce the light available to shorter plants and can help stabilise fluctuating temperatures. For example, trees increase air humidity, provide shade and reduce wind, which moderates local temperatures.

Secondary succession

Secondary succession happens on land that's been cleared of all the plants, but where the soil remains, e.g. after a forest fire or where a forest has been cut down by humans. The established community of species is usually destroyed, but without too much disturbance to the soil. It can occur during any stage (including the climax community) after the pioneer stage.

The process of secondary succession is similar to primary succession, but because there's already a soil layer, secondary succession starts at a later stage — and the pioneer species are larger plants, e.g. shrubs.

┌─ **Example — secondary succession** ─────────

An investigation was carried out into secondary succession following controlled burning in an Indonesian grassland. The investigators recorded the percentage cover of plant species at nearly 300 sites, 3 years, 4 years and 9 years after burning.

Data showed a fall in the percentage cover of a species of grass, a rise in the percentage cover of a species of bracken, and a rise in shrubs and young trees (see Figure 4).

Figure 3: *Secondary succession following a forest fire.*

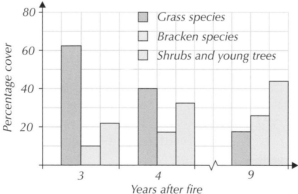

Figure 4: *Graph to show the change in percentage cover of species on an Indonesian grassland following a fire.*

Legend:
- Grass species
- Bracken species
- Shrubs and young trees

(y-axis: Percentage cover, values 20, 40, 60, 80)
(x-axis: Years after fire, values 3, 4, 9)

Tip: The main difference between the two types of succession is that soil is present at the start of secondary succession but not in primary succession. Secondary succession also tends to reach the climax community more quickly as a result.

Ash from the fire caused the pH of the soil to increase (become more alkaline). The results show that the percentage cover of plants was initially dominated by grass (the pioneer species), which was able to tolerate the alkaline conditions. Larger plants then began to grow and out-competed the grasses by changing the abiotic conditions, making it harder for the grasses to survive. For example, they cast shade, reducing the amount of light available to the grasses for photosynthesis and growth, causing their percentage cover to fall. The addition of organic material from the bracken to the soil altered the soil conditions, making it harder for the grass seeds to germinate.

Tip: Remember, in both primary and secondary succession, the species at each stage change the local abiotic conditions. This allows species that are better adapted for the improved conditions to move in and out-compete the species already there.

Climatic climax communities

Which species make up the climax community depends on what the climate's like in an ecosystem. The climax community for a particular climate is called its **climatic climax**.

Examples

- In a temperate climate, e.g. the UK, there's plenty of available water, mild temperatures and not much change between the seasons. The climatic climax will contain large trees because they can grow in these conditions once deep soils have developed (see Figure 5).

- In a polar climate there's not much available water, temperatures are low and there are massive changes between the seasons. Large trees won't ever be able to grow in these conditions, so the climatic climax contains only herbs or shrubs, but it's still the climax community (see Figure 6).

Figure 5: The climax community in many parts of Britain is deciduous woodland.

Figure 6: The climax community in most of Greenland is arctic tundra.

Tip: 'Remains viable for' means how long the plant seeds are capable of germinating (sprouting).

Practice Questions — Application

A team analysed data on ecological changes in part of a national park. Their results are shown in the graph below.

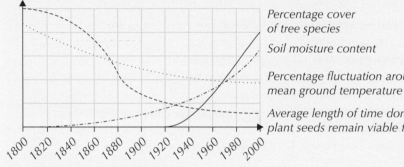

Percentage cover of tree species

Soil moisture content

Percentage fluctuation around mean ground temperature

Average length of time dominant plant seeds remain viable for

Time (years)

Q1 What type of succession is shown on the graph? Explain your answer.

Q2 Describe the characteristics of the dominant plant community between 1800 and 1860.

Q3 Describe and suggest an explanation for the change shown in the average length of time dominant plant seeds remain viable for.

Q4 During what time period would you expect to see a high percentage of plants whose seeds require high light intensity for germination? Explain your answer.

Q5 Describe and suggest an explanation for the change in the soil moisture content shown on the graph.

Practice Questions — Fact Recall

Q1 What is succession?

Q2 Which type of succession happens in areas with no soil?

Q3 What is a climax community?

Q4 Suggest an event that could cause secondary succession.

Q5 What is a climatic climax community?

Exam Tip
You need to be able to use the correct ecological terms (like primary succession, climax community, etc.) in your exam — and spell them correctly too.

2. Conservation

Lots of things humans do endanger species and cause the loss of habitats. Happily, all is not lost — there are things we can do to protect them.

What is conservation?

Conservation is the protection and management of species and habitats. It's a dynamic process as conservation methods need to be adapted to the constant changes (caused naturally and by humans) that occur within ecosystems.

The importance of conservation

Conservation is important for many reasons, for example, economic ones. Ecosystems provide resources for lots of things that humans need, e.g. rainforests contain species that provide things like drugs, clothes and food. These resources are economically important because they're traded on a local and global scale. If the ecosystems aren't conserved, the resources that we use now will be lost, so there will be less trade in the future.

Some people also think we should conserve species simply because it's the right thing to do, e.g. most people think organisms have a right to exist, so they shouldn't become extinct as a result of human activity. Also, many species and habitats bring joy to lots of people because they're attractive to look at. The species and habitats may be lost if they aren't conserved, so future generations won't be able to enjoy them.

There are ecological reasons for conservation too, as conserving species and habitats can help to prevent climate change. E.g. when trees are burnt, CO_2 is released into the atmosphere, which contributes to global warming. If the trees are conserved, this doesn't happen. Conserving species and habitats also helps to prevent the disruption of food chains. Disruption of food chains can have knock-on effects on other organisms, e.g. some species of bear feed on salmon, which feed on herring — if the number of herring decreases it can affect both the salmon and the bear populations.

Conflicts in conservation

Not everyone agrees with every conservation measure though, as some conservation methods can cause conflict.

--- Examples ---

Conflict with people's livelihoods

The conservation of the Siberian tiger in Russia affects people who make money from killing the tigers and selling their fur (there's conflict between the conservationists and the hunters).

Conflict with other species

Peregrine falcons are an endangered species. To help recover their numbers in part of America, peregrine falcons were encouraged to nest in an area that was also used by other birds, including red knots.

A study has found that the peregrine falcons have caused a decline in the local population of red knots through reducing the available habitats (see Figure 1).

Learning Objectives:

- Be able to use your knowledge and understanding to present scientific arguments and ideas relating to the conservation of species and habitats.
- Understand that conservation of habitats frequently involves management of succession.

Specification Reference 3.4.7

Tip: Remember, an ecosystem is made up of all the living and non-living things in an area (see page 7).

Tip: Take a look at pages 64-65 for more on climate change.

Figure 1: *Conservation of peregrine falcons (top) has caused a local decline in red knots (bottom).*

Conservation methods

Different species and habitats need to be conserved in different ways. Here are some examples of the different conservation methods that can be used.

1. Management of succession

Human activities can prevent succession, stopping a climax community from developing. When succession is stopped artificially like this the climax community is called a **plagioclimax**.

> **Example**
>
> A regularly mown grassy field won't develop shrubs and trees (woody plants), even if the climate of the ecosystem could support them. The growing points of the woody plants are cut off by the lawnmower, so larger plants can't establish themselves.
>
> The longer the interval between mowing, the further succession can progress and the more diversity increases. But with more frequent mowing, succession can't progress and diversity will be lower — only the grasses can survive being mowed. Mowing doesn't just affect plants, it can affect the wider biodiversity of the area. For example, removing the woody plants destroys habitats for insects, decreasing the number of insect species.

Conservation sometimes involves preventing succession in order to preserve an ecosystem in its current stage.

> **Example**
>
> There are large areas of moorland in Scotland that provide habitats for many species of plants and animals. If the moorland was left to natural processes, succession would lead to a climax community of spruce forest. This would mean the loss of the moorland habitat and could lead to the loss of some of the plants and animals that currently live there. Preventing succession keeps the moorland ecosystem intact. There are a couple of ways to manage succession to conserve the moorland ecosystem:
>
> ▪ Animals are allowed to graze on the land. This is similar to mowing — the animals eat the growing points of the shrubs and trees, which stops them from establishing themselves and helps to keep vegetation low.
>
> ▪ Managed fires are lit. After the fires, secondary succession will occur on the moorland — the plant species that grow back first (pioneer species) are the species that are being conserved, e.g. heather. Larger plant species will take longer to grow back and will be removed again the next time the moor's burnt.

2. Seedbanks

A seedbank is a store of lots of seeds from lots of different plant species. They help to conserve species by storing the seeds of endangered plants. They also help to conserve different varieties of each species by storing a range of seeds from plants with different characteristics, e.g. seeds from tall sunflowers and seeds from short sunflowers. If the plants become extinct in the wild the stored seeds can be used to grow new plants.

Seedbanks are a good way of conserving plant species — large numbers of species can be conserved because seeds don't need much space. Seeds can also be stored anywhere and for a long time, as long as it's cool and dry. But there are disadvantages — the seeds have to be regularly tested to see if they're still viable (whether they can grow into a plant), which can be expensive and time-consuming.

Tip: The method used to manage succession always depends on the environment, e.g. clearing winter scrub (grasses and low shrubs) that would otherwise build up and dry out the land is useful to prevent wetland becoming woodland.

Tip: There are lots of ways of managing succession to aid conservation, some of which involve altering the abiotic conditions. For example, ditches and sluices can be used to control the water content of the soil.

Figure 2: *Grazing sheep (top) and managed fires (bottom) have been used to halt succession and conserve Scottish moorland.*

Exam Tip
The only conservation method you need to know about is managing succession. However, it's a good idea to know about the other ways, because you could be given data in the exam that was collected using any of these methods.

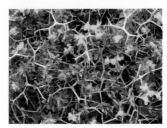

Figure 3: Seeds from the Cretan vetch are stored at the Millennium Seedbank.

3. Captive breeding

Captive breeding programmes involve breeding animals in controlled environments. Species that are endangered, or already extinct in the wild, can be bred in captivity to help increase their numbers. However, there are some problems with captive breeding programmes, e.g. animals can have problems breeding outside their natural habitat, which can be hard to recreate in a zoo.

Example

Pandas (see Figure 4) are bred in captivity because their numbers are critically low in the wild. However, they don't reproduce as successfully in captivity as they do in the wild.

Animals bred in captivity can be reintroduced to the wild. This increases their numbers in the wild, which can help to conserve their numbers or bring them back from the brink of extinction. Reintroducing animals into the wild can cause problems though, e.g. reintroduced animals could bring new diseases to habitats, harming other species living there.

Figure 4: Pandas have poor breeding rates in captivity.

4. Relocation

Relocating a species means moving a population of a species to a new location because they're directly under threat, e.g. from poaching, or the habitat they're living in is under threat, e.g. from rising sea levels. The species is moved to an area where it's not at risk (e.g. a protected national park, see below), but with a similar environment to where it's come from, so the species is still able to survive.

Example

The Northern quoll (see Figure 5) is an endangered species found in Australia. The native population in the north plummeted, so conservationists moved 64 individuals to two of Australia's islands. It was thought the Northern quoll would have a better chance of survival on the islands because there were no known predators, and after five years their populations were found to have increased dramatically.

Relocation is often used for species that only exist in one place (if that population dies out, the species will be extinct). It helps to conserve species because they're relocated to a place where they're more likely to survive, so their numbers may increase. Relocating species can cause problems though, e.g. native species in the new area may be out-competed by the species that's moved in and become endangered themselves.

Figure 5: Relocation of the Australian Northern quoll has helped conserve the species.

5. Protected areas

Protected areas, such as national parks and nature reserves, protect habitats (and so protect the species in them) by restricting urban development, industrial development and farming. Habitats in protected areas can be managed to conserve them.

Example

Some woodlands are managed by coppicing — cutting down trees in a way that lets them grow back, so they don't need to be replanted. This helps to conserve the woodland, but allows some wood to be harvested.

Tip: Conserving the area a species lives in can have wider benefits than just conserving the species itself. For example, it can help other species by providing habitats for them.

There are problems with using protected areas to conserve habitats though, e.g. national parks are also used as tourist destinations (many are funded by revenue from the tourists that visit). This means there's conflict between the need to conserve the habitats and the need to allow people to visit and use them.

Tip: To answer these questions, you might need to take a look back at pages 77-79 to remind yourself about how succession works.

Exam Tip
You always need to read exam questions carefully, but that's especially true when you're given data on a topic you know really well. It's dead easy to give a general answer based on what you know when actually the question wants you to use the data you're given.

Tip: When a question says 'suggest' you're not expected to know the exact answer — you're expected to use your knowledge to come up with a sensible answer.

Practice Questions — Application

Succession in an area of steppe (grassland) can result in a forest. A nature reserve wishes to conserve the steppe landscape by managing succession. Grazing, mowing and fire were used on three areas that were then left for a set amount of time. The results were compared to a control area which was left undisturbed for the same length of time. The data is shown on the bar chart below.

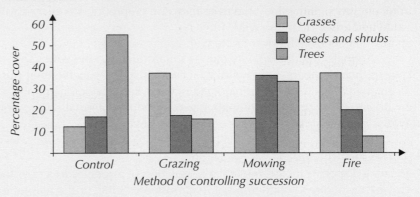

Q1 a) Describe what the results show about the effectiveness of the three methods of managing succession.

b) Suggest two advantages of controlling succession by grazing rather than by fire.

Q2 The government wish to conserve the steppe as it is a natural habitat of saiga antelope, which is an endangered species. They hope that saiga antelope bred in a zoo can be released onto the reserve.

Suggest an advantage and disadvantage of releasing saiga antelope bred in zoo.

Practice Questions — Fact Recall

Q1 What is conservation?

Q2 Briefly discuss some of the reasons for and against conservation.

Q3 What is a plagioclimax?

Q4 Explain why trees will not grow in a regularly mown field.

Q5 Describe how a managed fire can be used to prevent succession, in order to preserve an ecosystem in its current stage.

3. Conservation Evidence and Data

Learning Objectives:
- Be able to evaluate evidence and data concerning issues relating to the conservation of species and habitats and consider conflicting evidence.
- Be able to explain how conservation relies on science to inform decision-making.

Specification Reference 3.4.7

You need to be able to evaluate data on conservation. Sometimes though, it can be a bit tricky — especially when data sets show conflicting trends...

Evaluating evidence on conservation

You need to be able to evaluate any evidence or data about conservation projects and research that the examiners throw at you — so here's an example I made earlier...

HOW SCIENCE WORKS

⌐ Example ─────────────────────────────────────

In recent years, native British bluebells have become less common in woodland areas. It's thought that this is due to the presence of non-native Spanish bluebells, which compete with the native species for a similar niche.

An experiment was carried out to see if removing the invasive Spanish species would help to conserve the native species. Each year for 15 years the percentage cover of native species was estimated in a 50 m by 50 m area of woodland using random sampling and 250, 1 m² quadrats. After five years, all the Spanish bluebells were removed. A similar sized control woodland in which the Spanish bluebells remained untouched was also studied. The results are shown below.

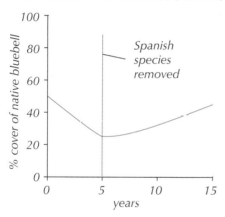

Figure 1: Percentage cover of native British bluebells in a woodland.

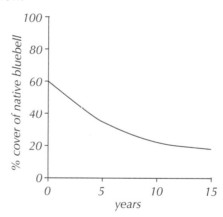

Figure 2: Control experiment.

Tip: A niche is the role of a species within its habitat (see page 7). If you need a reminder about using quadrats, take a look at page 14.

You might be asked to:

Describe the data

- For the first five years, the percentage cover of native bluebells fell from 50% to around 25%. After the Spanish species was removed, it increased from around 25% to around 45% in ten years.

- The control experiment shows a fairly steady drop in native bluebell percentage cover from 60% to 20% over the 15 years.

Draw conclusions

The removal of Spanish bluebells resulted in an increase in the percentage cover of native bluebells over a ten year period. This suggests that the recent decrease in native British bluebells is due to competition with the Spanish bluebells.

Figure 3: Some attempts to conserve British bluebells (top) have involved removing Spanish bluebells (bottom).

Evaluate the method

- The effects of some other variables (e.g. changing weather) were removed by the control experiment, where the percentage cover of native bluebells continued to fall throughout the 15 year study. This makes the data more reliable.
- The study area and sample size were quite large, giving more accurate data.
- Random sampling removed bias — the data's more likely to be an accurate estimate of the whole area.

Conflicting evidence

The evidence from one study alone wouldn't usually be enough to conclude that there's a link between decreasing percentage cover of native bluebells, and the presence of Spanish bluebells. Similar studies would be carried out to investigate the link.

If these studies came to the same conclusion, the conclusion would become increasingly accepted. Sometimes studies come up with conflicting evidence though — evidence that leads to a different conclusion than other studies.

There's more about interpreting data on pages 232-234.

Example

Another study was carried out to investigate the effect on native bluebells of removing Spanish bluebells.

It was similar to the study on the previous page except a 20 m by 20 m area was sampled using a random sample of 20 quadrats, and no control woodland was used.

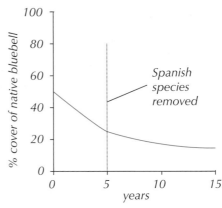

Figure 4: Percentage cover of native British bluebells in a woodland.

You might be asked to:

Describe the data

In the first five years, the percentage cover of native bluebells fell from 50% to around 25%. After the Spanish species was removed, it kept decreasing to around 15% after the full 15 years.

Draw conclusions

The removal of the Spanish bluebells had no effect on the decreasing percentage cover of native bluebells — which conflicts with the study on the previous page.

Evaluate the method

- There wasn't a control woodland, so the continuing decrease in native bluebell cover after the removal of the Spanish bluebells could be due to another factor, e.g. cold weather in years 5-10.
- The study area and sample size were quite small, giving a less accurate total percentage cover.

Tip: Ecosystems are such complicated things that studies can sometimes throw up conflicting data — which can be both really interesting and a bit of pain if the data's reliable. But the first thing you should always do when you get conflicting data is look at the methodology — chances are something in the method has caused the conflict.

Conservation and decision making

Scientists carry out research to provide information about conservation issues. This information can then be used to make informed decisions about which species and habitats need to be conserved, and the best way to conserve them. For example, the study on page 85 showed that native bluebell coverage increased after the removal of Spanish bluebells, which suggests that the decrease in native bluebell coverage is due to competition with the Spanish species. It provides evidence that there's a conservation issue (native bluebells are decreasing) and a way to solve it (remove the Spanish species).

Many conservation decisions have been made using the results of scientific research — take a look at these examples:

Tip: Take a look at page 6 for more on how society uses science to make decisions.

Examples

African elephants

- Between 1970 and 1989 the number of African elephants dropped from around 3 million to around 50 000 because they were being hunted for their ivory tusks (see Figure 5).

- In 1989, the Convention on International Trade in Endangered Species banned ivory trade to end the demand for elephant tusks so that fewer elephants would be killed for their tusks.

Peregrine falcons

- The commonly used pesticide DDT was found to have contributed to the loss of half of the peregrine falcon population in the UK in the 1950s and 1960s. DDT built up in the food chain and caused the falcon eggs to have thin shells. This meant the eggs were crushed and the chicks weren't hatched.

- The use of DDT as a pesticide was banned in the UK in 1984 to try to conserve and increase peregrine falcon numbers.

Sea turtles

- The numbers of some species of sea turtle have dropped so low that they're now endangered. Many eggs are removed from the beaches by poachers before the turtles hatch and reach the sea (see Figure 6).

- Conservation agencies have set up hatching programmes where eggs are taken away from beaches and looked after until they hatch. The young turtles are then released into the sea.

Hedgerows

- A reduction in the size of hedgerows in farmers' fields was found to cause a decrease in biodiversity in the British countryside.

- The government provides subsidies to encourage farmers to plant hedgerows and leave margins of ground unharvested around fields. This increases the size of hedgerows and conserves biodiversity.

Whales

- Whale numbers were found to have dropped massively due to whale hunting.

- Commercial whaling was banned in 1986 by the International Whaling Commission in order to conserve whale numbers.

Figure 5: Research showing a decline in elephant populations due to hunting for their ivory tusks has led to a ban on the sale of ivory.

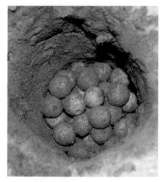

Figure 6: Poachers often remove turtle eggs from beaches before turtles can hatch.

Tip: Harrowing is where the surface of the soil is broken up and smoothed over. This makes the soil better for seed growth.

The diversity of native plants on certain areas of grassland has been reduced by the invasion of non-native species. A team wishing to conserve the native species investigated two methods. The first involved harrowing the soil and dispersing native seeds, and the second involved continual grazing by sheep. These methods were each conducted on 14 fields, and their effects were compared to a control field (which was left untouched). The fields were left for four years. The results were averaged and are shown below.

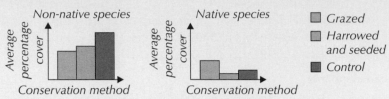

Q1   Describe the results shown in the graph.

Q2   a) Which method of conservation was most successful? Give a reason for your answer.

b) Suggest why the method you named in part a) worked and why the other did not.

Q3   A second team conducted an investigation using the same methods. Each method was used on a single field and the fields were left for six years. Their results are shown in the bar chart below.

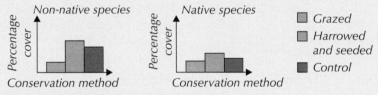

Describe the difference in the results between the two investigations and suggest why this might have occurred.

Section Summary

Make sure you know:
- That succession is the process by which an ecosystem changes over time, and how this happens.
- That succession begins with a pioneer species, which are specialised to cope with hostile conditions.
- That at each stage in succession, species change the abiotic environment so that it becomes more suitable for other species, increasing species diversity.
- That succession ends with a climax community (the largest and most complex community of plants that can be supported by the ecosystem), and that the climax community for a particular climate is called the climatic climax community.
- That primary succession happens on newly formed land that has no soil, whereas secondary succession happens on land that's been cleared of all plants but where the soil remains.
- That conservation is the protection and management of species and habitats.
- That conservation often involves management of succession, e.g. by mowing, grazing or lighting fires.
- How to evaluate evidence and data relating to conservation, and consider conflicting evidence.
- How science relating to conservation is used to inform decision-making.

1   A nature reserve has taken over management of a small area of woodland, home to an endangered species of bird. The nature reserve wants to change how the woodland is managed in order to conserve the bird species, and is investigating using coppicing.

Coppicing is where trees are periodically cut down near to the ground so that many new stems can grow from the stump. In the first three years following coppicing the trees establish themselves, in years 4-10 the canopy closes (becomes dense) and in years 11-15 the trees mature.

The nature reserve has found a study that investigated the effect of coppicing on the endangered bird species. The results are shown below.

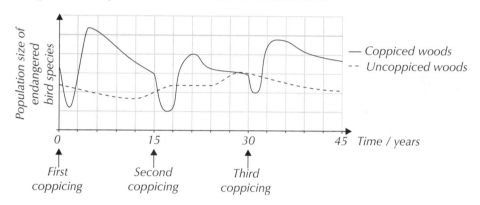

1 (a)   Describe and explain the trends shown on the graph.

(6 marks)

1 (b)   A nearby reserve coppices part of its the woodland every 15 years. Since they began coppicing, they have kept close records of the effect this has had on woodland biodiversity, the number of an endangered bird species and the income generated from the woodland. This is all shown in the graph below.

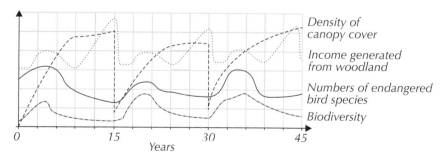

1 (b) (i)   Suggest an explanation for the trend in income generated by the woodland.

(4 marks)

1 (b) (ii)   Describe the trend in biodiversity shown on the graph and suggest explanations for this trend.

(6 marks)

2   An area of heathland in a national park is home to an endangered plant species which needs high light intensity and acidic soils to grow successfully. The park managers have decided to halt succession on the heath and are exploring ways in which to do this. They are considering burning the heathland every fifty years.

2 (a)   Burning the heathland leads to secondary succession.
Describe the process of secondary succession.

(5 marks)

2 (b)   Suggest two reasons why burning the heathland every fifty years might not help to conserve the endangered plant species.

(2 marks)

The managers have found data from another heathland which halted succession by burning every 20 years. The data is shown on the graph below.

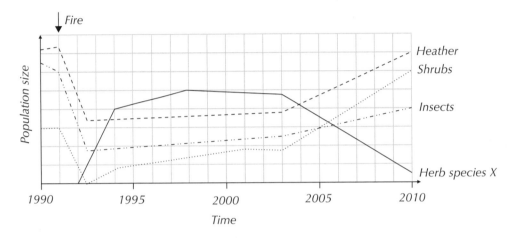

2 (c)   Describe and explain the changes in the population sizes of heather, shrubs and insects between 1991 and 2000.

(3 marks)

2 (d)   Herb species X is a pioneer species.
2 (d) (i)   Explain what is meant by the term 'pioneer species'.

(1 mark)

2 (d) (ii)   Explain why the pioneer species in primary and secondary succession are rarely the same species.

(2 marks)

2 (d) (iii)   Describe and suggest an explanation for the change in the population size of the herb species shown in the graph over the twenty year period.

(3 marks)

2 (e) (i)   The managers have met opposition against the use of fire to halt succession. Some campaigners against the use of fire have used the data shown above to argue that insect populations do not recover following heathland fires.

Explain why their conclusion is not valid.

(2 marks)

2 (e) (ii)   Explain an alternative way in which the plant species could be conserved.

(3 marks)

1. Genetic Terms

Inheritance is all about how you got the genes you have and how likely you are to pass them on to your children. But before you start exploring this section, you really need to get to grips with the basic terms described below.

Basic terms and definitions
Genes and alleles

A **gene** is a sequence of bases on a DNA molecule that codes for a protein (polypeptide) which results in a characteristic.

You can have one or more versions of the same gene. These different versions are called **alleles**. The order of bases in each allele is slightly different — that's because each allele codes for different versions of the same characteristic. Alleles are represented using letters.

Examples
- There are many different alleles for eye colour. The allele for brown eyes is shown using a B, and the allele for blue eyes uses b.
- Pea plants have a gene for seed shape. The allele for a round seed shape is shown using a R, and the allele for wrinkled seed shape uses r.

Most plants and animals, including humans, have two alleles of each gene, one from each parent. That's because we inherit one copy of each chromosome of a pair from our parents. The allele of each gene is found at a fixed position, called a **locus**, on each chromosome in a pair (see Figure 1).

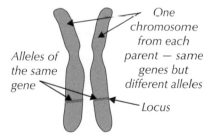

Alleles of the same gene

One chromosome from each parent — same genes but different alleles

Locus

Figure 1: *Diagram showing a locus on a pair of chromosomes.*

Genotype

The genotype of an organism is its genetic constitution, or put another way, the different alleles an organism has. This could be a list of all its alleles but usually it's just the alleles for one characteristic at a time.

Examples
- One person may have the genotype BB for eye colour and another person Bb.
- One pea plant might have the genotype RR for seed shape and another pea plant rr.

Phenotype

The phenotype of an organism is 'the expression of the genetic constitution and its interaction with the environment'. This just means what characteristics an organism has as a result of both its genes and the effect the environment has on its genes.

Learning Objectives:
- Know that alleles are one or more alternative versions of the same gene.
- Understand that there may be multiple alleles of a single gene.
- Know that genotype is the genetic constitution of an organism.
- Know that phenotype is the expression of the genetic constitution and its interaction with the environment.
- Know that alleles may be dominant, recessive or codominant.
- Know that alleles at a specific locus may be either homozygous or heterozygous.

Specification Reference 3.4.8

Tip: A base is a nitrogen-containing molecule that forms part of a DNA nucleotide.

┌ **Examples** ─────────────────────────────────
- One person may have brown eyes and another may have blue eyes.
- One pea plant may have round seeds and another may have wrinkled seeds.

Dominant and recessive alleles

An allele whose characteristic appears in the phenotype even when there's only one copy is called a dominant allele. Dominant alleles are shown by a capital letter. Recessive alleles are those whose characteristics only appear in the phenotype if two copies are present. They're shown by lower case letters.

┌ **Examples** ─────────────────────────────────
- The allele for brown eyes, B, is dominant, so if a person's genotype is Bb or BB they'll have brown eyes. The allele for blue eyes, b, is recessive, so a person will only have blue eyes if their genotype is bb.
- The allele for round seed shape, R, is dominant, so if a pea plant's genotype is Rr or RR it will have round seeds. The allele for wrinkled seed shape, r, is recessive, so a pea plant will only have wrinkled seeds if its genotype is rr.

Codominant alleles

Some alleles are both expressed in the phenotype because neither one is recessive. They are said to be codominant alleles.

┌ **Examples** ─────────────────────────────────
- Snapdragon plants can have alleles for red flowers or white flowers. Neither allele is recessive so a snapdragon plant with one copy of each allele will have pink flowers.
- The alleles for haemoglobin are codominant because they're both expressed in the phenotype (see page 95).

Homozygous and heterozygous

If an organism carries two copies of the same allele it's said to be homozygous. If an organism carries two different alleles then it's heterozygous.

┌ **Examples** ─────────────────────────────────
- The genotypes BB and bb are homozygous and the genotype Bb is heterozygous.
- The genotypes RR and rr are homozygous and the genotype Rr is heterozygous.

Practice Questions — Application

Q1 In owl monkeys, the allele T codes for a tufted tail and t codes for a non-tufted tail. For each of following the genotypes, give the owl monkey's phenotype: A — Tt, B — TT, C — tt.

Q2 The yellow colour pea seed allele is dominant to the green allele.
   a) What would be the phenotype of a pea seed with the alleles Yy?
   b) Give the genotype of a homozygous pea seed that's yellow.
   c) Give the genotype of a green pea seed.

2. Genetic Diagrams — Simple Monohybrid Crosses

Learning Objective:
- Be able to use fully labelled genetic diagrams to predict the results of monohybrid crosses involving dominant, recessive and codominant alleles.

Specification Reference 3.4.8

Genetic diagrams show how alleles could be passed on to the next generation.

What are genetic diagrams?

Individuals have two alleles for each gene. Gametes (sex cells) contain only one allele for each gene. When gametes from two parents fuse together, the alleles they contain form the genotype of the offspring produced.

Genetic diagrams show the possible genotypes of offspring, so they can be used to predict the genotypes and phenotypes of the offspring that would be produced if two parents are crossed (bred). You need to know how to use genetic diagrams to predict the results of various crosses.

Monohybrid inheritance

Monohybrid inheritance is the inheritance of a single characteristic (gene) controlled by different alleles. **Monohybrid crosses** show the likelihood of alleles (and so different versions of the characteristic) being inherited by offspring of particular parents. The example below shows how wing length can be inherited in fruit flies.

Figure 2a: Photo of a fruit fly with normal wings.

┌─ **Example** ─────────────────────────────

The allele for normal wings is dominant, so it's shown by a capital letter N. Any flies that have even one N allele will have normal wings. The allele for vestigial (little) wings is recessive, so it's shown by the letter n. Only flies that have two n alleles will have vestigial wings.

The genetic diagram in Figure 1 shows a cross between one homozygous parent with normal wings (NN) and one homozygous parent with vestigial wings (nn). The normal winged parent can only produce gametes with the allele for normal wings (N). The vestigial winged parent can only produce gametes with the allele for vestigial wings (n).

Here's how to draw a genetic diagram for this cross:

Step 1: Make sure you're clear what the letters mean.

> N — normal wings allele
> n — vestigial (little) wings allele

Figure 2b: Photo of a fruit fly with vestigial wings.

Step 2: Show the parents' genotype at the top.

Step 3: The middle circles show the possible gametes. Put one of each letter into a circle.

Step 4: The lines show all the possible ways the gametes could combine. Fill in the possible combinations in the bottom boxes.

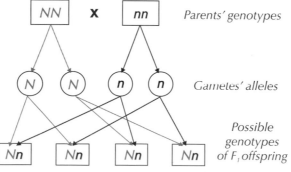

Figure 1: Genetic diagram showing a single generation monohybrid cross between homozygous parents.

All offspring produced are heterozygous (Nn), as one allele is inherited from each parent.

Tip: The first set of offspring is called the F_1 generation.

Tip: A monohybrid cross with two homozygous parents will <u>always</u> produce <u>all heterozygous</u> offspring in the F_1 generation.

Tip: The learning objective says you must be able to use <u>fully labelled diagrams</u>. So make sure you understand what each stage of a diagram shows, and what the letters represent.

The genetic diagram in Figure 3 shows a cross between two parents from the F_1 generation (both heterozygous). Just follow the same steps as on the previous page, but this time the gametes produced by each F_1 offspring may contain the allele for either normal (N) or vestigial wings (n).

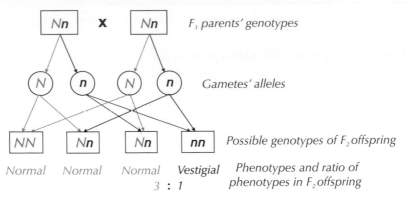

Figure 3: Genetic diagram showing a monohybrid cross between heterozygous parents.

Tip: The second set of offspring is called the F_2 generation.

The F_2 offspring could have either normal or vestigial wings. But there's a 75% chance they'll have the normal wings phenotype (genotype of NN or Nn) and a 25% chance they'll have the vestigial wings phenotype (genotype nn). So you'd expect a 3:1 ratio of normal : vestigial wings in the offspring.

Whenever you do a monohybrid cross with two heterozygous parents you get a 3:1 ratio of dominant : recessive characteristic.

Punnett squares

Exam Tip
In the exam, you might have to use a genetic diagram to work out all sorts of information. For example, the ratio of possible offspring, the probability of certain offspring occurring, the phenotype or genotype of offspring... You might have to draw a diagram yourself to work out the answer, or you might have to complete a cross.

A Punnett square is just another way of showing a genetic diagram — they're also used to predict the genotypes and phenotypes of offspring. The Punnett squares below show the same crosses from the previous page and above.

— Example — how to draw a Punnett square —

Step 1: Work out the alleles the gametes would have.

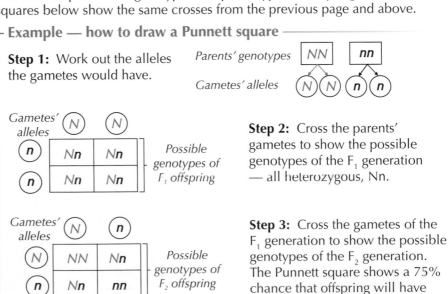

Step 2: Cross the parents' gametes to show the possible genotypes of the F_1 generation — all heterozygous, Nn.

Tip: It's up to you how you work out phenotypes, genotypes or ratios — you can use a diagram or a Punnett square, whichever you find easier. The steps are the same, so just take your time and go through it carefully.

Step 3: Cross the gametes of the F_1 generation to show the possible genotypes of the F_2 generation. The Punnett square shows a 75% chance that offspring will have normal wings and a 25% chance that they'll have vestigial wings, i.e. a 3:1 ratio.

Monohybrid inheritance of codominant alleles

Occasionally, alleles show codominance — both alleles are expressed in the phenotype, and neither one is recessive. One example in humans is the allele for sickle-cell anaemia, a genetic disorder caused by a mutation in the haemoglobin gene. It causes red blood cells to be sickle-shaped (crescent-shaped) — see page 221 for more.

see page 221 for more.

Tip: Haemoglobin is a protein found in red blood cells — its role is to carry oxygen around the body.

Example

People who are homozygous for normal haemoglobin (H^NH^N) don't have the disease. People who are homozygous for sickle haemoglobin (H^SH^S) have sickle-cell anaemia — all their blood cells are sickle shaped. People who are heterozygous (H^NH^S) have an in-between phenotype, called the sickle-cell trait — they have some normal haemoglobin and some sickle haemoglobin. The two alleles are codominant because they're both expressed in the phenotype.

The genetic diagram in Figure 5 shows the possible offspring from crossing two parents with sickle-cell trait (heterozygous).

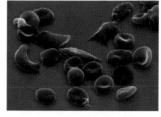

Figure 4: A coloured scanning electron micrograph (SEM) of normal red blood cells (red) and sickle-shaped cells (pink).

Figure 5: Genetic diagram showing a monohybrid cross of codominant alleles.

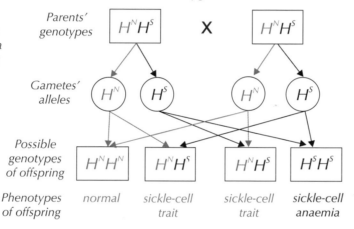

This cross has produced a 1:2:1 ratio of normal: sickle-cell trait: sickle-cell anaemia, or normal homozygous : heterozygous : disorder homozygous.

Tip: When alleles show codominance they're represented in a slightly different way to normal — you show the main gene as a normal capital letter (H) and then the alleles as superscript capitals (H^S or H^N), because neither is recessive.

Practice Questions — Application

Q1 The allele for tall pea plants is dominant over the allele for dwarf pea plants. Give the possible genotype(s) of offspring produced if a homozygous tall pea plant is crossed with a homozygous dwarf pea plant. Show your working.

Q2 Polydactyly is a genetic disorder where a baby is born with extra fingers or toes. The disorder is caused by a dominant allele. What is the probability of a baby being born with the condition if a heterozygous sufferer and a parent without the disorder have a child? Show your working.

Q3 In one organism, the alleles for skin colour show codominance. Any organisms that are homozygous with blue alleles are blue in colour. Organisms that are homozygous with yellow alleles are yellow in colour. Heterozygous organisms are yellow and blue striped. What colour ratio of organisms would be produced if a heterozygous parent was crossed with a homozygous blue parent? Show your working.

Exam Tip
If you're not given letters to use for a genetic diagram, just choose sensible ones yourself, e.g. T for tall dominant allele and t for dwarf recessive allele.

Exam Tip
If you're asked to find the probability of something, you can write it as a fraction (e.g. ¾), a decimal (e.g. 0.75) or a percentage (e.g. 75%).

Learning Objective:

- Be able to use fully labelled genetic diagrams to predict the results of crosses involving sex-linked characteristics and multiple alleles.

Specification Reference 3.4.8

3. Genetic Diagrams — Sex-linked and Multiple Allele Crosses

Sex-linked and multiple allele crosses aren't much different to the monohybrid crosses you've already come across. These examples still only involve one gene, it's just the gene can be associated with the sex of the offspring, or it can have more than two alleles.

Inheritance of sex-linked characteristics

The genetic information for gender (sex) is carried on two sex chromosomes. In mammals, females have two X chromosomes (XX) and males have one X chromosome and one Y chromosome (XY).

Figure 1 is a genetic diagram that shows how gender is inherited. From this you can see that the probability of having male offspring is 50% and the probability of having female offspring is 50%.

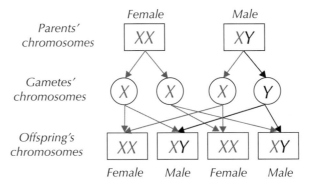

Figure 1: *Genetic diagram showing the inheritance of gender.*

Exam Tip
In the exam you could be asked to give the probability of producing a certain gender with a particular genotype, for example, a boy with blue eyes. You work out the probability of a child having blue eyes first and then divide it by 2, to include the 1 in 2 chance of having a boy. (This isn't the same thing as a sex-linked characteristic though.)

Some characteristics are **sex-linked**. That means the alleles that code for them are located on a sex chromosome. The Y chromosome is smaller than the X chromosome and carries fewer genes. So most genes on the sex chromosomes are only carried on the X chromosome (called X-linked genes).

As males only have one X chromosome they often only have one allele for sex-linked genes. So because they only have one copy they express the characteristic of this allele even if it's recessive. This makes males more likely than females to show recessive phenotypes for genes that are sex-linked.

Genetic disorders caused by faulty alleles located on sex chromosomes include colour blindness and haemophilia. The faulty alleles for both of these disorders are carried on the X chromosome and so are called X-linked disorders. Y-linked disorders do exist but are less common.

Example

Figure 2 on the next page shows a genetic diagram for colour blindness. Colour blindness is a sex-linked disorder caused by a faulty allele carried on the X chromosome. As it's sex-linked both the chromosome and the allele are represented in the genetic diagram, e.g. X^n, where X represents the X chromosome and n the faulty allele for colour vision. The Y chromosome doesn't have an allele for colour vision so is just represented by Y.

Females would need two copies of the recessive allele to be colour blind, while males only need one copy. This means colour blindness is much rarer in women than men.

Tip: The faulty allele for colour vision is represented by a lower case 'n', so you know its a recessive allele.

Here's how to draw a Punnett square for this sex-linked cross:

Step 1: Make sure you're clear what the letters mean. You need to show X and Y chromosomes too this time. You usually show them as a capital X and Y and then have the genes as superscript letters.

N — normal colour vision allele
n — faulty colour vision allele
X — female Y — male

Carrier female   Normal male

Parents' genotypes $X^N X^n$ $X^N Y$

Step 2: Work out the alleles the gametes would have.

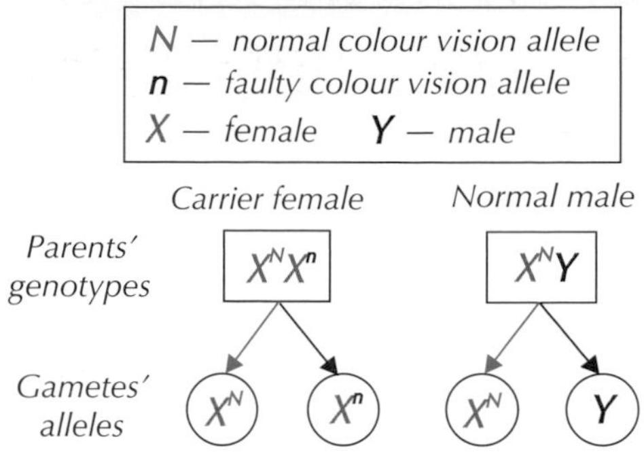

Gametes' alleles X^N X^n X^N Y

Step 3: Cross the parents' gametes to show the possible offspring.

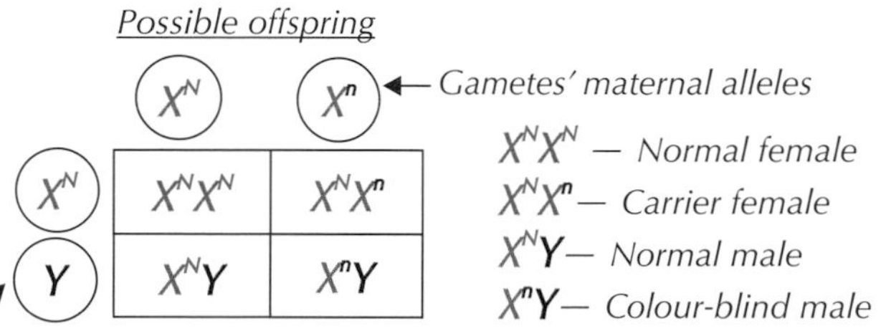

Possible offspring

Gametes' maternal alleles

	X^N	X^n
X^N	$X^N X^N$	$X^N X^n$
Y	$X^N Y$	$X^n Y$

Gametes' paternal alleles

$X^N X^N$ — Normal female
$X^N X^n$ — Carrier female
$X^N Y$ — Normal male
$X^n Y$ — Colour-blind male

Figure 2: *Punnett square showing the inheritance of colour-blindness.*

Tip: This cross isn't any harder than the simple monohybrid ones you saw on pages 93-95. Just follow the same steps to work out all the possible combinations of gametes and what they would mean.

Tip: A carrier is a person carrying an allele which is not expressed in the phenotype but that can be passed on to offspring. Males can't be carriers of X-linked disorders because they only have one copy of each chromosome, so if they have the allele they have the disease — whether it's recessive or not.

Multiple allele crosses

Inheritance is more complicated when there are more than two alleles of the same gene (multiple alleles).

Example

In the ABO blood group system in humans there are three alleles for blood type:

- I^O is the allele for blood group O.
- I^A is the allele for blood group A.
- I^B is the allele for blood group B.

Allele I^O is recessive. Alleles I^A and I^B are codominant — people with genotype $I^A I^B$ will have blood group AB.

Figure 3 shows a cross between a heterozygous person with blood group A and a heterozygous person with blood group B.

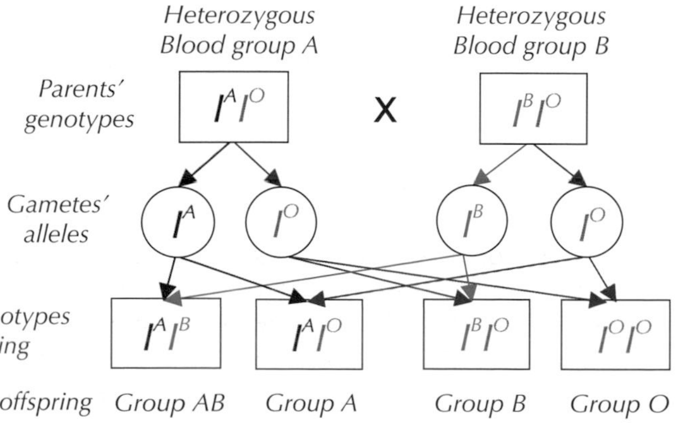

Tip: Recessive blood groups are normally really rare, but it just so happens that loads of people in Britain are descended from people who were $I^O I^O$, so O's really common.

Figure 3: *Genetic diagram showing the inheritance of blood group.*

Heterozygous Blood group A   Heterozygous Blood group B

Parents' genotypes $I^A I^O$ X $I^B I^O$

Gametes' alleles I^A I^O I^B I^O

Possible genotypes of offspring $I^A I^B$ $I^A I^O$ $I^B I^O$ $I^O I^O$

Phenotypes of offspring   Group AB   Group A   Group B   Group O

Any offspring could have one of four different blood groups (A, B, O or AB).

Tip: Make sure you really know your definitions, especially homozygous, heterozygous, genotype and phenotype (see pages 91-92).

Q1 Fragile X syndrome is an X-linked dominant disorder. A male sufferer and a heterozygous female sufferer have a child. Give the possible genotypes and phenotypes of the child.

Q2 The stripping pattern of cats can be determined by three alleles — Ta for Abyssinian, T for the mackerel phenotype and tb for blotched. Abyssinian is dominant to both of the other alleles, mackerel is dominant to blotched only and blotched is recessive to all. (So the dominance of the alleles is Ta > T > tb.)

What are the possible striping patterns of offspring if a TaT cat and a tbtb cat breed together?

Q3 Duchenne muscular dystrophy is a form of muscular dystrophy that causes muscle breakdown and difficulties walking and breathing. It is caused by a recessive X-linked allele.   What is the probability of having a child with Duchenne muscular dystrophy if a normal male has a child with a carrier female?

Q4 The colour of one species of moth is controlled by three alleles — pale typical (m), darkly mottled insularia (M') and nearly black melanic (M). The table below shows all possible genotype combinations and their phenotypic outcomes.

Genotype	Phenotype
mm	Typical
MM	Melanic
M'M'	Insularia
mM	Melanic
mM'	Insularia
MM'	Melanic

a) Describe the dominance of the different alleles.

b) A homozygous melanic and a typical pale moth breed. Show all the possible results of this cross.

Tip: This last question is a bit tricky — try drawing a basic cross and see what you get.

Q5 Hypertrichosis pinnae (extremely hairy ears) was once thought to be a Y-linked characteristic. If this were true, why might a father with 'bald' ears whose child has hairy ears, be suspicious of his wife?

Practice Questions — Fact Recall

Q1 Give the chromosomes that determine sex in a male and a female.

Q2 What is the probability of having a female child?

Q3 Some characteristics are sex-linked. What does this mean?

Q4 Why are X-linked disorders more common in males than females?

4. Genetic Pedigree Diagrams

These are the final type of genetic diagram you need to know about, I promise.

What are genetic pedigree diagrams?

Genetic pedigree diagrams show how an inherited trait (characteristic) runs in a group of related individuals. You might have to interpret genetic pedigree diagrams to work out the genotypes or potential phenotypes of individuals.

Learning Objective:

- Be able to use fully labelled genetic diagrams to predict the results of different crosses.

Specification Reference 3.4.8

Example

Cystic fibrosis (CF) is an inherited disorder that causes the production of a thick mucus, which affects the lungs and digestive system. It's caused by a faulty recessive allele (f). A person will only have CF if they're homozygous for the allele (ff) — they must inherit one recessive allele from each parent. If a person is heterozygous (Ff), they won't have CF but they'll be a carrier.

The genetic pedigree diagram below shows how CF runs in one particular family. You can use the key, the relationship lines and what you've learnt so far about inheritance to make predictions about the genotypes of each individual and any future offspring.

Tip: A carrier has a faulty recessive allele but doesn't have any symptoms of the disorder.

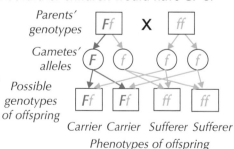

A key will show what the shapes represent:
- ■ Unaffected male
- ● Unaffected female
- ▢ Male with CF
- ○ Female with CF

Two parents are joined by a horizontal line.

A vertical line goes from parents to children.

Children have a vertical line above them.

This female has CF (ff), but neither of her parents do. She must have inherited an f allele from each parent, so both parents must be carriers (Ff).

This male has CF (ff), like his mother (ff). He's inherited an f allele from each parent, so his father must be a carrier (Ff).

From the information in the diagram you could be asked to do genetic crosses to work out the probability that further children would have CF or be a carrier. E.g. to work out the chances of the next child born to individuals 4 and 5 having CF you would cross Ff (individual 4) and ff (individual 5) — as shown opposite. Two out of the four genotypes produced by the cross are ff, so the chances of the next child being born with CF is 50%.

Parents' genotypes: Ff X ff

Gametes' alleles: F, f, f, f

Possible genotypes of offspring: Ff, Ff, ff, ff

Phenotypes of offspring: Carrier, Carrier, Sufferer, Sufferer

---

Practice Questions — Application

Huntington's disease is caused by a dominant allele. The genetic pedigree diagram shows the inheritance of Huntington's disease in one family.

Q1 What is the genotype of individual 1?

Q2 What would be the possible genotypes of the offspring produced by a cross between individuals 3 and 5?

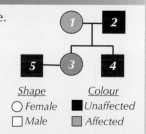

Shape	Colour
○ Female	■ Unaffected
□ Male	▦ Affected

Exam Tip
It's highly likely you'll get asked these kinds of questions in the exam, e.g. you're given a diagram but asked to work out other crosses from it. Work things out slowly and sensibly, looking at one thing at a time.

Learning Objectives:

- Know that species exist as one or more populations.
- Understand the concepts of gene pool and allele frequency.
- Know what the Hardy-Weinberg principle is and the conditions under which the principle applies.
- Understand that the Hardy-Weinberg principle provides a mathematical model which predicts that allele frequencies will not change from generation to generation.
- Be able to calculate allele, genotype and phenotype frequencies from appropriate data and from the Hardy-Weinberg equation: $p^2 + 2pq + q^2 = 1$, where p is the frequency of the dominant allele and q is the frequency of the recessive allele.

Specification Reference 3.4.8

5. The Hardy-Weinberg Principle

A little bit of maths now... but I promise it's not too bad. Basically, you can use two fairly simple equations to work out allele, genotype and phenotype frequencies for a whole population — which is more useful than it sounds.

Gene pools and other terms

You need to get to grips with some key terms before you start playing around with equations and numbers:

- A **species** is defined as a group of similar organisms that can reproduce to give fertile offspring.
- A **population** is a group of organisms of the same species living in a particular area. Species can exist as one or more populations, e.g. there are populations of the American black bear (*Ursus americanus*) in parts of America and in parts of Canada.
- The **gene pool** is the complete range of alleles present in a population. How often an allele occurs in a population is called the **allele frequency**. It's usually given as a percentage of the total population, e.g. 35%, or a decimal, e.g. 0.35.

What is the Hardy-Weinberg principle?

The Hardy-Weinberg principle is a mathematical model that predicts the frequencies of alleles in a population won't change from one generation to the next. But this prediction is only true under certain conditions:

- It has to be a large population where there's no immigration, emigration, mutations or natural selection (see pages 104-105).
- There needs to be random mating — all possible genotypes can breed with all others.

The Hardy-Weinberg equations (see below) can be used to estimate the frequency of particular alleles and genotypes within populations. They can also be used to test whether or not the Hardy-Weinberg principle applies to particular alleles in particular populations, i.e. to test whether selection or any other factors are influencing allele frequencies. If frequencies do change between generations in a large population then there's a pressure of some kind (see pages 102-103).

The Hardy-Weinberg equations

There are two Hardy-Weinberg equations you need to be able to use — one is used for working out allele frequency and the other one is usually used when you're dealing with genotype (and phenotype) frequencies.

Allele frequency

The total frequency of all possible alleles for a characteristic in a certain population is 1.0. So the frequencies of the individual alleles (the dominant one and the recessive one) must add up to 1.0. Here's that idea in an equation:

Tip: If the frequencies for two alleles add up to <u>more than one</u>, they're not alleles for the same gene (characteristic). If they come to <u>less than one</u>, there are more than two alleles for that gene.

$$p + q = 1$$

Where...
p = the frequency of the dominant allele
q = the frequency of the recessive allele

Genotype frequency

The total frequency of all possible genotypes for one characteristic in a certain population is 1.0. So the frequencies of the individual genotypes must add up to 1.0. But remember there are three genotypes — homozygous recessive, homozygous dominant and heterozygous. Here's the second equation:

$$p^2 + 2pq + q^2 = 1$$

Where...
p^2 = frequency of homozygous dominant genotype
$2pq$ = frequency of heterozygous genotype
q^2 = frequency of homozygous recessive genotype

Tip: Remember, homozygous dominant means two copies of the dominant allele (e.g. BB), homozygous recessive means two copies of the recessive allele (e.g. bb) and heterozygous means one copy of each allele (e.g. Bb).

Uses of the Hardy-Weinberg principle

The best way to understand how to use the principle and the equations is to follow through some examples.

Predicting allele frequency

You can figure out the frequency of one allele if you know the frequency of the other:

┌─ Example ─────────────────────────────────

- A species of plant has either red or white flowers. Allele R (red) is dominant and allele r (white) is recessive. If the frequency of R is 0.4 in Population X, what is the frequency of r?

- You know the frequency of one allele and just need to find the frequency of the other using $p + q = 1$ (where p = dominant allele, R, and q = recessive allele, r). So:

$$p + q = 1$$
$$R + r = 1$$
$$0.4 + r = 1$$
$$r = 1 - 0.4 = 0.6$$

So the frequency of the r allele in Population X is 0.6.

Exam Tip
Make sure you learn both equations and when to use them — you won't be given the equations in your exam.

You can also figure out allele frequencies if you're given information about genotype (or phenotype) frequencies:

┌─ Example ─────────────────────────────────

- There are two alleles for flower colour (R and r), so there are three possible genotypes — RR, Rr and rr. If the frequency of genotype RR is 0.56 in Population Y, what is the allele frequency of r?

- You know that RR is the homozygous dominant genotype, so RR = p^2. You also know that the allele frequency for R = p, so:

$$p^2 = 0.56$$
$$p = \sqrt{0.56} = 0.75, \text{ so } R = 0.75$$

You also know that $p + q = 1$, where p = the dominant allele, R, and q = the recessive allele, r. So:

$$p + q = 1$$
$$R + r = 1$$
$$0.75 + r = 1$$
$$r = 1 - 0.75 = 0.25$$

So the frequency of the r allele (white) in Population Y is 0.25.

Tip: Remember, genotype is the genes an organisms has (e.g. Rr) and phenotype is the expression of this genotype in the environment (e.g. red flowers).

Predicting genotype frequency

Here you're after genotype, so it's p^2, q^2 or $2pq$ you need to find:

Example

- If there are two alleles for flower colour (R and r), there are three possible genotypes — RR, Rr and rr. In Population Z, the frequency of genotype RR is 0.34 and the frequency of genotype Rr is 0.27. Find the frequency of rr in Population Z.
- $p^2 + 2pq + q^2 = 1$, where p^2 = homozygous dominant genotype, RR, $2pq$ = heterozygous genotype, Rr, and q^2 = homozygous recessive genotype, rr. So:

$$p^2 + 2pq + q^2 = 1$$
$$RR + Rr + rr = 1$$
$$0.34 + 0.27 + rr = 1$$
$$rr = 1 - 0.34 - 0.27 = 0.39$$

So the frequency of the rr genotype in Population Z is 0.39.

Exam Tip

It's easier than it might seem to decide which equation to use.
If you're given one allele frequency and asked to find the other it's the simple equation.
If you know two out of the three genotype or phenotype frequencies, you can find the other frequency using the big equation. For anything else you'll probably need to use a combination of equations.

Predicting the percentage of a population that has a certain genotype

You're looking at genotype again, so it's ultimately something to do with p^2, q^2 or $2pq$. But you might have to use a combination of equations to get there:

Example

- The frequency of cystic fibrosis (genotype ff) in the UK is currently approximately 1 birth in 2000. Use this information to estimate the percentage of people in the UK that are cystic fibrosis carriers (Ff).
- To do this you need to find the frequency of the heterozygous genotype Ff, i.e. $2pq$, using both equations. (You can't just use the big one as you only know one of the three genotypes — q^2.)

First calculate q:

Frequency of cystic fibrosis (homozygous recessive, ff) is 1 in 2000

$$ff = q^2 = \frac{1}{2000} = 0.0005. \text{ So } q = \sqrt{0.0005} = 0.022$$

Next calculate p:

Use $p + q = 1$, rearranged: $p = 1 - q = 1 - 0.022 = 0.978$

Then calculate $2pq$:

$$2pq = 2 \times p \times q = 2 \times 0.978 \times 0.022 = 0.043$$

The frequency of genotype Ff is 0.043, so the percentage of the UK population that are carriers is $0.043 \times 100 = 4.3\%$.

Tip: The more examples you practise, the more confident you'll be at working out allele, genotype and phenotype frequencies when it comes to your exam.

Showing if any external factors are affecting allele frequency

The Hardy-Weinberg principle predicts that the frequencies of alleles in a population won't change from one generation to the next as long as the population is large, there's no immigration, emigration, mutations or natural selection, and mating is totally random.

So if you use the Hardy-Weinberg equations to discover that allele frequency has changed from one generation to the next, then the Hardy-Weinberg principle doesn't apply to that population. This means that one (or more) of the factors listed above must be affecting allele frequency. For example, immigration might have occurred.

Tip: The effect of natural selection on allele frequency is covered in more depth on pages 104-105.

Example

- If the frequency of cystic fibrosis is measured 50 years later it might be found to be 1 birth in 3000. Use this information to decide if the Hardy-Weinberg principle applies to this population.

- Start by estimating the frequency of the recessive allele (f) in the population, i.e. q.

To calculate q:

Frequency of cystic fibrosis (homozygous recessive, ff) is 1 in 3000

$$ff = q^2 = \frac{1}{3000} = 0.00033$$

So, $q = \sqrt{0.00033} = 0.018$

The frequency of the recessive allele is now 0.018, compared to 0.022 currently (see previous page). As the frequency of the allele has changed between generations the Hardy-Weinberg principle doesn't apply.

Tip: You don't always need to use all of the equation. You can just use the parts you want to find out, e.g. you know p and q and need to find the frequency of the heterozygous genotype, so just do $2pq$.

Practice Questions — Application

Q1 In a human population, the allele frequency for the recessive albino allele is measured over generations as shown in the table below.

a) Calculate the frequency of the pigmented (non-albino) allele in generation 1.

b) Calculate the frequency of the heterozygous genotype in generation 1.

c) Does the Hardy-Weinberg principle apply to this population? Explain your answer.

Generation	Allele frequency
1	0.10
4	0.07
7	0.03

Q2 ADA deficiency is an inherited metabolic disorder caused by a recessive allele. The recessive allele frequency in a population is 0.16. What is the frequency of the homozygous dominant genotype in the same population?

Q3 Seed texture in pea plants is controlled by two alleles, the dominant round allele and the recessive wrinkled allele. 31% of a population have wrinkled seeds. What percentage of the population have a heterozygous genotype?

Figure 1: G H Hardy (top) and Wilhelm Weinberg (bottom) actually came up with the ideas behind the Hardy-Weinberg principle independently from one another.

Practice Questions — Fact Recall

Q1 Define the term population.

Q2 Explain what is meant by the term gene pool.

Q3 Define the term allele frequency.

Q4 Describe the Hardy-Weinberg principle and the conditions under which it is true.

Q5 Write down the two Hardy-Weinberg equations and describe what each component represents.

- Understand differential reproductive success and its effect on the allele frequency within a gene pool.

- Understand stabilising and directional selection.

- Be able to use both specific examples and unfamiliar information to explain how selection produces changes within a species.

- Be able to interpret data relating to the effect of selection in producing change within populations.

- Understand that the geographic separation of populations of a species can result in the accumulation of differences in the gene pools.

- Understand the importance of geographic isolation in the formation of new species.

Specification Reference 3.4.8

6. Allele Frequency and Speciation

The Hardy-Weinberg principle holds true if no external factors affect allele frequency. But that's not really the case in the real world...

Differential reproductive success

Sometimes the frequency of an allele within a population changes. This can happen when the allele codes for a characteristic that affects the chances of an organism surviving. Not all individuals are as likely to reproduce as each other. There's differential reproductive success in a population — individuals that have an allele that increases their chance of survival are more likely to survive, reproduce and pass on their genes (including the beneficial allele), than individuals with different alleles. This means that a greater proportion of the next generation inherit the beneficial allele. They, in turn, are more likely to survive, reproduce and pass on their genes. So the frequency of the beneficial allele increases from generation to generation. This process is called **natural selection**.

Allele frequency patterns

Stabilising selection and directional selection are types of natural selection that affect allele frequency in different ways. Having different frequencies of alleles means there's always a range of different characteristics in a population.

Stabilising selection

This is where individuals with alleles for characteristics towards the middle of the range are more likely to survive and reproduce. It occurs when the environment isn't changing, and it reduces the range of possible phenotypes.

┌─ **Example** ─────────────────────────────────

In any mammal population there's a range of fur length. In a stable climate, having fur at the extremes of this range reduces the chances of surviving as it's harder to maintain the right body temperature, so mammals with very short or very long fur have a selective disadvantage. Mammals with alleles for average fur length are the most likely to survive, reproduce and pass on their alleles. These mammals have a selective advantage, so these alleles for average fur length increase in frequency.

     Over time, the proportion of the population with average fur length increases and the range of fur lengths decreases — as shown in Figure 1. In the offspring graph the range of fur lengths has decreased, which results in a narrower graph. The proportion with average length fur has increased, resulting in a taller graph in the average fur length region.

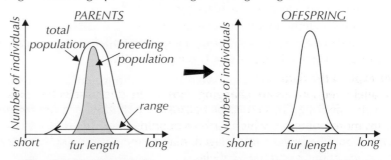

Figure 1: Graphs that show stabilising selection across generations.

Directional selection

This is where individuals with alleles for characteristics of an extreme type are more likely to survive and reproduce. This could be in response to an environmental change.

Tip: With data that shows <u>stabilising</u> selection, the mean <u>stays</u> in the middle. With data that shows <u>directional</u> selection, the mean moves in one <u>direction</u> or the other.

Example

Cheetahs are the fastest animals on land. It's likely that this characteristic was developed through directional selection, as individuals that have alleles for speed are more likely to catch prey than slower individuals. They have a select advantage so they're more likely to survive, reproduce and pass on their alleles.

Over time, the frequency of alleles for high speed increases and the population becomes faster — as shown in Figure 2. In the offspring graph, the average speed (dotted line) has moved towards the extreme, faster end.

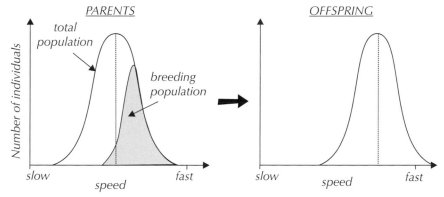

Figure 2: Graphs that show directional selection across generations.

Exam Tip
Make sure you know the differences between the two types of selection. You could be asked to interpret data that shows one of the types of selection and explain why the change has come about.

Interpreting data on allele frequencies

You could be asked to interpret data on allele frequency and the different types of selection in the exam. Here's an example to give you an idea...

Exam Tip
Here the data here shows phenotype, but in the exam you could get genotype or allele-specific data — the idea is still the same.

Example

There are two common forms of the peppered moth in the UK — one dark coloured and one pale. The allele for dark colouring is dominant (M) over the allele for pale colouring (m). The table on the right shows m allele frequency in a population of peppered moths between 1852 and 1860, and the number of coal-powered factories in the area over the same period.

Year	Number of coal-powered factories	Frequency
1852	1	0.75
1854	3	0.70
1856	5	0.63
1858	7	0.47
1860	10	0.39

Figure 3: Two colours of peppered moth on the bark of a tree.

You might be asked to describe the data...
The frequency of the m allele decreases from 0.75 to 0.39 as the number of factories increases. So the frequency of the M allele must increase from 0.25 to 0.61 (remember: $p + q = 1$, see page 100).

...or explain the data
The allele frequencies are changing, most likely due to selective pressure for dark colouring. This could be because of pollution — more factories means more pollution, which darkens buildings etc. The dark coloured moths would be better camouflaged, making them more likely to survive, reproduce and pass on the M allele.

Exam Tip
Regardless of whether it's stabilising or directional selection, you need to make sure you get in the phrase 'more likely to survive, reproduce and pass on their alleles'.

Tip: Selective pressures are things like climate, food sources and habitat, which cause some individuals to have an advantage over others. E.g. a warm climate causes individuals who can store more water, sweat less or have thinner fur to have an advantage.

Geographical isolation and speciation

Selective pressures can lead to genetic changes within a single population. But if that single population gets split and isolated into two groups, then different selective pressures can lead to the development of a new species — this is called **speciation**.

Speciation occurs when populations of the same species become reproductively isolated. This can happen when a physical barrier, e.g. a flood or an earthquake, divides a population of a species, causing some individuals to become separated from the main population. This is known as **geographical isolation**.

Populations that are geographically separated will experience slightly different conditions. For example, there might be a different climate on each side of the physical barrier. The populations will experience different selective pressures and so different changes in allele frequencies:

Exam Tip
It's important to use the correct terminology in the exam, so make sure you understand and can use all the words here. You'll pick up marks for correct spelling too.

- Different alleles will be more advantageous in the different populations, so natural selection occurs. For example, if geographical separation places one population in a colder climate than before, longer fur length will be beneficial. Directional selection will then act on the alleles for fur length in this population, changing the frequency of the allele for longer fur length.

- Allele frequencies will also change as mutations (see p. 184) will occur independently in each population.

The changes in allele frequency will lead to differences accumulating in the gene pools of the separated populations, causing changes in phenotype frequencies. Eventually, individuals from the different populations will have changed so much that they won't be able to breed with one another to produce fertile offspring — they'll have become reproductively isolated. The two groups will have become separate species — see Figure 5.

Tip: A species is a group of individual organisms that can breed together to produce fertile offspring.

Figure 4: A drawing by Charles Darwin of four species of finch found in the Galapagos Islands. 'Darwin's finches' are often seen as a classical example of speciation.

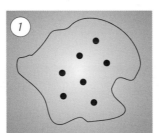

Population of individuals
• = individual organism

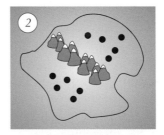

Physical barriers stop interbreeding between populations.

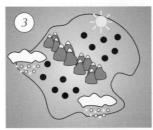

Populations adapt to new environments.

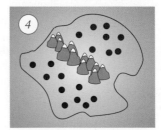

Differences accumulate in the gene pool leading to development of new species.

Figure 5: Diagram showing how geographical isolation could lead to reproductive isolation and so speciation.

Practice Questions — Application

Q1 The graph shows the fur length for a herd of caribou in 1850 and again 100 years later. In 1850 the population were moved from an area in the Arctic to an area much further south.

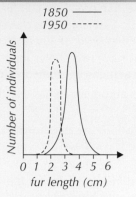

a) Calculate the range of fur lengths for 1950.

b) What kind of selection does the graph show? Explain your answer.

c) Use your knowledge of selection to explain the results.

Tip: To help you answer Q1 c), remember the caribou were moved to an area further <u>south</u> than the cold Arctic.

Q2 Darwin observed 14 different species of finch on the Galapagos Islands in the Pacific Ocean. Each species of finch is unique to a single island and each island has a unique food source on it. Although the finches are all similar, the size and shapes of their beaks differ. Use your knowledge of selection and speciation to explain how these different species came about.

Q3 The frequency of an allele involved in fur colouring was calculated for two populations of woodland mammal found in the north and south of a large forest. The results are shown in the table below. In 1999 a fire destroyed thousands of square miles of trees in the north of the forest.

| Year | Allele frequency | |
	North	South
1994	0.31	0.17
1996	0.33	0.17
1998	0.33	0.19
2000	0.48	0.32
2002	0.52	0.24

Tip: Take your time looking at any data you're given — make sure you really understand what the table in Q3 is showing you before you attempt to answer the questions.

a) The allele frequency for the southern population peaked in 2000. Suggest an explanation for this.

b) The allele is involved in the production of dark fur. Use this information to explain how natural selection might have accounted for the results for the northern population.

c) Further investigation revealed further, different allele frequency changes between the different populations since the fire, leading some scientists to suggest that speciation had occurred. How could this theory be tested?

Practice Questions — Fact Recall

Q1 What is meant by differential reproductive success?

Q2 Explain the differences between stabilising and directional selection.

Q3 What is meant by the term geographical isolation?

Q4 Briefly describe the process of speciation.

Section Summary

Make sure you know...

- That there can be one or more versions of the same gene and that these are called alleles.

- That most plants and animals have two alleles for each gene and that they are found at the same position (called a locus) on each chromosome in a pair.

- That genotype is what alleles an organism has and that phenotype is how these alleles show themselves.

- That alleles whose characteristic is always shown in the phenotype are called dominant, that those only shown in the phenotype if you have two copies are called recessive, and that codominant alleles both show in the phenotype.

- That if an organism has two different alleles for the same characteristic it's heterozygous, but if it has two versions of the same allele it's homozygous.

- That genetic diagrams show how the alleles of two parents could come together to give all the possible genotypes of their offspring.

- How to draw and use genetic diagrams showing monohybrid crosses involving dominant, recessive and codominant alleles, and sex-linked characteristics and multiple alleles, to make predictions about offspring.

- That genetic pedigree diagrams show how inherited characteristics run through families.

- How to use genetic pedigree diagrams to predict genotypes and phenotypes, and to predict the results of crosses.

- That species exist as one or more populations and that the full range of alleles in a population is its gene pool.

- That how often an allele occurs in a population is called allele frequency, which can be given as a percentage or as a decimal.

- That the Hardy-Weinberg principle is a mathematical model that predicts that allele frequencies will not change from generation to generation, so long as there's no immigration, emigration, mutations or natural selection, and mating is totally random.

- The Hardy-Weinberg equations $p + q = 1$ and $p^2 + 2pq + q^2 = 1$, and that p is the frequency of the dominant allele, q is the frequency of the recessive allele, p^2 is the frequency of homozygous dominant genotype, $2pq$ is the frequency of heterozygous genotype, and q^2 is the frequency of homozygous recessive genotype.

- How to use the Hardy-Weinberg equations and any data you are given to calculate allele, genotype and phenotype frequencies.

- That differential reproductive success means not all individuals are as likely to reproduce as each other, as some will have characteristics (alleles) that make them more likely to survive, reproduce and pass on their alleles.

- That differential reproductive success can cause a change in allele frequency within a gene pool.

- That differential reproductive success can cause stabilising selection, where individuals with alleles for characteristics towards the middle of the range are more likely to survive, reproduce and pass on their alleles.

- That differential reproductive success can cause directional selection, where individuals with alleles for characteristics at an extreme of the range are more likely to survive, reproduce and pass on their alleles.

- How to use your knowledge about differential reproductive success to interpret data and explain how selection produces changes within a species.

- That if populations of the same species are geographically isolated it can result in differences in the gene pools that can eventually lead to the formation of new species (speciation).

Exam-style Questions

1   The human alleles for normal haemoglobin (H^N) and sickle haemoglobin (H^S) show codominance. Individuals homozygous for the sickle allele have sickle-cell anaemia, which means their red blood cells are sickle-shaped. Heterozygous individuals have sickle-cell trait, which means they have some normal and some sickle-shaped cells. Below is a pedigree diagram showing haemoglobin phenotypes in one family.

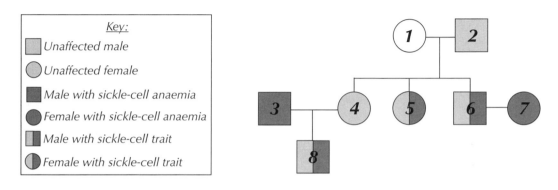

Key:
- Unaffected male
- Unaffected female
- Male with sickle-cell anaemia
- Female with sickle-cell anaemia
- Male with sickle-cell trait
- Female with sickle-cell trait

1 (a) (i)   Explain what is meant by the term homozygous.

(1 mark)

1 (a) (ii)   What is the genotype for individual 1? Explain your answer.

(2 marks)

1 (a) (iii)   If individuals 6 and 7 have a child, what is the chance of them having a girl with sickle-cell trait? Show your working.

(2 marks)

1 (b)   Malaria is an infectious disease caused by infection of the red blood cells. It results in a fever, coma and even death. Sickle-shaped red blood cells offer protection against malaria. This means individuals with sickle-cell trait are more tolerant to malaria infection and show less severe symptoms if they get infected.

The table below shows estimates of sickle haemoglobin allele frequency in various regions of the world and the prevalence of malaria in that area.

Region	Allele Frequency	Prevalence of malaria
Northern Europe	0 - 0.025	None
India	0 - 0.05	Low to moderate
Central Africa	0.05 - 0.125	High

Describe and explain the relationship between sickle allele frequency and prevalence of malaria.

(3 marks)

2 The diagram shows an experiment conducted with fruit flies. One population was split in two and each population was fed a different food. After many generations the populations were placed together and it was found that they couldn't breed together.

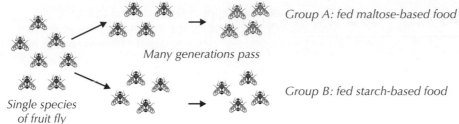

Single species of fruit fly

Many generations pass

Group A: fed maltose-based food

Group B: fed starch-based food

2 (a) What evidence shows that speciation occurred?

(1 mark)

2 (b) Explain why the experiment resulted in speciation.

(3 marks)

2 (c) The frequencies of some alleles in the Group A population are shown in the table.

Generation	White eyes alleles	Blood eyes allele	Normal wings allele
A	0.68	0.14	0.79
E	0.56	0.16	0.82
I	0.61	0.14	0.83

2 (c) (i) Is eye colour controlled by white and blood alleles only?
Use evidence from the table to support your answer.

(1 mark)

2 (c) (ii) The gene for wings has two alleles — the dominant normal wings allele and the recessive vestigial (little) wings allele. What percentage of the population in generation E would be heterozygous for wings? Show your working.

(2 marks)

3 Haemophilia is most often a sex-linked characteristic caused by a recessive faulty allele carried on the X chromosome in humans.

3 (a) Explain what is meant by a sex-linked recessive characteristic.

(2 marks)

3 (b) A male haemophilia sufferer and a homozygous normal female are considering having children.

What would be the probability of them having a child that suffers from haemophilia? Show your working.

(2 marks)

1. Survival and Response

In order to survive, organisms need to respond to what's going on around them. Otherwise they'd find themselves in a pretty unfavourable position...

Responding to the environment

Organisms increase their chances of survival by responding to changes in their external environment, e.g. by avoiding harmful environments such as places that are too hot or too cold. They also respond to changes in their internal environment to make sure that the conditions are always optimal for their metabolism (all the chemical reactions that go on inside them). Any change in the internal or external environment, e.g. a change in temperature, light intensity or pressure, is called a **stimulus**.

Simple responses

Simple organisms, e.g. woodlice, have simple responses to keep them in a favourable environment. Their response can either be tactic or kinetic:

Tactic response (taxis) — directional movement in response to a stimulus. The direction of the stimulus affects the response.

> **Example**
>
> Woodlice show a tactic response to light — they move away from a light source. This helps them survive as it keeps them concealed under stones during the day (where they're safe from predators) and keeps them in damp conditions (which reduces water loss).
>
>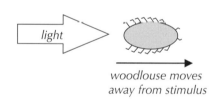
>
> light
>
> woodlouse moves away from stimulus

Kinetic response (kinesis) — non-directional (random) movement in response to a stimulus. The intensity of the stimulus affects the response.

> **Example**
>
> Woodlice show a kinetic response to humidity. In high humidity they move slowly and turn less often, so that they stay where they are. As the air gets drier, they move faster and turn more often, so that they move into a new area. This response helps woodlice move from drier air to more humid air, and then stay put. This improves the survival chances of the organism — it reduces their water loss and it helps to keep them concealed.

Practice Questions — Fact Recall

Q1 Why is it important that organisms respond to stimuli?

Q2 What is a tactic response?

Q3 What is a kinetic response?

Learning Objectives:

- Understand that organisms increase their chances of survival by responding to changes in their environment.
- Know that taxes and kineses are simple responses that can keep a mobile organism in a favourable environment.

Specification Reference 3.5.1

Tip: Simple responses are automatic responses to a stimulus — the organism doesn't 'choose' where to move.

Tip: If an organism moves <u>towards</u> a stimulus it's a <u>positive</u> taxis, and if it moves <u>away</u> from a stimulus it's a <u>negative</u> taxis. So in the first example, woodlice show a negative taxis to light.

Tip: Taxes is the plural of taxis, kineses is the plural of kinesis.

Tip: The word before 'taxis' tells you what the organism is responding to, e.g. <u>photo</u>taxis is a response to <u>light</u>.

Learning Objectives:

- Understand that in nervous communication, electrical impulses are passed along the length of a nerve cell.

- Know that nerve cells stimulate their target cells by secreting chemical neurotransmitters directly on to them.

- Know that nervous communication results in rapid, short-lived and localised responses.

- Understand the importance of simple reflexes in avoiding damage to the body.

- Know a simple reflex arc involving three neurones.

- Know that mammalian hormones are substances that stimulate their target cells via the blood system.

- Know that hormonal communication results in slow, long-lasting and widespread responses.

Specification References 3.5.1 and 3.5.2

Tip: Electrical impulses are also called nerve impulses.

Tip: The CNS is part of the nervous system, made up of the brain and spinal cord (see page 140 for more).

2. Nervous and Hormonal Communication

In order to respond to changes in the environment, an organism needs to pass messages between different areas of its body. In animals this communication is carried out using nerve impulses, hormones or a combination of both.

Receptors and effectors

Receptors detect stimuli — they can be cells, or proteins on cell surface membranes. There are loads of different types of receptors that detect different stimuli, e.g. baroreceptors are a type of receptor that detect changes in blood pressure.

Effectors are cells that bring about a response to a stimulus, to produce an effect. Effectors include muscle cells and cells found in glands, e.g. the pancreas. Receptors communicate with effectors via the nervous system or the hormonal system, or sometimes using both.

The nervous system

Neurones (nerve cells)

The nervous system is made up of a complex network of cells called neurones. There are three main types of neurone:

1. **Sensory neurones** transmit electrical impulses from receptors to the central nervous system (CNS).

2. **Motor neurones** transmit electrical impulses from the CNS to effectors.

3. **Relay neurones** (also called intermediate neurones, interneurones or association neurones) transmit electrical impulses between sensory neurones and motor neurones.

Nervous communication

A stimulus is detected by receptor cells and an electrical impulse is sent along a sensory neurone. When an electrical impulse reaches the end of a neurone chemicals called **neurotransmitters** take the information across the gap (called a synapse) to the next neurone, which then sends an electrical impulse (see p. 128). The CNS processes the information, decides what to do about it and sends impulses along motor neurones to an effector (see Figure 1).

Figure 1: The pathway of nervous communication.

┌─ Example ─────────────────────────────

A real-life example of nervous communication is when you see a friend waving to you and you wave back in response:

- **Stimulus** — you see a friend waving.

- **Receptors** — light receptors (photoreceptors) in your eyes detect the wave. The electrical impulse is carried by a sensory neurone to the CNS.

- **CNS** — processes information and decides what to do about it. An electrical impulse is sent along a motor neurone.

- **Effectors** — muscle cells are stimulated by the motor neurone.

- **Response** — muscles contract to make your arm wave.

The nervous response

When an electrical impulse reaches the end of a neurone, neurotransmitters are secreted directly onto cells (e.g. muscle cells) — so the nervous response is localised. Neurotransmitters are quickly removed once they've done their job, so the response is short-lived. Electrical impulses are really fast, so the response is rapid — this allows animals to react quickly to stimuli.

Tip: The cells that neurotransmitters are released onto are called target cells — they have specific receptors for the neurotransmitters (see page 128 for more).

Simple reflexes

A simple reflex is a rapid, involuntary response to a stimulus. The pathway of communication goes through the spinal cord but not through conscious parts of the brain, so the response happens automatically. Because you don't have to spend time deciding how to respond, information travels really fast from receptors to effectors.

Simple reflexes are protective — they help organisms to avoid damage to the body because the response happens so quickly.

Tip: Nervous impulses that involve the conscious brain are voluntary responses — you have to think about them. Reflexes don't involve the conscious brain so they're involuntary responses — your body responds without thinking about it first.

The reflex arc

The pathway of neurones linking receptors to effectors in a simple reflex is called a reflex arc. Three neurones are involved — a sensory neurone, a relay neurone and a motor neurone (see Figure 2).

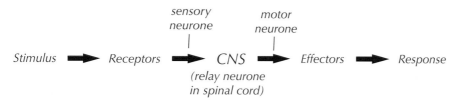

Figure 2: The pathway of nervous communication in a simple reflex arc.

--- Example ---

A real-life example of a simple reflex is the hand-withdrawal response to heat:

- **Stimulus** — you touch a hot surface.
- **Receptors** — thermoreceptors (heat receptors) in your skin detect the heat stimulus. A sensory neurone carries the impulse to the CNS.
- **CNS** — a relay neurone in your spinal cord carries the impulse to a motor neurone.
- **Effectors** — the motor neurone carries the impulse to muscle cells in your biceps.
- **Response** — your biceps muscle contracts to pull your hand away from the heat source and stop your hand from being damaged.

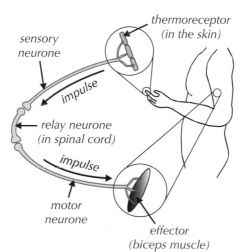

Exam Tip
You need to learn a simple reflex arc involving three neurones for your exam. The hand-withdrawal response to heat is a really common example.

Tip: If there's a relay neurone involved in the simple reflex arc then it's possible to override the reflex, e.g. in the example on the left your brain could tell your hand to withstand the heat.

The hormonal system

The hormonal system in mammals is made up of **glands** and **hormones**:

- A gland is a group of cells that are specialised to secrete a useful substance, such as a hormone, e.g. the pancreas secretes insulin.

- Hormones are 'chemical messengers'. Many hormones are proteins or peptides (e.g. insulin), and some are steroids (e.g. progesterone).

Hormones are secreted when a gland is stimulated. Glands can be stimulated by a change in concentration of a specific substance (sometimes another hormone). They can also be stimulated by electrical impulses.

Hormonal communication

Hormones diffuse directly into the blood, then they're taken around the body by the circulatory system. They diffuse out of the blood all over the body but each hormone will only bind to specific receptors for that hormone, found on the membranes of some cells — these are called **target cells**. The hormones trigger a response in the target cells (the effectors).

Stimulus ➡ *Receptors* ➡ *Hormone* ➡ *Effectors* ➡ *Response*

Figure 3: *The pathway of hormonal communication.*

Figure 4: *A growth hormone molecule (pink) bound to a growth hormone receptor (yellow and beige) in the membrane of the target cell.*

Example

A real-life example of hormonal communication is the process the body uses to increase blood glucose concentration when it's lower than normal:

- **Stimulus** — low blood glucose concentration.

- **Receptors** — receptors on pancreas cells detect the low blood glucose concentration.

- **Hormone** — the pancreas releases the hormone glucagon into the blood.

- **Effectors** — target cells in the liver detect glucagon and convert glycogen into glucose.

- **Response** — glucose is released into the blood, so glucose concentration increases.

Tip: There's more on glucagon and how blood glucose concentration is controlled on pages 157-158.

The hormonal response

Hormones aren't released directly onto their target cells — they must travel in the blood to get there. This means that chemical communication (by hormones) is slower than electrical communication (by nerves). They aren't broken down as quickly as neurotransmitters, so the effects of hormones can last for much longer. Hormones are transported all over the body, so the response may be widespread if the target cells are widespread.

Nervous vs hormonal response

Here's a table summarising the key differences between the nervous and hormonal systems:

Nervous System	Hormonal System
Electrical impulses carried by neurones	Hormones carried in the blood
Fast response	Slow response
Localised effect	Widespread effect
Short-lived effect	Long-lasting effect

Q1 Look at the three scenarios below.

> **Scenario 1:** The adrenal gland releasing DHT, resulting in poor hair growth.
>
> **Scenario 2:** Stepping on a drawing pin and immediately pulling the foot up off the pin.
>
> **Scenario 3:** Hearing music and deciding to tap the foot.

Match each scenario to the type of communication involved:

A — nervous response   **B** — hormonal response   **C** — simple reflex

Give evidence from the text to support each of your answers.

Q2 The knee-jerk reflex involves lightly tapping a person on the patellar tendon (just below the knee-cap) with a tendon hammer. When this happens, the quadriceps muscle (in the thigh) immediately contracts, causing the person's lower leg to jerk forward.

a) This response is a reflex. Suggest one way in which the response would differ if it was not a reflex.

b) Name the stimulus and the effector in the knee-jerk reflex.

c) The knee-jerk reflex is unusual because the sensory neurone synapses directly onto the motor neurone in the spinal cord.

   i)   Describe how this differs from a simple reflex, such as the hand-withdrawal response to heat.

   ii) Suggest what effect tapping the patellar tendon might have in someone with a spinal cord injury. Explain your answer.

d) Suggest the purpose of the knee-jerk reflex.

Tip: When you're asked to 'suggest' answers, you're not expected to be able to give an exact, detailed answer. Instead, you're expected to use your knowledge to make educated and plausible suggestions.

Practice Questions — Fact Recall

Q1 What is the role of a receptor?

Q2 Give two types of cell that act as effectors.

Q3 Describe the pathway of nervous communication from stimulus to response, in a voluntary response.

Q4 Explain why nervous communication leads to a localised and short-lived response.

Q5 Why do simple reflexes help an organism to avoid damage to their body?

Q6 Where are hormones secreted from?

Q7 Give two types of stimuli that trigger hormone secretion.

Q8 Why is hormonal communication generally slower than nervous communication?

Q9 Explain why a hormonal response may be widespread and long-lasting.

3. Chemical Mediators

Chemical mediators are another form of cellular communication in mammals.

Learning Objectives:
- Know that some mammalian cells release local chemical mediators which only affect cells in their local vicinity.
- Know that histamine and prostaglandins are local chemical mediators.

Specification Reference 3.5.2

What is a chemical mediator?

A chemical mediator is a chemical messenger that acts locally (i.e. on nearby cells). Communication using chemical mediators is similar to communication using hormones (see p. 114) — cells release chemicals that bind to specific receptors on target cells to cause a response. But there are a few differences:

- Chemical mediators are secreted from cells that are all over the body (not just from glands).
- Their target cells are right next to where the chemical mediator's produced. This means they stimulate a local response (not a widespread one).
- They only have to travel a short distance to their target cells, so produce a quicker response than hormones (which are transported in the blood).

Tip: Even though chemical mediators have a similar mode of action to hormones, they're not part of the hormonal system.

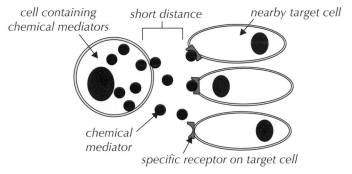

Figure 1: *Chemical mediators being released onto their target cells.*

Histamine and prostaglandins

You need to know about two types of chemical mediator — histamine and prostaglandins.

Histamine

Histamine is a chemical mediator that's stored in mast cells and basophils (types of cell in the immune system). It's released in response to the body being injured or infected. It increases the permeability of the capillaries nearby to allow more immune system cells to move out of the blood to the infected or injured area.

Figure 2: *Transmission electron microscope (TEM) image of a mast cell. The red granules contain histamine and are released into surrounding tissues when the mast cell is activated i.e. by injury or infection.*

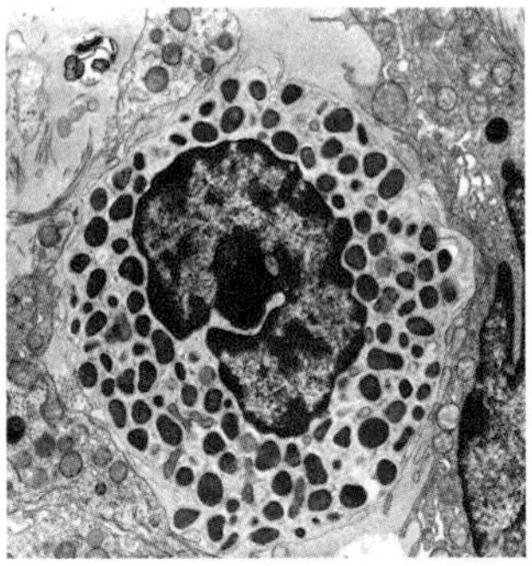

Prostaglandins

Prostaglandins are a group of chemical mediators that are produced by most cells of the body. They're involved in loads of things like inflammation, fever, blood pressure regulation and blood clotting. E.g. one type of prostaglandin is released from blood vessel epithelium cells and causes the muscles around them to relax.

Practice Questions — Fact Recall

Q1 Why do chemical mediators only produce a local response?

Q2 Why do chemical mediators produce a faster response than hormones?

Q3 What triggers the release of histamine?

Q4 Name one type of local chemical mediator other than histamines.

4. Receptors

Receptors detect stimuli. They're the first cell involved in the chain of communication... and you need to know how they work.

How receptors work

Receptors are specific — they only detect one particular stimulus, e.g. light or pressure or glucose concentration. There are many different types of receptor that each detect a different type of stimulus. Some receptors are cells, e.g. photoreceptors are receptor cells that connect to the nervous system (see page 119). Some receptors are proteins on cell surface membranes, e.g. glucose receptors are proteins found in the cell membranes of some pancreatic cells.

Receptors in the nervous system convert the energy of the stimulus into the electrical energy used by neurones. Here's how they work...

The resting potential

When a nervous system receptor is in its resting state (not being stimulated), there's a difference in charge between the inside and the outside of the cell — the inside is negatively charged relative to the outside (see Figure 1). This means there's a **voltage** across the membrane. Voltage is also known as **potential difference**. The potential difference when a cell is at rest is called its **resting potential**. The resting potential is generated by ion pumps and ion channels (see p. 121).

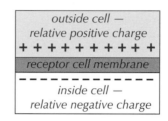

Figure 1: *Relative charges either side of a receptor cell membrane at rest.*

The generator potential

When a stimulus is detected, the cell membrane is excited and becomes more permeable, allowing more ions to move in and out of the cell — altering the potential difference. The change in potential difference due to a stimulus is called the **generator potential**. A bigger stimulus excites the membrane more, causing a bigger movement of ions and a bigger change in potential difference — so a bigger generator potential is produced (see Figure 2).

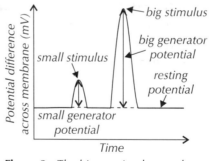

Figure 2: *The bigger stimulus produces the bigger generator potential.*

The action potential

If the generator potential is big enough it'll trigger an action potential — an electrical impulse along a neurone. An action potential is only triggered if the generator potential reaches a certain level called the **threshold level**. If the stimulus is too weak the generator potential won't reach the threshold, so there's no action potential (see Figure 3).

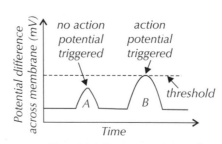

Figure 3: *Generator potential not reaching the threshold (A) and reaching the threshold (B).*

Learning Objectives:

- Understand how a generator potential is created when a receptor is stimulated.
- Know the basic structure of a Pacinian corpuscle as an example of a receptor.
- Be able to use the Pacinian corpuscle as an example to illustrate:
  - that receptors only respond to specific stimuli.
  - that stimulation of receptor membranes produces deformation of stretch-mediated sodium channels, which leads to the establishment of a generator potential.
- Be able to explain how the distribution of rods and cones, and the connections they make in the optic nerve, lead to differences in sensitivity and visual acuity.

  Specification Reference 3.5.1

Tip: Potential difference across a cell membrane is usually measured in millivolts (mV).

Tip: There's much more on action potentials on pages 122-123.

Pacinian corpuscles

Pacinian corpuscles are mechanoreceptors — they detect mechanical stimuli, e.g. pressure and vibrations. They're found in your skin. Pacinian corpuscles contain the end of a sensory neurone, imaginatively called a sensory nerve ending. The sensory nerve ending is wrapped in loads of layers of connective tissue called lamellae.

When a Pacinian corpuscle is stimulated, e.g. by a tap on the arm, the lamellae are deformed and press on the sensory nerve ending. This causes deformation of **stretch-mediated sodium channels** in the sensory neurone's cell membrane — see Figure 5. The sodium ion channels open and sodium ions diffuse into the cell, creating a generator potential. If the generator potential reaches the threshold, it triggers an action potential.

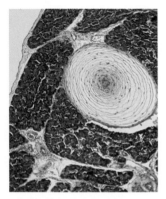

Figure 4: Light micrograph showing a section of a Pacinian corpuscle at rest.

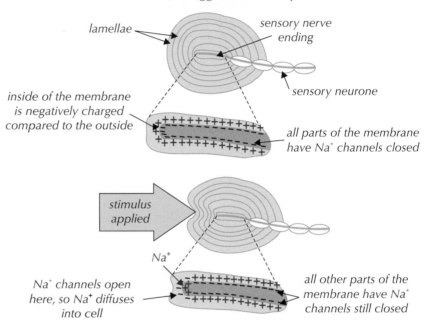

Figure 5: A Pacinian corpuscle at rest (above) and during stimulation (below).

Practice Questions — Application

Q1 For a particular receptor cell, an action potential is triggered when the generator potential reaches –60 mV.

a) What name is given to the value at which an action potential will be triggered?

The graph below shows generator potentials in the receptor cell.

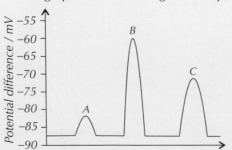

b) Which curve shows a generator potential that would trigger an action potential? Give a reason for your answer.

c) What is the resting potential of this receptor cell?

Q2 Suggest how a person's response to vibration might be altered if they were to take a drug that blocks stretch-mediated sodium channels.

Photoreceptors

Photoreceptors are receptors in your eye that detect light. Light enters the eye through the pupil, and the amount of light that enters is controlled by the muscles of the iris. Light rays are focused by the lens onto the retina, which lines the inside of the eye. The retina contains the photoreceptor cells.

The fovea is an area of the retina where there are lots of photoreceptors. Nerve impulses from the photoreceptor cells are carried from the retina to the brain by the optic nerve, which is a bundle of neurones. Where the optic nerve leaves the eye is called the blind spot — there aren't any photoreceptor cells, so it's not sensitive to light.

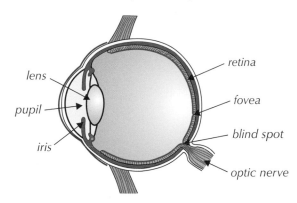

Figure 6: Cross-section of an eye.

How photoreceptors work

Light enters the eye, hits the photoreceptors and is absorbed by light-sensitive pigments. Light bleaches the pigments, causing a chemical change and altering the membrane permeability to sodium. A generator potential is created and if it reaches the threshold, a nerve impulse is sent along a bipolar neurone. Bipolar neurones connect photoreceptors to the optic nerve, which takes impulses to the brain (see Figure 7).

Tip: Light goes straight through the neurones to the photoreceptors.

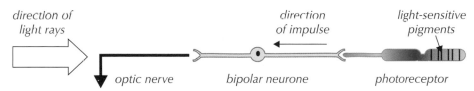

Figure 7: Nervous communication in the eye.

Rods and cones

The human eye has two types of photoreceptor — rods and cones. Rods are mainly found in the peripheral parts of the retina, and cones are found packed together in the fovea — see Figure 9.

Rods only give information in black and white (monochromatic vision), but cones give information in colour (trichromatic vision). There are three types of cones — red-sensitive, green-sensitive and blue-sensitive. They're stimulated in different proportions so you see different colours.

Figure 8: A section through a human retina. Light entering the eye from the left hits the photoreceptors (yellow), which connect to neurones (red).

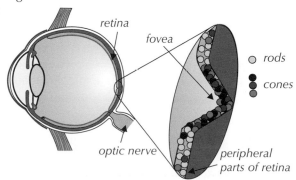

Figure 9: Diagram showing the location of rods and cones.

Sensitivity

Rods are very sensitive to light (they fire action potentials in dim light). This is because many rods join one neurone, so many weak generator potentials combine to reach the threshold and trigger an action potential.

Cones are less sensitive than rods (they only fire action potentials in bright light). This is because one cone joins one neurone, so it takes more light to reach the threshold and trigger an action potential.

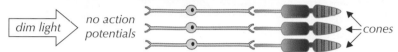

Visual acuity

Visual acuity is the ability to tell apart points that are close together. Rods give low visual acuity because many rods join the same neurone, which means light from two objects close together can't be told apart.

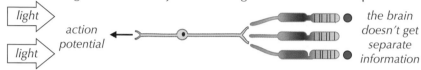

Cones give high visual acuity because cones are close together and one cone joins one neurone. When light from two points hits two cones, two action potentials (one from each cone) go to the brain — so you can distinguish two points that are close together as two separate points.

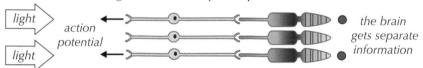

Summary table of rods and cones

Rods	Cones
Mainly located in the peripheral parts of the retina	Mainly located in the fovea
Give information in black and white	Give information in colour
Many rods join one neurone	One cone joins one neurone
High sensitivity to light	Low sensitivity to light
Give low visual acuity	Give high visual acuity

Practice Questions — Fact Recall

Q1 Explain how a generator potential is produced.

Q2 What type of stimulus does a Pacinian corpuscle respond to?

Q3 Describe the structure of a Pacinian corpuscle.

Q4 Explain how the presence of a stimulus triggers an action potential in a Pacinian corpuscle.

Q5 Explain why cones give a higher visual acuity than rods.

Q6 Other than visual acuity, give three differences between rods and cones.

Figure 10: A scanning electron microscope (SEM) image of rod (white) and cone (green) cells in the retina.

Tip: Someone with a low visual acuity will have blurry vision.

Tip: Remember, cones are packed closely together.

5. The Nervous Impulse

Nervous impulses are the electrical charges transmitted along a neurone. They're created by the movement of sodium and potassium ions.

The resting membrane potential

In a neurone's resting state (when it's not being stimulated), the outside of the membrane is positively charged compared to the inside. This is because there are more positive ions outside the cell than inside. So the membrane is polarised — there's a difference in charge. The voltage across the membrane when it's at rest is called the resting potential — it's about –70 mV.

Movement of sodium and potassium ions

The resting potential is created and maintained by **sodium-potassium pumps** and **potassium ion channels** in a neurone's membrane (see Figure 1).

- Sodium-potassium pumps use **active transport** to move three sodium ions (Na^+) out of the neurone for every two potassium ions (K^+) moved in. ATP is needed to do this.

- Potassium ion channels allow **facilitated diffusion** of potassium ions (K^+) out of the neurone, down their concentration gradient.

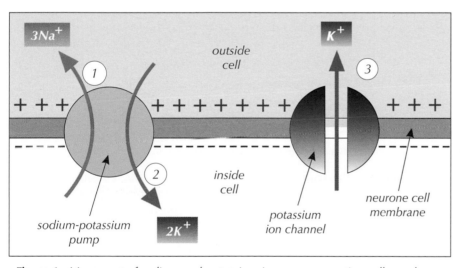

Figure 1: *Movement of sodium and potassium ions across a resting cell membrane.*

1. The sodium-potassium pumps move sodium ions out of the neurone, but the membrane isn't permeable to sodium ions, so they can't diffuse back in. This creates a sodium ion **electrochemical gradient** (a concentration gradient of ions) because there are more positive sodium ions outside the cell than inside.

2. The sodium-potassium pumps also move potassium ions in to the neurone.

3. When the cell's at rest, most potassium ion channels are open. This means that the membrane is permeable to potassium ions, so some diffuse back out through potassium ion channels.

Even though positive ions are moving in and out of the cell, in total more positive ions move out of the cell than enter. This makes the outside of the cell positively charged compared to the inside.

Learning Objectives:

- Understand how a resting potential is established in terms of differential membrane permeability, electrochemical gradients and the movement of sodium and potassium ions.

- Understand how changes in membrane permeability lead to depolarisation and the generation of an action potential.

- Understand the nature and importance of the refractory period in producing discrete impulses.

- Understand the all-or-nothing principle of an action potential.

- Know the structure of a myelinated motor neurone.

- Understand how an action potential is passed along non-myelinated and myelinated axons, resulting in nerve impulses.

- Know how myelination, saltatory conduction, axon diameter and temperature affect the speed of conduction.

Specification Reference 3.5.2

Tip: The neurone cell membrane also has sodium ion channels (see next page) but these are closed when the cell's at rest.

Tip: Remember, sodium-potassium pumps are SOPI — Sodium Out, Potassium In.

Action potentials

Tip: These sodium ion channels are <u>voltage-gated</u> — they only open when the potential difference reaches a certain voltage.

When a neurone is stimulated, other ion channels in the cell membrane, called sodium ion channels, open. If the stimulus is big enough, it'll trigger a rapid change in potential difference. This causes the cell membrane to become **depolarised** (it's no longer polarised). The sequence of events that happen are known as an action potential — see Figure 2.

Exam Tip
You don't have to learn the mV values given here — they're only approximate and vary from neurone to neurone. Don't be thrown in the exam if you're given a graph with different values.

Exam Tip
You might be asked to explain the shape of this graph in your exam, so make sure you know what's happening at each point.

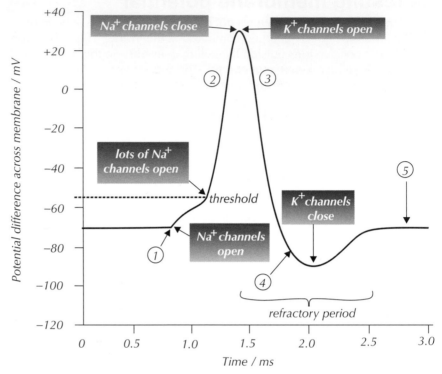

Figure 2: A graph to show the changes in potential difference across a neurone cell membrane during an action potential.

Tip: The graph below shows when the <u>sodium ion channels</u> (orange) are open during an action potential (dotted line):

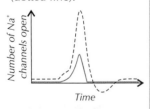

And this graph shows when the <u>potassium ion channels</u> (blue) are open:

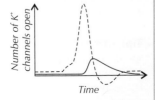

1. **Stimulus** — this excites the neurone cell membrane, causing sodium ion channels to open. The membrane becomes more permeable to sodium, so sodium ions diffuse into the neurone down the sodium ion electrochemical gradient. This makes the inside of the neurone less negative.

2. **Depolarisation** — if the potential difference reaches the threshold (around −55 mV), more sodium ion channels open. More sodium ions diffuse into the neurone.

3. **Repolarisation** — at a potential difference of around +30 mV the sodium ion channels close and potassium ion channels open. The membrane is more permeable to potassium so potassium ions diffuse out of the neurone down the potassium ion concentration gradient. This starts to get the membrane back to its resting potential.

4. **Hyperpolarisation** — potassium ion channels are slow to close so there's a slight 'overshoot' where too many potassium ions diffuse out of the neurone. The potential difference becomes more negative than the resting potential (i.e. less than −70 mV).

5. **Resting potential** — the ion channels are reset. The sodium-potassium pump returns the membrane to its resting potential by pumping sodium ions out and potassium ions in, and maintains the resting potential until the membrane's excited by another stimulus.

The refractory period

After an action potential, the neurone cell membrane can't be excited again straight away. This is because the ion channels are recovering and they can't be made to open — sodium ion channels are closed during repolarisation and potassium ion channels are closed during hyperpolarisation. This period of recovery is called the refractory period (see Figure 3).

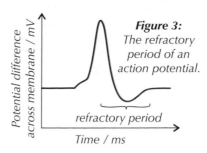

Figure 3: *The refractory period of an action potential.*

The refractory period acts as a time delay between one action potential and the next. This makes sure that action potentials don't overlap but pass along as discrete (separate) impulses. The refractory period also makes sure action potentials are unidirectional (they only travel in one direction).

Waves of depolarisation

When an action potential happens, some of the sodium ions that enter the neurone diffuse sideways. This causes sodium ion channels in the next region of the neurone to open and sodium ions diffuse into that part. This causes a wave of depolarisation to travel along the neurone. The wave moves away from the parts of the membrane in the refractory period because these parts can't fire an action potential.

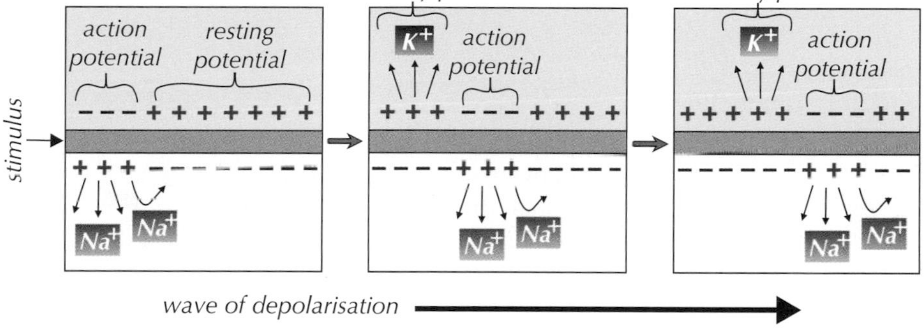

Tip: A wave of depolarisation is like a Mexican wave travelling through a crowd — sodium ions rushing inwards causes a wave of activity along the membrane.

Figure 4: *The movement of ions across a neurone cell membrane during a wave of depolarisation.*

Tip: The electrical impulse can be said to 'propagate' along the neurone. This just describes the wave-like movement of the action potential.

All-or-nothing principle

Once the threshold is reached, an action potential will always fire with the same change in voltage, no matter how big the stimulus is. If the threshold isn't reached, an action potential won't fire (see Figure 5). This is the **all-or-nothing** nature of action potentials.

A bigger stimulus won't cause a bigger action potential but it will cause them to fire more frequently (see Figure 6).

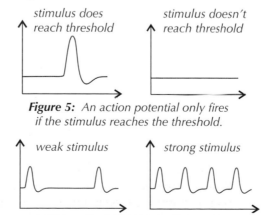

Figure 5: *An action potential only fires if the stimulus reaches the threshold.*

Figure 6: *A bigger stimulus causes more frequent action potentials.*

Tip: The all-or-nothing principle stops the brain from getting over-stimulated by not responding to very small stimuli.

Speed of conduction

Three factors affect the speed of conduction of action potentials:

1. Myelination

Some neurones, including many motor neurones, are myelinated — they have a **myelin sheath** (see Figure 8). The myelin sheath is an electrical insulator. It's made of a type of cell called a **Schwann cell**. Between the Schwann cells are tiny patches of bare membrane called the **nodes of Ranvier**. Sodium ion channels are concentrated at the nodes of Ranvier.

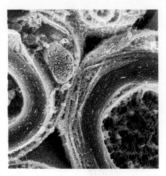

Figure 7: A cross-section through a myelinated neurone. The myelin sheath (orange/brown) surrounds the axon (dark brown).

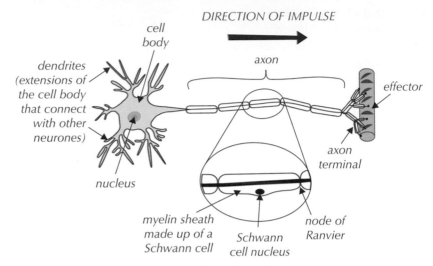

Figure 8: Structure of a myelinated motor neurone.

Saltatory conduction

In a myelinated neurone, depolarisation only happens at the nodes of Ranvier (where sodium ions can get through the membrane). The neurone's cytoplasm conducts enough electrical charge to depolarise the next node, so the impulse 'jumps' from node to node. This is called saltatory conduction and it's really fast — see Figure 10.

In a non-myelinated neurone, the impulse travels as a wave along the whole length of the axon membrane (see Figure 11). This is slower than saltatory conduction (although it's still pretty quick).

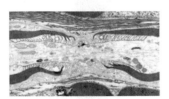

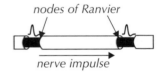

Figure 10: Saltatory conduction along a myelinated neurone.

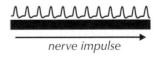

Figure 11: Conduction along a non-myelinated neurone.

Figure 9: A section through a myelinated neurone. The area where there is no myelin sheath (blue) is a node of Ranvier.

Tip: If you imagine a Mexican wave travelling through a crowd, then saltatory conduction is like every tenth person doing the wave instead of everyone doing the wave — so it travels much faster.

2. Axon diameter

Action potentials are conducted quicker along axons with bigger diameters because there's less resistance to the flow of ions than in the cytoplasm of a smaller axon. With less resistance, depolarisation reaches other parts of the neurone cell membrane quicker.

3. Temperature

The speed of conduction increases as the temperature increases too, because ions diffuse faster. The speed only increases up to around 40 °C though — after that the proteins begin to denature and the speed decreases.

Tip: The pumps and channels that move ions across the membrane are proteins, so these will denature at high temperatures.

Practice Questions — Application

The graph below shows the changes in potential difference across a neurone cell membrane during an action potential.

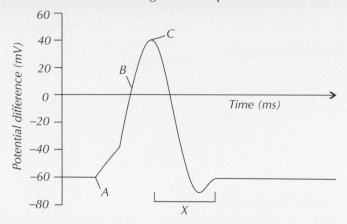

Tip: Remember, the potential difference is the voltage across the membrane.

Q1 Describe the different events occurring at points A, B and C.

Q2 What is the threshold level for this action potential?

Q3 What is the resting potential of this neurone cell membrane?

Q4 a) Explain the shape of the curve during the period marked X.

   b) What name is given to the period marked X?

Q5 How would the graph look if a bigger stimulus triggered the action potential? Explain your answer.

Exam Tip
Always be clear in your exam answers as to whether you're talking about sodium ions (Na^+) or potassium ions (K^+) — don't just write 'sodium', 'potassium' or 'ions'.

Practice Questions — Fact Recall

Q1 Which two proteins in a neurone's cell membrane are responsible for creating and maintaining the resting membrane potential?

Q2 Following a stimulus, explain how the opening of sodium ion channels affects the potential difference across a neurone cell membrane.

Q3 Describe and explain the movement of sodium ions if the potential difference across a neurone cell membrane reaches the threshold level.

Q4 a) After an action potential, why can't the neurone cell membrane be excited again straight away?

   b) What two effects does this have on the conduction of action potentials along a neurone?

Q5 Explain how waves of depolarisation are produced.

Q6 Describe the structure of a myelinated neurone.

Q7 How does conduction along a myelinated neurone differ compared to conduction along a non-myelinated neurone?

Q8 Give two factors, other than myelination, that affect the conduction of action potentials.

Exam Tip
In your exam, be careful not to use phrases like 'ions move across the membrane' — you need to make it clear whether they're moving into or out of the cell.

Exam-style Questions

1   The diagram below shows the structure of a myelinated motor neurone.

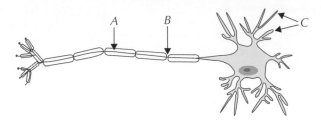

1 (a) (i)   Name the type of cell that forms structure A.

(1 mark)

1 (a) (ii)   Name the structures labelled B and C.

(2 marks)

1 (b)   Guillain-Barré syndrome is an auto-immune disease whereby the myelin sheath around certain neurones is damaged.

1 (b) (i)   Explain the function of myelin in a normal motor neurone.

(2 marks)

1 (b) (ii)   Use your knowledge of myelination to explain how Guillain-Barré syndrome can result in muscle weakness and paralysis.

(2 marks)

1 (c)   The graph below shows three action potentials recorded across the membrane of a myelinated axon (axon X).

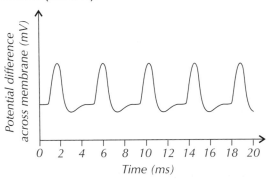

1 (c) (i)   Explain why the action potentials don't overlap.

(3 marks)

1 (c) (ii)   If the action potentials continue at the same frequency, calculate the number of action potentials along the axon in 500 ms.

(2 marks)

1 (c) (iii)   At the same temperature, another myelinated axon (axon Y) conducted 140 action potentials in 500 ms. Use your answer to **(c)(ii)** to suggest whether axon X or axon Y has the biggest diameter. Explain your answer.

(3 marks)

2   A bee sting will activate an immune response. The affected area will quickly become red and inflamed as a result of chemicals, such as histamine, released by immune cells to increase the permeability of capillaries at the site of the sting.

2 (a)   What name is given to chemical messengers such as histamine?

(1 mark)

2 (b)   Explain why the release of histamine results in the area around the bee sting becoming inflamed quickly.

(2 marks)

Antihistamine drugs work by blocking histamine receptors on target cells.

2 (c)   Suggest how the body's response to a bee sting would be affected if an antihistamine had been taken shortly before being stung.

(2 marks)

3   The diagram below shows a neurone cell membrane at two different times during one action potential.

Time 1

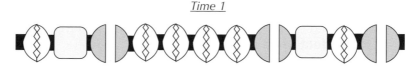

Time 2

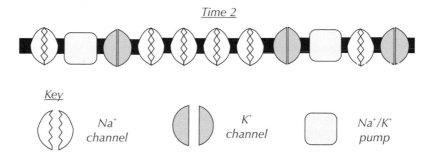

Key

Na⁺ channel   K⁺ channel   Na⁺/K⁺ pump

3 (a)   Describe the stages of the action potential that are occurring at Times 1 and 2. Use evidence from the diagram to support your answer.

(6 marks)

3 (b)   The neurone cell membrane shows sodium-potassium (Na⁺/K⁺) pumps.

3 (b) (i)   Describe the movement of sodium and potassium ions across a sodium-potassium pump.

(3 marks)

3 (b) (ii)   Explain why a sodium-potassium pump is needed by the neurone cell membrane after Time 2.

(3 marks)

3 (c)   Tetrodotoxin is a chemical that blocks sodium ion channels.

Use your knowledge of action potentials to explain the effect that tetrodotoxin is likely to have upon the nervous system.

(3 marks)

- Know the detailed structure of a synapse.
- Be able to explain unidirectionality in synaptic transmission.
- Understand the sequence of events involved in transmission across a cholinergic synapse.
- Know the detailed structure of a neuromuscular junction.
- Understand the sequence of events involved in transmission across a neuromuscular junction.
- Be able to explain inhibition, and spatial and temporal summation.
- Be able to predict and explain the effects of specific drugs on a synapse, when provided with information. (Recall of the names and mode of action of individual drugs is not required.)

Specification Reference 3.5.2

6. Synaptic Transmission

If you've ever wanted to know more about neurones and how they pass on information, well now's your chance...

Synapses and neurotransmitters

A synapse is the junction between a neurone and another neurone, or between a neurone and an effector cell, e.g. a muscle or gland cell. The tiny gap between the cells at a synapse is called the synaptic cleft. The presynaptic neurone (the one before the synapse) has a swelling called a synaptic knob. This contains synaptic vesicles filled with chemicals called neurotransmitters — see Figure 1.

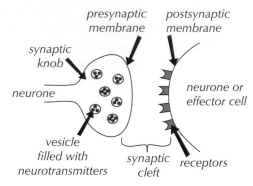

Figure 1: *The structure of a typical synapse.*

Effect of an action potential

When an action potential reaches the end of a neurone it causes neurotransmitters to be released into the synaptic cleft. They diffuse across to the postsynaptic membrane (the one after the synapse) and bind to specific receptors. When neurotransmitters bind to receptors they might trigger an action potential (in a neurone), cause muscle contraction (in a muscle cell), or cause a hormone to be secreted (from a gland cell).

Because the receptors are only on the postsynaptic membranes, synapses make sure impulses are **unidirectional** — the impulse can only travel in one direction. Neurotransmitters are removed from the cleft so the response doesn't keep happening, e.g. they're taken back into the presynaptic neurone or they're broken down by enzymes (and the products are taken into the neurone).

Acetylcholine

There are many different neurotransmitters. You need to know about one called **acetylcholine** (**ACh**), which binds to cholinergic receptors. Synapses that use acetylcholine are called **cholinergic synapses**.

Cholinergic synapses

This is how a nerve impulse is transmitted across a cholinergic synapse:

1. Arrival of an action potential

An action potential arrives at the synaptic knob of the presynaptic neurone. The action potential stimulates voltage-gated calcium ion channels in the presynaptic neurone to open. Calcium ions (Ca^{2+}) diffuse into the synaptic knob. (They're pumped out afterwards by active transport.)

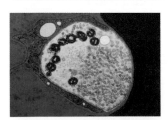

Figure 2: *A synaptic knob (yellow) containing vesicles (large red circles).*

Tip: Voltage-gated ion channels are channels that only open when the potential difference across a membrane reaches a certain voltage.

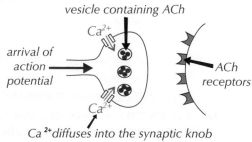

Ca^{2+} diffuses into the synaptic knob

2. Fusion of the vesicles

The influx of calcium ions into the synaptic knob causes the synaptic vesicles to fuse with the presynaptic membrane. The vesicles release the neurotransmitter acetylcholine (ACh) into the synaptic cleft by exocytosis.

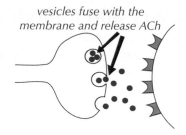

vesicles fuse with the membrane and release ACh

Exam Tip
"The influx of calcium ions..." means that the calcium ions have flowed into the synaptic knob. You'll lose out on marks in the exam if you talk about an influx of calcium ions out of the synaptic knob.

3. Diffusion of ACh

ACh diffuses across the synaptic cleft and binds to specific cholinergic receptors on the postsynaptic membrane. This causes sodium ion channels in the postsynaptic neurone to open. The influx of sodium ions causes an action potential on the postsynaptic membrane (if the threshold is reached). ACh is removed from the synaptic cleft so the response doesn't keep happening. It's broken down by an enzyme called acetylcholinesterase (AChE) and the products are re-absorbed by the presynaptic neurone and used to make more ACh.

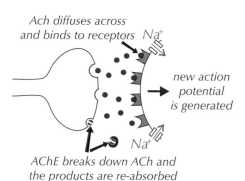

Ach diffuses across and binds to receptors Na^+

new action potential is generated

AChE breaks down ACh and the products are re-absorbed Na^+

Tip: Look back at page 122 if you need a reminder of how action potentials are generated.

Neuromuscular junctions

A neuromuscular junction is a specialised cholinergic synapse between a motor neurone and a muscle cell. Neuromuscular junctions use the neurotransmitter acetylcholine (ACh), which binds to cholinergic receptors called nicotinic cholinergic receptors.

Tip: ACh and AChF are used in cholinergic synapses and in neuromuscular junctions.

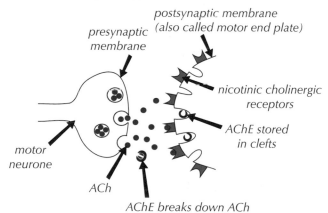

postsynaptic membrane (also called motor end plate)

presynaptic membrane

nicotinic cholinergic receptors

AChE stored in clefts

motor neurone

ACh

AChE breaks down ACh

Figure 3: *The structure of a neuromuscular junction.*

Neuromuscular junctions work in the same way as cholinergic synapses, but there are a few differences:

- The postsynaptic membrane has lots of folds that form clefts. These clefts store the enzyme that breaks down ACh (acetylcholinesterase — AChE).
- The postsynaptic membrane has more receptors than other synapses.
- When a motor neurone fires an action potential, it always triggers a response in a muscle cell. This isn't always the case for a synapse between two neurones (see page 130).

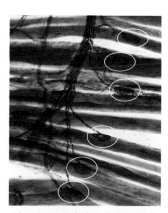

Figure 4: *A light micrograph showing neuromuscular junctions (circled) on skeletal muscle.*

Excitatory and inhibitory neurotransmitters

Tip: 'Depolarise' means making the potential difference across the neurone membrane more positive. 'Hyperpolarise' means making the potential difference across the membrane more negative. (See page 122 for more.)

Neurotransmitters are excitatory or inhibitory. Excitatory neurotransmitters depolarise the postsynaptic membrane, making it fire an action potential if the threshold is reached.

Example

Acetylcholine is an excitatory neurotransmitter — it binds to cholinergic receptors to cause an action potential in the postsynaptic membrane.

Inhibitory neurotransmitters hyperpolarise the postsynaptic membrane, preventing it from firing an action potential.

Example

GABA is an inhibitory neurotransmitter — when it binds to its receptors it causes potassium ion channels to open on the postsynaptic membrane, hyperpolarising the neurone.

Summation at synapses

Tip: Summation is where the sum total of lots of smaller impulses triggers an action potential.

If a stimulus is weak, only a small amount of neurotransmitter will be released from a neurone into the synaptic cleft. This might not be enough to excite the postsynaptic membrane to the threshold level and stimulate an action potential. Summation is where the effect of neurotransmitters released from many neurones (or one neurone that's stimulated a lot in a short period of time) is added together. It means synapses accurately process information, finely tuning the response. There are two types of summation:

1. Spatial summation

Spatial summation is where two or more presynaptic neurones release their neurotransmitters at the same time onto the same postsynaptic neurone. The small amount of neurotransmitter released from each of these neurones can be enough altogether to reach the threshold in the postsynaptic neurone and trigger an action potential — see Figure 5.

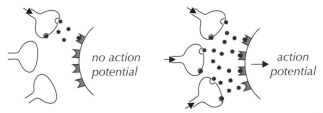

Figure 5: *One presynaptic neurone only releases a few neurotransmitters (left) but three presynaptic neurones release enough to trigger an action potential (right).*

2. Temporal summation

Temporal summation is where two or more nerve impulses arrive in quick succession from the same presynaptic neurone. This makes an action potential more likely because more neurotransmitter is released into the synaptic cleft — see Figure 6.

Tip: Impulses have to follow each other very quickly, otherwise the neurotransmitter will be removed from the cleft before it's reached a level high enough to trigger an action potential.

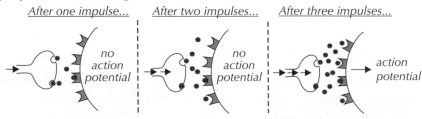

Figure 6: *The effects of temporal summation at a synapse.*

Drugs at synapses

Drugs can affect synaptic transmission. They can do this in various ways.
For example, some drugs are the same shape as neurotransmitters so they
mimic their action at receptors (these drugs are called agonists).
This means more receptors are activated.

Example

Nicotine mimics acetylcholine
so binds to nicotinic cholinergic
receptors in the brain.

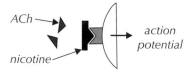

Some drugs block receptors so they can't be activated by
neurotransmitters (these drugs are called antagonists). This means fewer
receptors (if any) can be activated.

Example

Curare blocks the effects of acetylcholine
by blocking nicotinic cholinergic
receptors at neuromuscular junctions,
so muscle cells can't be stimulated.
This results in the muscle being paralysed.

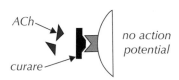

Some drugs inhibit the enzyme that breaks down neurotransmitters
(they stop it from working). This means there are more neurotransmitters in
the synaptic cleft to bind to receptors and they're there for longer.

Example

Nerve gases stop acetylcholine
from being broken down in the
synaptic cleft. This can lead to
loss of muscle control.

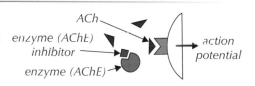

Some drugs stimulate the release of neurotransmitter from the
presynaptic neurone so more receptors are activated.

Example

Amphetamines force a
neurotransmitter called dopamine
out of synaptic vesicles and into
the synaptic cleft. This increases
the effect of dopamine,
e.g. it increases alertness.

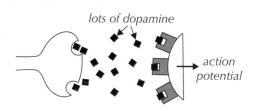

Some drugs inhibit the release of neurotransmitters from the
presynaptic neurone so fewer receptors are activated.

Example

Opioids block calcium ion
channels in the presynaptic
neurone. This means
fewer vesicles fuse with the
presynaptic membrane so less
neurotransmitter is released.

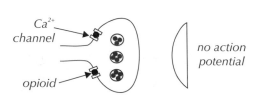

Exam Tip
You don't have to
learn the names of
all the drugs given
here but make sure
you understand how
they affect synaptic
transmission. In the
exam, you could be
given information
about a particular drug
you've not come across
before and be asked to
predict the effects the
drug would have at a
synapse.

Q1 Lambert–Eaton myasthenic syndrome (LEMS) is an autoimmune disorder where antibodies are formed against calcium ion channels in the neuromuscular junction, preventing the channels from working properly. Suggest what the main symptom of LEMS might be. Explain your answer.

Q2 Endorphins are endogenous opioid peptides that function as inhibitory neurotransmitters. Endorphins bind to opioid receptors on neurones that transmit pain signals.

   a) Suggest what effect endorphins have on the sensation of pain. Explain your answer.

   b) Morphine is an opioid drug that's very similar in structure to an endorphin molecule. Suggest what effect taking morphine will have on a person's sensation of pain. Explain your answer.

Q3 Acetylcholine (Ach) is involved in many functions in the body, including saliva production. Carbachol is a drug that binds and activates cholinergic receptors. Predict the effect of carbachol on saliva production and explain your answer.

Practice Questions — Fact Recall

Q1 The diagram on the right shows a cholinergic synapse. Name the structures labelled A to G on the diagram.

Q2 Give three types of cell that have receptors for neurotransmitters.

Q3 Explain why impulses at a synapse are unidirectional.

Q4 At a cholinergic synapse:

   a) Describe and explain the movement of calcium ions following the arrival of an action potential at a presynaptic neurone.

   b) Explain how acetylcholine (ACh) leaves the presynaptic neurone and causes an action potential in the postsynaptic neurone.

Q5 Why is it important that ACh is removed from the synaptic cleft by being broken down by the enzyme AChE?

Q6 What is a neuromuscular junction?

Q7 Give three ways in which a neuromuscular junction differs from a cholinergic synapse.

Q8 What effect does an inhibitory neurotransmitter have on a postsynaptic membrane?

Q9 Explain how an action potential may be more likely as a result of:

   a) spatial summation,

   b) temporal summation.

7. Effectors — Muscles

Now that you've learnt how a stimulus is detected and how the signal is transmitted along neurones, it's on to effectors. Muscles are effectors — they contract in response to nervous impulses.

Types of muscle

There are three different types of muscle in the body:

- **Smooth muscle** contracts without conscious control. It's found in walls of internal organs (apart from the heart), e.g. stomach, intestine and blood vessels.
- **Cardiac muscle** contracts without conscious control (like smooth muscle) but it's only found in the heart.
- **Skeletal muscle** (also called striated, striped or voluntary muscle) is the type of muscle you use to move, e.g. the biceps and triceps move the lower arm.

You need to know the ins and outs of skeletal muscle for the exam...

Skeletal muscle

Skeletal muscle is made up of large bundles of long cells, called muscle fibres. The cell membrane of muscle fibre cells is called the sarcolemma. Bits of the sarcolemma fold inwards across the muscle fibre and stick into the sarcoplasm (a muscle cell's cytoplasm). These folds are called transverse (T) tubules and they help to spread electrical impulses throughout the sarcoplasm so they reach all parts of the muscle fibre — see Figure 1.

A network of internal membranes called the sarcoplasmic reticulum runs through the sarcoplasm. The sarcoplasmic reticulum stores and releases calcium ions that are needed for muscle contraction. Muscle fibres have lots of mitochondria to provide the ATP that's needed for muscle contraction. They are multinucleate (contain many nuclei) and have lots of long, cylindrical organelles called **myofibrils**. Myofibrils are made up of proteins and are highly specialised for contraction (see next page).

Learning Objectives:

- Know the gross and microscopic structure of skeletal muscle.
- Know the ultrastructure of a myofibril.
- Understand the sliding filament theory of muscle contraction.
- Understand the roles of calcium ions and tropomyosin in the cycle of actin-myosin cross bridge formation.
- Understand the roles of actin, myosin, calcium ions and ATP in myofibril contraction.
- Understand the role of ATP and phosphocreatine (PCr) in providing energy supply during muscle contraction.
- Know the structure, location and general properties of slow and fast skeletal muscle fibres.

Specification Reference 3.5.3

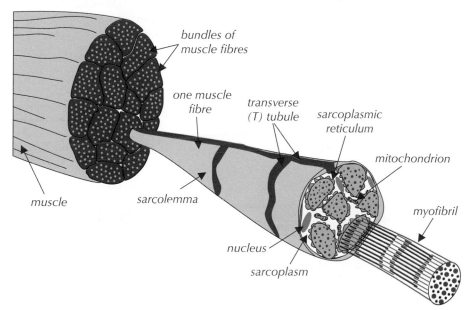

Figure 1: Diagram showing the structure of skeletal muscle and a muscle fibre.

bundles of muscle fibres

one muscle fibre

transverse (T) tubule

sarcoplasmic reticulum

mitochondrion

muscle

sarcolemma

myofibril

nucleus

sarcoplasm

Figure 2: *A scanning electron microscope (SEM) of a section of muscle fibre with myofibrils (pink and yellow) bundled together.*

Tip: Microfibrils are <u>organelles</u> within the cell (muscle fibre).

Myofibrils

Tip: There's more detail on the way myosin and actin work in muscle contraction on pages 135-137.

Tip: To remember which band is which, think: d<u>a</u>rk = **A**-bands and l<u>i</u>ght = **I**-bands.

Myofibrils contain bundles of thick and thin myofilaments that move past each other to make muscles contract. The thick myofilaments are made of the protein **myosin** and the thin myofilaments are made of the protein **actin**.

If you look at a myofibril under an electron microscope, you'll see a pattern of alternating dark and light bands (see Figures 3 and 4). Dark bands contain the thick myosin filaments and some overlapping thin actin filaments — these are called A-bands. Light bands contain thin actin filaments only — these are called I-bands.

A myofibril is made up of many short units called **sarcomeres**. The ends of each sarcomere are marked with a Z-line. In the middle of each sarcomere is an M-line. The M-line is the middle of the myosin filaments. Around the M-line is the H-zone. The H-zone only contains myosin filaments.

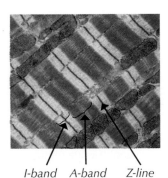

I-band   A-band   Z-line

Figure 3: *A transmission electron microscope (TEM) of myofibrils showing the banding of myosin (red) and actin (yellow).*

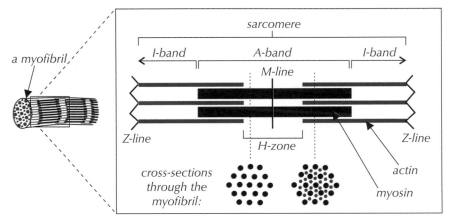

Figure 4: *The structure of a sarcomere — a unit of a myofibril.*

The sliding filament theory

Muscle contraction is explained by the sliding filament theory. This is where myosin and actin filaments slide over one another to make the sarcomeres contract — the myofilaments themselves don't contract. The simultaneous contraction of lots of sarcomeres means the myofibrils and muscle fibres contract. Sarcomeres return to their original length as the muscle relaxes.

Tip: <u>A</u> bands are the only ones that stay the s<u>a</u>me length.

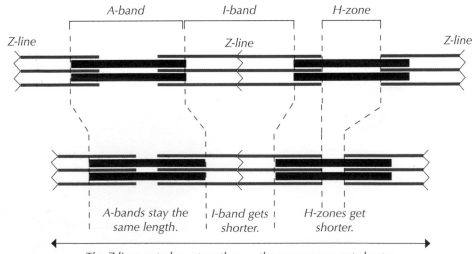

Figure 5: *Sarcomeres during relaxation (top) and contraction (bottom).*

Q1 Cross sections from three different sites along a sarcomere are shown below. Which cross-section(s) could be from:

a) an I-band?

b) an M-line?

c) an A-band?

d) a Z-line?

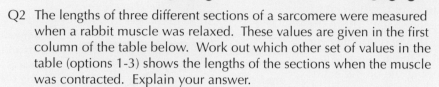

> **Tip:** The diagrams in Q1 might look a bit odd at first, but with a bit of logical thinking you should be able to work out the answers.
> It might help if you sketch out the sarcomere structure with the bands on, so you can see what's happening.

Q2 The lengths of three different sections of a sarcomere were measured when a rabbit muscle was relaxed. These values are given in the first column of the table below. Work out which other set of values in the table (options 1-3) shows the lengths of the sections when the muscle was contracted. Explain your answer.

	Relaxed (μm)	Option 1 (μm)	Option 2 (μm)	Option 3 (μm)
A-band	1.5	1.5	1.2	1.5
I-band	0.8	0.5	0.5	1
H-zone	0.7	0.2	0.7	0.2

Myosin and actin filaments

Muscle contraction involves myosin and actin filaments sliding over one another. Here's a bit more detail about the two types of filament:

Myosin filaments

Myosin filaments have globular heads that are hinged, so they can move back and forth. Each myosin head has a binding site for actin and a binding site for ATP — see Figure 6.

Actin filaments

Actin filaments have binding sites for myosin heads, called actin-myosin binding sites. Two other proteins called **tropomyosin** and **troponin** are found between actin filaments. These proteins are attached to each other (troponin holds tropomyosin in place) and they help myofilaments move past each other (see Figure 6).

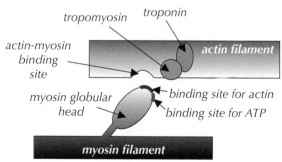

Figure 6: The structure of myosin and actin filaments.

> **Tip:** This diagram has been simplified — troponin and tropomyosin are actually joined in a long chain that coils round the actin filament.

Binding sites in resting muscles

For myosin and actin filaments to slide past each other, the myosin head needs to bind to the actin-myosin binding site on the actin filament. In a resting (unstimulated) muscle the actin-myosin binding site is blocked by tropomyosin — see Figure 7. This means myofilaments can't slide past each other because the myosin heads can't bind to the actin filaments.

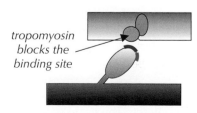

Figure 7: Actin and myosin filaments in resting muscle.

Muscle contraction

Tip: If you can't remember your sarcolemma from your sarcoplasmic reticulum then take a look back at page 133.

Arrival of an action potential

When an action potential from a motor neurone stimulates a muscle cell, it depolarises the sarcolemma. Depolarisation spreads down the T-tubules to the sarcoplasmic reticulum. This causes the sarcoplasmic reticulum to release stored calcium ions (Ca^{2+}) into the sarcoplasm. This influx of calcium ions into the sarcoplasm triggers muscle contraction.

Calcium ions bind to troponin, causing it to change shape. This pulls the attached tropomyosin out of the actin-myosin binding site on the actin filament. This exposes the binding site, which allows the myosin head to bind. The bond formed when a myosin head binds to an actin filament is called an **actin-myosin cross bridge** — see Figure 8.

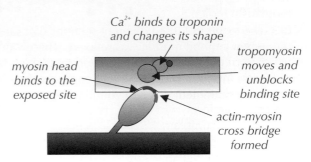

Ca²⁺ binds to troponin and changes its shape

myosin head binds to the exposed site

tropomyosin moves and unblocks binding site

actin-myosin cross bridge formed

Figure 8: *Formation of an actin-myosin cross bridge.*

Movement of the actin filament

Tip: The movement of the myosin head to the side is called a 'power stroke'.

Calcium ions also activate the enzyme ATPase, which breaks down ATP (into ADP + Pi) to provide the energy needed for muscle contraction. The energy released from ATP moves the myosin head to the side, which pulls the actin filament along in a kind of rowing action (see Figure 9).

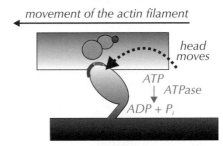

movement of the actin filament

head moves

$$ATP \downarrow ATPase$$
$$ADP + P_i$$

Figure 9: *Movement of the myosin head.*

Breaking of the cross bridge

Tip: As the actin filaments are being moved along, the I-bands are getting shorter and the Z-lines are moving closer together.

ATP also provides the energy to break the actin-myosin cross bridge, so the myosin head detaches from the actin filament after it's moved. The myosin head then returns to it's starting position, and reattaches to a different binding site further along the actin filament — see Figure 10. A new actin-myosin cross bridge is formed and the cycle is repeated (attach, move, detach, reattach to new binding site...).

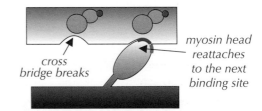

cross bridge breaks

myosin head reattaches to the next binding site

Figure 10: *Myosin head forms a new actin-myosin cross bridge.*

Many actin-myosin cross bridges form and break very rapidly, pulling the actin filament along — which shortens the sarcomere, causing the muscle to contract. The cycle will continue as long as calcium ions are present and bound to troponin.

Return to resting state

When the muscle stops being stimulated, calcium ions leave their binding sites on the troponin molecules and are moved by active transport back into the sarcoplasmic reticulum (this needs ATP too).

The troponin molecules return to their original shape, pulling the attached tropomyosin molecules with them. This means the tropomyosin molecules block the actin-myosin binding sites again — see Figure 11. Muscles aren't contracted because no myosin heads are attached to actin filaments (so there are no actin-myosin cross bridges). The actin filaments slide back to their relaxed position, which lengthens the sarcomere.

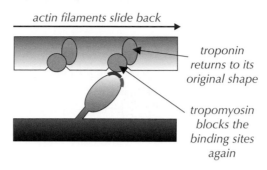

actin filaments slide back

troponin returns to its original shape

tropomyosin blocks the binding sites again

Figure 11: *Blocking of the actin-myosin binding sites as the muscle returns to its resting state.*

Practice Questions — Application

Q1 The graph below shows the calcium ion concentration in the sarcoplasm of a muscle fibre over time.

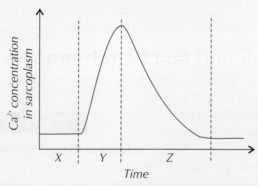

Ca²⁺ concentration in sarcoplasm (Ca^{2+} concentration in sarcoplasm)

X   Y   Z

Time

a) During what time period (X, Y or Z):

   i)   is the muscle fibre the longest length? Explain your answer.

   ii) would Ca^{2+} ions be bound to troponin? Explain your answer.

   iii) would ATPase be activated? Explain your answer.

b) Describe the movement of calcium ions during time the period Z.

c) Describe the event that causes an increase in Ca^{2+} ions in the sarcoplasm at the beginning of time period Y.

Q2 Cardiac muscle in the heart has some similarities to skeletal muscle, for example, it has both actin and myosin filaments. Patients who suffer from heart failure may be given positive inotropic agents — these are substances which increase the level of calcium ions in the cytoplasm of muscle cells.

Use your knowledge of muscle contraction to explain why this treatment may be used.

Tip: Have a flick back to pages 43-49 if you need to remind yourself of the processes involved in aerobic and anaerobic respiration.

Energy for muscle contraction

So much energy is needed when muscles contract that ATP gets used up very quickly. ATP has to be continually generated so exercise can continue — this happens in three main ways:

1. Aerobic respiration

Most ATP is generated via oxidative phosphorylation in the cell's mitochondria. Aerobic respiration only works when there's oxygen so it's good for long periods of low-intensity exercise, e.g. a long walk.

2. Anaerobic respiration

ATP is made rapidly by glycolysis. The end product of glycolysis is pyruvate, which is converted to lactate by lactate fermentation. Lactate can quickly build up in the muscles and cause muscle fatigue. Anaerobic respiration is good for short periods of hard exercise, e.g. a 400 m sprint.

Tip: Many activities use a combination of these systems.

3. ATP-phosphocreatine (PCr) system

ATP is made by phosphorylating ADP — adding a phosphate group taken from PCr. The equation for this is shown in Figure 12. PCr is stored inside cells and the ATP-PCr system generates ATP very quickly. PCr runs out after a few seconds so it's used during short bursts of vigorous exercise, e.g. a tennis serve. The ATP-PCr system is anaerobic (it doesn't need oxygen) and it's alactic (it doesn't form any lactate).

$$ADP + PCr \rightarrow ATP + Cr \text{ (creatine)}$$

Figure 12: *Phosphorylation of ADP by PCr.*

Slow twitch and fast twitch muscle fibres

Skeletal muscles are made up of two types of muscle fibres — slow twitch and fast twitch. Different muscles have different proportions of slow and fast twitch fibres. The two types have different properties:

Slow twitch muscle fibres

Slow twitch muscle fibres contract slowly and can work for a long time without getting tired. This makes them good for endurance activities, e.g. long-distance running and maintaining posture. High proportions of slow twitch muscle fibres are found in the muscles you use for posture, such as the muscles in the back and in the calves.

Energy is released slowly through aerobic respiration (see above) in slow twitch muscle fibres. They have lots of mitochondria and blood vessels to supply the muscles with oxygen. The mitochondria are mainly found near to the edge of muscle fibres, so that there's a short diffusion pathway for oxygen from the blood vessels to the mitochondria. Slow twitch muscle fibres are also rich in myoglobin, a red-coloured protein that stores oxygen, so they're reddish in colour.

Figure 13: *Cross section of a muscle showing fast twitch fibres (dark pink) and slow twitch fibres (light pink).*

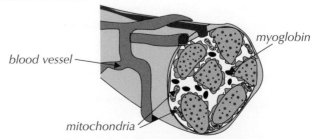

Figure 14: *A slow twitch muscle fibre.*

Fast twitch muscle fibres

Fast twitch muscle fibres contract very quickly but also get tired quickly. This makes them good for short bursts of speed and power, e.g. sprinting and eye movement. High proportions of fast twitch muscle fibres are found in muscles you use for fast movement, such as the legs, arms and eyes.

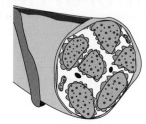

Figure 15: *A fast twitch muscle fibre, with few blood vessels, myoglobin or mitochondria.*

Energy is released quickly through anaerobic respiration using glycogen in fast twitch muscle fibres. They also have stores of PCr so that energy can be generated very quickly when needed (see previous page). Fast twitch muscle fibres have few mitochondria or blood vessels. They don't have much myoglobin either, so they can't store much oxygen — this gives them more of a whitish colour.

Tip: Cells are able to store excess glucose as glycogen, which can be converted back into glucose when needed.

Practice Question — Application

Q1 A marathon runner runs 25 miles at a steady pace. She then speeds up for the 26th mile and sprints the last 385 yards to the finish line.

   a) Discuss the ways in which the marathon runner is most likely to generate ATP during the course of the race.

   b) Is the marathon runner likely to have a greater proportion of fast twitch or slow twitch muscle fibres in her leg muscles? Give a reason for your answer.

Practice Questions — Fact Recall

Q1 Describe the structure and function of T-tubules.

Q2 Describe the structure of an A-band in a myofibril and describe its appearance under an electron microscope.

Q3 What is the sliding filament theory of muscle contraction?

Q4 Name the two proteins found between actin filaments that help myofilaments slide past each other.

Q5 Explain how calcium ions in the sarcoplasm allow the formation of actin-myosin cross bridges.

Q6 Describe the role of ATP in muscle contraction.

Q7 a) Describe how ATP is generated in the ATP-phosphocreatine system.

   b) Give one advantage and one disadvantage of generating ATP via the ATP-phosphocreatine system.

   c) Give two other ways in which ATP can be generated.

Q8 Give two ways in which slow twitch muscle fibres are adapted for their function.

Learning Objective:
- Understand the role of chemoreceptors and pressure receptors, the autonomic nervous system and effectors in controlling heart rate.

Specification Reference 3.5.1

8. Control of Heart Rate

You can't consciously control your heart rate — it's controlled by a part of the nervous system called the autonomic nervous system, which does it for you.

Structure of the nervous system

The nervous system is split into two different systems — the central nervous system (CNS) and the peripheral nervous system. The CNS is made up of the brain and spinal cord, whereas the peripheral nervous system is made up of the neurones that connect the CNS to the rest of the body.

The peripheral nervous system also has two different systems — the somatic and autonomic nervous systems. The somatic nervous system controls conscious activities, e.g. running and playing video games. The autonomic nervous system controls unconscious activities, e.g. digestion.

The autonomic nervous system is split into the sympathetic and parasympathetic nervous systems, which have opposite effects on the body. The sympathetic nervous system is the 'fight or flight' system that gets the body ready for action. The parasympathetic system is the 'rest and digest' system that calms the body down. The autonomic nervous system is involved in the control of heart rate (see below). The structure of the nervous system is summarised below:

Tip: To help you remember the difference between the sympathetic and parasympathetic nervous systems, remember: sympathetic for stress, parasympathetic for peacefulness.

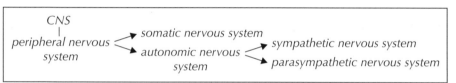

Communication between the heart and brain

There's a small mass of tissue in the wall of the right atrium of the heart called the sinoatrial node (SAN). The SAN generates electrical impulses that cause the cardiac muscles to contract. The rate at which the SAN fires (i.e. heart rate) is unconsciously controlled by a part of the brain called the medulla.

Tip: The medulla's full name is the medulla oblongata.

Animals need to alter their heart rate to respond to internal stimuli, e.g. to prevent fainting due to low blood pressure or to make sure the heart rate is high enough to supply the body with enough oxygen. Internal stimuli are detected by pressure receptors and chemical receptors:

Tip: The carotid arteries are major arteries in the neck.

- There are pressure receptors called baroreceptors in the aorta, the vena cava and carotid arteries. They're stimulated by high and low blood pressure.

- There are chemical receptors called chemoreceptors in the aorta, the carotid arteries and in the medulla. They monitor the oxygen level in the blood and also carbon dioxide and pH (which are indicators of O_2 level).

Electrical impulses from receptors are sent to the medulla along sensory neurones. The medulla processes the information and sends impulses to the SAN along sympathetic or parasympathetic neurones.

Control of heart rate in response to different stimuli
1. High blood pressure

Tip: Acetylcholine is a type of neurotransmitter. (see page 128 for more).

Baroreceptors detect high blood pressure and send impulses along sensory neurones to the medulla, which sends impulses along parasympathetic neurones. These secrete acetylcholine, which binds to receptors on the SAN. This causes the heart rate to slow down in order to reduce blood pressure back to normal.

2. Low blood pressure

Baroreceptors detect low blood pressure and send impulses along sensory neurones to the medulla, which sends impulses along sympathetic neurones. These secrete noradrenaline, which binds to receptors on the SAN. This causes the heart rate to speed up in order to increase blood pressure back to normal.

Tip: Noradrenaline is another type of neurotransmitter.

3. High blood O_2, low CO_2 or high blood pH levels

Chemoreceptors detect chemical changes in the blood and send impulses along sensory neurones to the medulla, which sends impulses along parasympathetic neurones. These secrete acetylcholine, which binds to receptors on the SAN. This causes the heart rate to decrease in order to return oxygen, carbon dioxide and pH levels back to normal.

Tip: The effectors in all of these situations are the cardiac muscles of the heart.

4. Low blood O_2, high CO_2 or low blood pH levels

Chemoreceptors detect chemical changes in the blood and send impulses along sensory neurones to the medulla, which sends impulses along sympathetic neurones. These secrete noradrenaline, which binds to receptors on the SAN. This causes the heart rate to increase in order to return oxygen, carbon dioxide and pH levels back to normal.

Tip: Low blood O_2, high CO_2 or low blood pH levels are a result of increased respiration.

The control of heart rate by the medulla is summarised below:

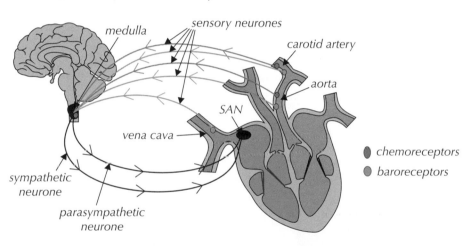

medulla — sensory neurones — carotid artery — aorta — SAN — vena cava — sympathetic neurone — parasympathetic neurone

● chemoreceptors
● baroreceptors

Practice Questions — Application

Q1 Anaemia is a condition in which the oxygen carrying capacity of the blood is reduced.

Use your knowledge of the control of heart rate to explain why a person with anaemia is likely to have a more rapid heart rate than someone without anaemia.

Practice Questions — Fact Recall

Q1 a) What is the overall role of the autonomic nervous system?

   b) Name the two divisions of the autonomic nervous system.

Q2 Name the part of the brain that controls heart rate.

Q3 a) What type of receptor detects a fall in blood pressure?

   b) Where are these receptors located in the body?

Tip: There are lots of receptors in the body that detect changes in blood chemistry — these questions refer to the ones that are used in controlling heart rate.

- Know that organisms increase their chance of survival by responding to changes in their environment.

- Know that tropisms are responses to directional stimuli that can maintain the roots and shoots of flowering plants in a favourable environment.

- Know that growth factors regulate growth in response to directional stimuli.

- Know that in flowering plants, specific growth factors diffuse from growing regions to other tissues.

- Understand the role of indoleacetic acid (IAA) in controlling tropisms in flowering plants.

Specification References 3.5.1 and 3.5.2

9. Responses in Plants

Just like animals, plants also respond to stimuli. Not surprisingly they use a different system to animals — it's all about tropisms and growth factors in the plant world...

Tropisms

Flowering plants, like animals, increase their chances of survival by responding to changes in their environment.

> **Examples**
> - They sense the direction of light and grow towards it to maximise light absorption for photosynthesis.
> - They can sense gravity, so their roots and shoots grow in the right direction.
> - Climbing plants have a sense of touch, so they can find things to climb and reach the sunlight.

A tropism is the response of a plant to a directional stimulus (a stimulus coming from a particular direction). Plants respond to stimuli by regulating their growth. A positive tropism is growth towards the stimulus, whereas a negative tropism is growth away from the stimulus.

Phototropism

Phototropism is the growth of a plant in response to light. Shoots are positively phototropic and grow towards light (see Figure 1). Roots are negatively phototropic and grow away from light (see Figure 2).

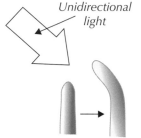
Unidirectional light

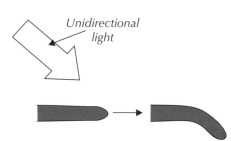
Unidirectional light

Figure 1: *Phototropism in shoots.*   **Figure 2:** *Phototropism in roots.*

Tip: Geotropism is sometimes referred to as gravitropism.

Geotropism

Geotropism is the growth of a plant in response to gravity. Shoots are negatively geotropic and grow upwards (see Figure 3). Roots are positively geotropic and grow downwards (see Figure 4).

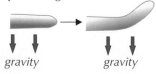
gravity   gravity

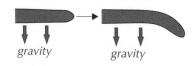
gravity   gravity

Figure 3: *Geotropism in shoots.*   **Figure 4:** *Geotropism in roots.*

Auxins

Plants respond to stimuli using growth factors — these are chemicals that speed up or slow down plant growth. Plant growth factors are produced in the growing regions of the plant (e.g. shoot tips, leaves) and they move to where they're needed in the other parts of the plant.

Figure 5: *A radish seedling showing negative geotropism.*

Growth factors called auxins are produced in the tips of shoots and diffuse backwards to stimulate the cell just behind the tips to elongate — this is where cell walls become loose and stretchy, so the cells get longer (see Figure 6). If the tip of a shoot is removed, no auxin will be available and the shoot stops growing.

Auxins stimulate growth in shoots but high concentrations inhibit growth in roots.

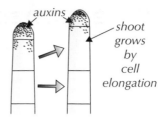

auxins

shoot grows by cell elongation

Figure 6: *Effect of auxins on shoot growth.*

Tip: There are other classes of growth factors that affect growth in different ways, e.g. a growth factor called gibberellin stimulates flowering and seed germination.

Indoleacetic acid (IAA)

Indoleacetic acid (IAA) is an important auxin that's produced in the tips of shoots in flowering plants. It's moved around the plant to control tropisms — it moves by diffusion and active transport over short distances, and via the phloem over long distances. This results in different parts of the plant having different amounts of IAA. The uneven distribution of IAA means there's uneven growth of the plant.

Tip: Phloem is a tissue which transport sugars around a plant.

┌─ **Example — phototropism** ──────────

IAA moves to the more shaded parts of the shoots and roots, so there's uneven growth.

IAA moves to this side — cells elongate and the shoot bends towards the light

IAA moves to this side — growth is inhibited so the root bends away from the light

Exam Tip
You need to learn these examples for the exam.

┌─ **Example — geotropism** ──────────

IAA moves to the underside of shoots and roots, so there's uneven growth.

IAA moves to this side — cells elongate so the shoot grows upwards

IAA moves to this side — growth is inhibited so the root grows downwards

Tip: Remember, root growth (but not shoot growth) is <u>inhibited</u> by high concentrations of IAA.

Interpreting experimental data about auxins

In the exam, you could be given some experimental data on auxins and then be asked to interpret the data. You could get something that looks a little like this:

HOW SCIENCE WORKS

Tip: There's more on pages 232-234 about interpreting experimental data.

┌─ **Example** ──────────

An experiment was carried out to investigate the role of auxin in shoot growth. Eight shoots, equal in height and mass, had their tips removed. Sponges soaked in glucose and either auxin or water were then placed where the tip should be. Four shoots were then placed in the dark (experiment A) and the other four shoots were exposed to a light source, directed at them from the right (experiment B) — see below.

Experiment A

Shoot minus the tip

A   B   C   D

Experiment B

A   B   C   D

light

Tip: Remember, growth factors are produced in shoot tips. So by removing the tips, any auxin already present is removed.

▨ *Sponge soaked in auxin and glucose*   ▨ *Sponge soaked in water and glucose*

After two days the amount of growth (in mm) and direction of growth was recorded. The results are shown in the table on the right.

	Growth			
	Shoot A	Shoot B	Shoot C	Shoot D
Experiment A (dark)	6 mm, right	6 mm, left	6 mm, straight	1 mm, straight
Experiment B (light)	8 mm, right	8 mm, right	8 mm, right	3 mm, straight

You could be asked to explain the data...

The results show how the movement of auxin controls phototropism in plant shoots. In experiment A shoot A, the auxin diffused straight down from the sponge into the left-hand side of the shoot. This stimulated the cells on this side to elongate, so the shoot grew towards the right. In shoot B, the opposite occurred, making the shoot grow towards the left. In shoot C, equal amounts of auxin diffused down both sides, making all the cells elongate at the same rate.

In experiment B, the shoots were exposed to a light source. The auxin diffused into the shoot and accumulated on the shaded side (left-hand side) regardless of where the sponge was placed. Shoots A, B and C all grew towards the right because most auxin accumulated on the left, stimulating cell elongation there.

You could be asked to comment on the experimental design...

A control (sponge soaked in water) was included to show that it was the auxin having an effect and nothing else. Glucose was included so that the shoots would have energy to grow in the dark (no photosynthesis can take place).

Tip: If you're asked about the design of an experiment, a good place to start is to think about what was used as a control.

Practice Questions —Application

Five shoots had their tips removed. Four of the stumps (where the tip should have been) were completely coated with a paste containing IAA and glucose. Each shoot received a different concentration of IAA but the same concentration of glucose. The remaining shoot had its stump completely coated with a paste containing glucose only. The plants were watered daily and grown in a dark environment for 30 days. Their height was recorded every 5 days. The results are shown in the table below.

	Height (cm)				
Days of growth	Control	Plant 1	Plant 2	Plant 3	Plant 4
0	2.4	1.2	3.2	3.5	5.4
5	2.5	1.8	4.9	4.1	7.1
10	2.6	2.6	7.0	4.9	8.5
15	2.6	4.2	9.2	6.0	10.6
20	2.7	5.9	11.6	6.9	12.3
25	2.7	8.2	13.9	7.1	14.9
30	2.8	9.9	16.3	8.2	16.9

Q1 What was the mean rate of growth for plant 1? Give your answer in mm/hour.

Q2 Which plant was given the highest concentration of IAA? Explain your answer.

Q3 Evaluate the method that was used in this experiment.

Tip: The units you need to give your answer in won't always be the same as the units given in the question.

Q1 What name is given to the growth of a plant in response to light?

Q2 Plant shoots are negatively geotropic. What does this mean?

Q3 What parts of a plant produce growth factors?

Q4 How do auxins affect plant growth?

Q5 What is indoleacetic acid (IAA) and where is it produced?

Q6 How does IAA move around a plant?

Q7 Explain how the distribution of IAA affects the growth of:

a) shoots in response to light.

b) roots in response to gravity.

Section Summary

Make sure you know:

- That organisms increase their chance of survival by responding to stimuli.

- That simple responses keep organisms in a favourable environment and can be tactic (directional movement in response to a stimulus) or kinetic (non-directional movement in response to a stimulus).

- That in nervous communication, electrical impulses are passed along neurones.

- That neurones release neurotransmitters onto target cells to trigger a response.

- That nervous communication results in rapid, short-lived and localised responses.

- That a simple reflex is a rapid, involuntary response to a stimulus that helps to protect the body from being damaged.

- A simple reflex arc involving three neurones, e.g. the hand-withdrawal response to heat.

- That hormones travel in the blood to target cells where they trigger a response.

- That hormonal communication results in slow, long-lasting and widespread responses.

- That chemical mediators, such as histamine and prostaglandins, only affect cells very close to where they're produced.

- That when a receptor cell is stimulated it causes a change in the potential difference across the membrane and that this is called a generator potential.

- The structure of a Pacinian corpuscle and that a Pacinian corpuscle only responds to specific (mechanical) stimuli — the stimulation of its membrane produces deformation of stretch-mediated sodium channels, which leads to production of a generator potential.

- That rods and cones are photoreceptors found within the retina and fovea of the eye. Many rods join one neurone, which makes them very sensitive to light but gives a low visual acuity. One cone joins one neurone, which makes them less sensitive to light than rods but gives a high visual acuity.

- How a resting membrane potential is established and maintained by sodium-potassium pumps and potassium ion channels in a neurone's cell membrane.

- That when sodium ion channels in the membrane open the membrane becomes more permeable to sodium ions and this causes depolarisation (the potential difference of the membrane becomes more positive), resulting in an action potential if the threshold level is reached.

- That the refractory period is when sodium and potassium ion channels are closed and can't be made to open again, and its importance in ensuring action potentials form discrete impulses and are unidirectional.

- That the all-or-nothing principle means that if the threshold is reached, an action potential will always fire with the same change in voltage and if the threshold isn't reached there'll be no action potential.

- The structure of a myelinated neurone including the dendrites, axon, axon terminal and myelin sheath.
- That action potentials are passed more quickly along myelinated neurones than unmyelinated neurones because impulses are only conducted at nodes of Ranvier (where sodium channels are concentrated so sodium ions get through the membrane).
- That bigger diameters and higher temperatures speed up the rate of conduction along a neurone.
- The detailed structure of a synapse including the synaptic knob, vesicles and postsynaptic membrane.
- That impulses at a synapse are unidirectional because only the postsynaptic membrane has receptors.
- How a nerve impulse is transmitted across a cholinergic synapse — voltage-gated calcium channels open, calcium ions diffuse into the synaptic knob and vesicles fuse with the presynaptic membrane. Acetylcholine (ACh) diffuses across the synaptic cleft to bind to cholinergic receptors on the postsynaptic membrane, which causes sodium ion channels to open and an influx of sodium ions triggers an action potential if the threshold is reached.
- The detailed structure of a neuromuscular junction (a synapse between a motor neurone and a muscle cell) and how a nerve impulse is transmitted across a neuromuscular junction.
- That inhibitory neurotransmitters hyperpolarise the postsynaptic membrane (make the potential difference more negative), preventing it from firing an action potential.
- That spatial summation is the total effect of all the neurotransmitters released from many neurones present at a synapse and that temporal summation is where two or more nerve impulses arrive in quick succession from the same presynaptic neurone.
- How to use information given about a drug to predict and explain the effects it will have at a synapse.
- That skeletal muscle is made up of large bundles of muscle fibres that contain transverse tubules, sarcolemma, sarcoplasm, sarcoplasmic reticulum, myofibrils, and lots of mitochondria and nuclei.
- That myofibrils contain thick myosin and thin actin filaments, and are divided into sarcomeres. A-bands on sarcomeres contain myosin and actin filaments, I-bands only contain actin filaments.
- The sliding filament theory — myosin and actin filaments slide over one another to make the sarcomeres contract (the myofilaments themselves don't contract).
- That calcium ions bind to troponin in muscle contraction, which pulls tropomyosin out of the actin-myosin binding site so that actin-myosin cross bridges can be formed.
- How actin, myosin, calcium ions and ATP work together to make a myofibril contract.
- That energy from ATP is used for muscle contraction and that ATP generation may involve the ATP-phosphocreatine (PCr) system.
- That slow twitch muscle fibres are good for endurance activities, release energy slowly through aerobic respiration and are found in muscles such as those used for posture.
- That fast twitch muscle fibres are good for short bursts of speed and power, release energy quickly through anaerobic respiration and are found in muscles, such as the eyes and legs, which are used for fast movement.
- That chemoreceptors and pressure receptors detect changes in blood chemistry or pressure and send impulses via the autonomic nervous system to the medulla.
- That the medulla sends signals via sympathetic or parasympathetic neurones to the SAN which controls heart rate.
- That tropisms are responses to directional stimuli (e.g. light or gravity) that can keep the shoots or roots of plants in a favourable environment, and that growth factors such as auxins regulate growth in response to these stimuli.
- That specific growth factors diffuse from growing regions (where they're produced) to other tissues.
- That indoleacetic acid (IAA) promotes growth in shoots but at high concentrations inhibits growth in roots. IAA controls the direction of plant growth in response to light (phototropism) by moving to the more shaded parts of shoots and roots, and it controls the direction of plant growth in response to gravity (geotropism) by moving to the underside of shoots and roots.

Exam-style Questions

1   A team of scientists investigated how low-intensity training affects the fibres in human skeletal muscle. Needle biopsies were taken from single muscle fibres in eight young, untrained men and the amount of GLUT4 was measured in slow and fast twitch muscle fibres. GLUT4 is a glucose transporter, a membrane protein that helps glucose to be transported across a plasma membrane.

The men then completed two weeks of low-intensity training and the amount of GLUT4 was measured again in the same way. The results are shown below. The values shown are means for the eight men.

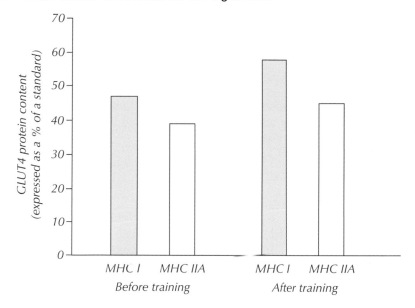

1 (a)   On the graph, MHC I refers to slow twitch muscle fibres and MHC IIA refers to fast twitch muscle fibres.

Describe what the results show.

(2 marks)

1 (b)   MHC stands for myosin heavy chain.

1 (b) (i)   Describe the structure of a myosin filament.

(3 marks)

    (ii)   Describe the role of the myosin filament and ATP in muscle contraction.

(6 marks)

1 (c)   With enough low-intensity training, a person may have a higher proportion of slow twitch muscle fibres than fast twitch muscle fibres.

Suggest a reason for this.

(1 mark)

1 (d)   Give one function of fast twitch muscle fibres and explain how they are adapted for this function.

(3 marks)

2 A neuromuscular junction is a specialised synapse between a motor neurone and a muscle cell.

2 (a) Explain how an action potential along a motor neurone results in a muscle being stimulated.

(6 marks)

2 (b) An action potential is more likely if two or more nerve impulses arrive in quick succession from the same presynaptic neurone.

2 (b) (i) What is the name given to this type of summation?

(1 mark)

2 (b) (ii) Explain why this type of summation makes an action potential more likely.

(5 marks)

2 (c) The drug tubocurarine blocks receptors at neuromuscular junctions.

Doctors use this drug as an anaesthetic as it temporarily paralyses muscles.
Suggest how tubocurarine works.

(4 marks)

3 Scientists took three Goosegrass seedlings and planted them in individual pots with soil taken from the same source. They let each seedling grow for 15 days in the conditions shown in the diagram below.

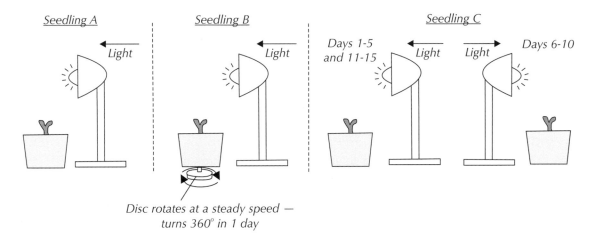

3 (a) Suggest what response the scientists were testing with this experiment.

(1 mark)

3 (b) The scientists didn't include a control in their experiment. Describe the conditions that should have been used for a seedling acting as a control.

(2 marks)

3 (c) Describe and explain the pattern of growth in the three plants you would expect to see by the end of the experiment.

(6 marks)

3 (d) Explain the role of growth factors in controlling the direction of growth in this experiment.

(4 marks)

1. Homeostasis Basics

The body has some pretty clever systems to control its internal environment...

What is homeostasis?

Changes in your external environment can affect your internal environment — the blood and tissue fluid that surrounds your cells. Homeostasis is the maintenance of a constant internal environment. It involves control systems that keep your internal environment roughly constant (within certain limits). This means your internal environment is kept in a state of dynamic equilibrium (i.e. fluctuating around a normal level). Keeping your internal environment constant is vital for cells to function normally and to stop them being damaged.

The importance of homeostasis

It's particularly important to maintain the right core body temperature and blood pH. This is because temperature and pH affect enzyme activity, and enzymes control the rate of **metabolic reactions** (chemical reactions in living cells). It's also important to maintain the right blood glucose concentration because cells need glucose for energy and blood glucose concentration affects the water potential of blood — see next page.

Temperature

The rate of metabolic reactions increases when the temperature's increased. More heat means more kinetic energy, so molecules move faster. This makes the substrate molecules more likely to collide with the enzymes' active sites. The energy of these collisions also increases, which means each collision is more likely to result in a reaction.

But, if the temperature gets too high (e.g. over 40 °C), the reaction essentially stops. The rise in temperature makes the enzyme's molecules vibrate more. If the temperature goes above a certain level, this vibration breaks some of the hydrogen bonds that hold the enzyme in its 3D shape. The active site changes shape and the enzyme and substrate no longer fit together. At this point, the enzyme is denatured — it no longer functions as a catalyst (see Figure 1).

If body temperature is too low enzyme activity is reduced, slowing the rate of metabolic reactions. The highest rate of enzyme activity happens at their optimum temperature — about 37 °C in humans (see Figure 1).

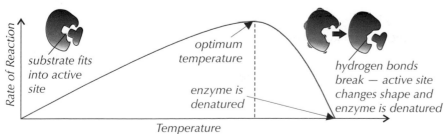

Figure 1: *Effect of temperature on the rate of a metabolic reaction.*

Learning Objectives:

- Understand that homeostasis in mammals involves physiological control systems that maintain the internal environment within restricted limits.
- Understand the importance of maintaining a constant core temperature and blood pH in relation to enzyme activity.
- Understand the importance of maintaining a constant blood glucose concentration in terms the water potential of blood and energy transfer.
- Know that negative feedback restores systems to their normal level.
- Understand that multiple negative feedback mechanisms give more control over changes in the internal environment.
- Know that positive feedback results in changes that are further away from the normal level.
- Know that positive feedback is often associated with a breakdown of control systems, e.g. in temperature control.
- Be able to interpret diagrams representing negative and positive feedback.

Specification Reference 3.5.4 and 3.5.5

pH

Tip: When an enzyme is denatured the reaction may still happen but it'll be too slow for the body's needs.

If blood pH is too high or too low (highly alkaline or acidic) enzymes become denatured (see Figure 2). The hydrogen bonds that hold them in their 3D shape are affected so the shape of the enzyme's active site is changed and it no longer works as a catalyst. The highest rate of enzyme activity happens at their optimum pH, so this is when metabolic reactions are fastest. Optimum pH is usually around pH 7 (neutral), but some enzymes work best at other pHs, e.g. enzymes found in the stomach work best at a low pH.

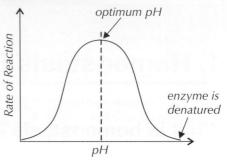

Figure 2: Effect of pH on a metabolic reaction.

Blood glucose concentration

If blood glucose concentration is too high the water potential of blood is reduced to a point where water molecules diffuse out of cells into the blood by osmosis. This can cause the cells to shrivel up and die (see Figure 3).

Tip: Water potential is the potential (likelihood) of water molecules to diffuse out of or into a solution.

Tip: Glucose is a solute. It lowers the water potential of the blood. Water molecules move by osmosis from an area of higher water potential (the cells) to an area of lower water potential (the blood).

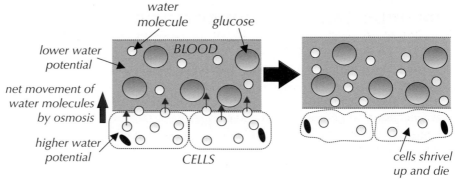

Figure 3: Effect of high blood glucose concentration on cells.

If blood glucose concentration is too low, cells are unable to carry out normal activities because there isn't enough glucose for respiration to provide energy.

Negative feedback

Homeostatic systems involve receptors, a communication system and effectors (see page 112). Receptors detect when a level is too high or too low, and the information's communicated via the nervous system or the hormonal system to effectors. The effectors respond to counteract the change — bringing the level back to normal. The mechanism that restores the level to normal is called a **negative feedback mechanism** — see Figure 4.

Tip: The 'level' in Figure 4 refers to something inside the body that needs to be controlled, e.g. temperature level, pH level, blood glucose level.

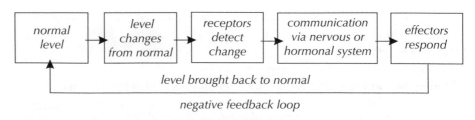

Figure 4: A negative feedback mechanism.

Negative feedback keeps things around the normal level.

Example

Body temperature is usually kept within 0.5 °C above or below 37 °C.

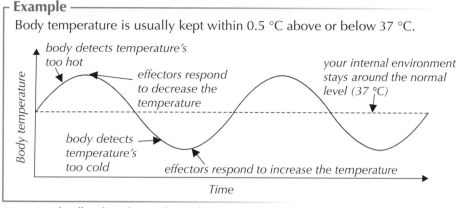

Tip: Negative feedback keeps the pH of the blood within the range 7.35 - 7.45.

Negative feedback only works within certain limits though — if the change is too big then the effectors may not be able to counteract it, e.g. a huge drop in body temperature caused by prolonged exposure to cold weather may be too large to counteract.

Multiple negative feedback mechanisms

Homeostasis involves multiple negative feedback mechanisms for each thing being controlled. This is because having more than one mechanism gives more control over changes in your internal environment than just having one negative feedback mechanism.

Having multiple negative feedback mechanisms means you can actively increase or decrease a level so it returns to normal, e.g. you have feedback mechanisms to reduce your body temperature and you also have mechanisms to increase it. If you only had one negative feedback mechanism, all you could do would be turn it on or turn it off. You'd only be able to actively change a level in one direction so it returns to normal. Only one negative feedback mechanism means a slower response and less control.

Tip: Think of this as trying to slow down a car with only an accelerator — all you can do is take your foot off the accelerator (you'd have more control with a brake too).

Positive feedback

Some changes trigger a positive feedback mechanism, which amplifies the change. The effectors respond to further increase the level away from the normal level. The mechanism that amplifies a change away from the normal level is called a **positive feedback mechanism** — see Figure 5.

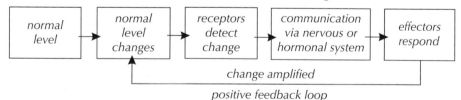

Figure 5: A positive feedback mechanism.

Positive feedback isn't involved in homeostasis because it doesn't keep your internal environment constant. Positive feedback is useful to rapidly activate processes in the body.

Example

During the formation of a blood clot after an injury, platelets become activated and release a chemical — this triggers more platelets to be activated, and so on. This means platelets very quickly form a blood clot at the injury site. (The process ends with negative feedback, when the body detects the blood clot has been formed.)

Figure 6: A person with hypothermia could be helped by being wrapped in a foil blanket as shown above. The foil blanket minimises further heat loss from the body so internal temperature should increase back to within normal limits.

Tip: 'Hypo' is often used to describe a condition where something being controlled (in this case body temperature) has fallen below its normal level —'hyper' is when it's gone above its normal level.

Breakdown of homeostatic systems

Positive feedback can also happen when a homeostatic system breaks down.

Example

Hypothermia is low body temperature (below 35 °C). It happens when heat's lost from the body quicker than it can be produced. As body temperature falls the brain doesn't work properly and shivering stops — this makes body temperature fall even more. Positive feedback takes body temperature further away from the normal level, and it continues to decrease unless action is taken.

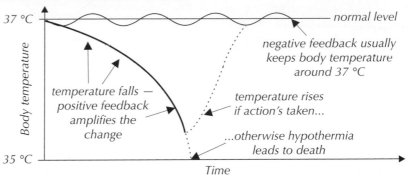

Practice Questions — Application

When low blood calcium concentration is detected, the secretion of parathyroid hormone (PTH) from the parathyroid gland is stimulated. When high blood calcium concentration is detected, the secretion of the hormone calcitonin, from the thyroid gland, is stimulated. These two hormones work via negative feedback mechanisms to control the blood calcium concentration. Their effects are shown on the graph.

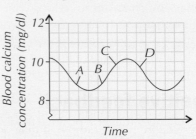

Q1 Suggest an explanation for the shape of the graph between:

a) A and B.   b) C and D.

Q2 Why is in beneficial to have both PTH and calcitonin controlling the concentration of calcium in the blood?

Q3 Suggest what could happen to the blood calcium concentration of someone who has had a parathyroid gland removed.
Explain your answer.

Practice Questions — Fact Recall

Q1 What is homeostasis?

Q2 Explain why is it important for the body to maintain its internal temperature within normal limits.

Q3 Why is it important that a constant blood glucose concentration is maintained?

Q4 Describe how positive feedback mechanisms differ from negative feedback mechanisms.

2. Control of Body Temperature

Some organisms can control their body temperature internally. Many different mechanisms allow them to do this and they're controlled by the brain.

Temperature control in ectotherms and endotherms

Animals are classed as either ectotherms (e.g. reptiles, fish) or endotherms (e.g. mammals, birds), depending on how they control their body temperature.

Ectotherms

Ectotherms can't control their body temperature internally — they control their temperature by changing their behaviour.

> **Example**
>
> A lizard is an ectotherm. When its internal temperature drops a lizard will move to find a warmer area, such as a place in the sunshine. When its internal temperature gets too high it will move to somewhere cooler such as a burrow beneath the sand.

This means the internal temperature of ectotherms depends on the external temperature (their surroundings).

Ectotherms have a variable metabolic rate because they can't keep their internal temperature constant. They generate very little heat themselves. This means the activity level of ectotherms depends on the external temperature too — they're more active at higher temperatures and less active at lower temperatures.

Endotherms

Endotherms control their body temperature internally by homeostasis, as well as by altering their behaviour.

> **Example**
>
> An elephant is an endotherm. Its temperature is mainly controlled internally by homeostasis, but it may also change its behaviour to control its temperature. For example, it may wallow in mud or flap its ears to help it cool down.

This means that, compared to ectotherms, the internal temperature of endotherms is less affected by the external temperature (within certain limits).

Endotherms have a constantly high metabolic rate because they can keep their internal temperature constant. They generate a lot of heat from metabolic reactions. This means the activity level of endotherms is largely independent of the external temperature — they can be active at any temperature (within certain limits).

Practice Questions — Application

Q1 On a thermal image, areas of heat radiation appear brightly coloured. On the right is a thermal image of a mouse and a snake.

a) What can you conclude about the temperature of the external environment when the image was taken? Explain your answer.

b) Would you expect the mouse or the snake to be more active at the time the image was taken? Explain your answer.

Learning Objectives:

- Know the different mechanisms for controlling temperature in an ectothermic reptile and an endothermic mammal.
- Understand the mechanisms involved in heat loss, production and conservation.
- Understand how the hypothalamus and the autonomic nervous system maintain a constant body temperature in mammals.

Specification Reference 3.5.4

Tip: In ectotherms, respiration and other metabolic reactions happen faster in warmer weather. This means in warmer weather more energy is available for faster movement etc, so ectotherms are more active in warmer weather.

Figure 1: *A lizard basking in the sun to warm up.*

Q2 In an experiment, the internal temperatures of a chuckwalla and
a hoatzin were recorded over a range of external temperatures
controlled by a heat source. The organisms were kept in enclosed
environments with a heat source. The results are shown in the
table below.

	Temperature (°C)				
External	20	24	28	32	38
Chuckwalla	26.7	30.4	37.7	40.1	43.2
Hoatzin	38.5	38.7	38.8	39.0	38.9

a) Use information from the table to explain which organism is an
ectotherm and which is an endotherm.

b) Will the metabolic reactions of the chuckwalla or the hoatzin be
most affected during this investigation? Explain your answer.

Mechanisms to change body temperature

Mammals use different mechanisms to lose heat, conserve heat and
produce heat.

Heat loss

1. **Sweating** — more sweat is secreted from sweat glands when the body's
    too hot. The water in sweat evaporates from the surface of the skin and
    takes heat from the body. The skin is cooled.

2. **Hairs lie flat** — mammals have a layer of hair that provides insulation
    by trapping air (air is a poor conductor of heat). When it's hot,
    erector pili muscles relax so the hairs lie flat. Less air is trapped, so the
    skin is less insulated and heat can be lost more easily.

3. **Vasodilation** — when it's hot, arterioles near the surface of the skin
    dilate (this is called vasodilation). More blood flows through the
    capillaries in the surface layers of the dermis. This means more heat is
    lost from the skin by radiation and the temperature is lowered.

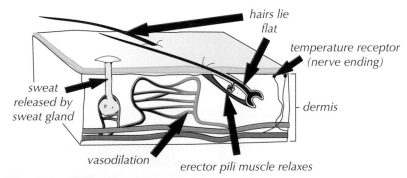

Figure 2: *Mechanisms of heat loss in a mammal.*

Heat production

1. **Shivering** — when it's cold, muscles contract in spasms. This makes the
    body shiver and more heat is produced from increased respiration.

2. **Hormones** — the body releases adrenaline and thyroxine. These increase
    metabolism and so more heat is produced.

Heat conservation

1. **Much less sweat** — less sweat is secreted from sweat glands when it's cold, reducing the amount of heat loss.

2. **Hairs stand up** — erector pili muscles contract when it's cold, which makes the hairs stand up. This traps more air and so prevents heat loss.

3. **Vasoconstriction** — when it's cold, arterioles near the surface of the skin constrict (this is called vasoconstriction) so less blood flows through the capillaries in the surface layers of the dermis. This reduces heat loss.

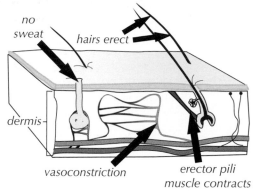

Figure 3: *Mechanisms of heat conservation in a mammal.*

Control of body temperature by the hypothalamus

Body temperature in mammals is maintained at a constant level by a part of the brain called the **hypothalamus**. The hypothalamus receives information about both internal and external temperature from **thermoreceptors** (temperature receptors):

- Information about internal temperature comes from thermoreceptors in the hypothalamus that detect blood temperature.

- Information about external temperature comes from thermoreceptors in the skin that detect skin temperature.

Thermoreceptors send impulses along sensory neurones to the hypothalamus, which sends impulses along motor neurones to effectors (muscles and glands). The neurones are part of the **autonomic nervous system**, so it's all done unconsciously. The effectors respond to restore the body temperature back to normal.

Rise in body temperature

When thermoreceptors detect body temperature is too high, they send impulses to the hypothalamus, which sends impulses to effectors. Effectors respond to increase heat loss from the body (e.g. sweat glands produce sweat) and to reduce the amount of heat that's produced by the body. Body temperature then returns to normal — see Figure 4.

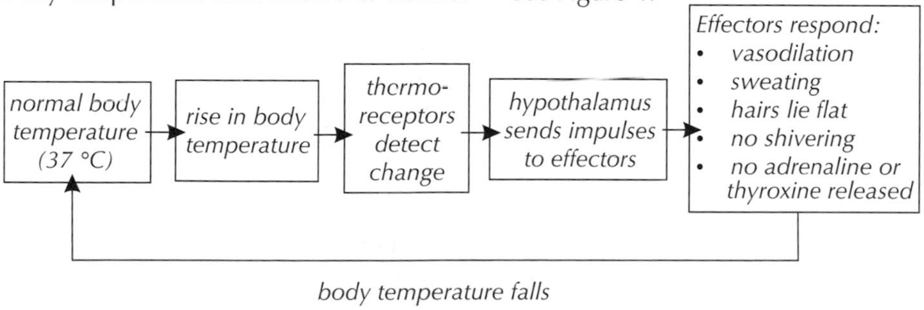

normal body temperature (37 °C) → rise in body temperature → thermoreceptors detect change → hypothalamus sends impulses to effectors → **Effectors respond:**
- vasodilation
- sweating
- hairs lie flat
- no shivering
- no adrenaline or thyroxine released

body temperature falls

Figure 4: *Negative feedback mechanism activated by a rise in body temperature*

Tip: Control of body temperature is called thermoregulation.

Tip: The levels of some things in our body are controlled by the nervous system (like body temperature here) and others are controlled by the hormonal system.

Tip: See page 140 for more about the autonomic nervous system.

Tip: When you feel hot (e.g. when you exercise) you might find yourself sweaty and red-faced — this is just your body's (unattractive) response to the rise in internal body temperature.

Fall in body temperature

When thermoreceptors detect body temperature is too low, they send impulses to the hypothalamus, which sends impulses to effectors. Effectors respond to produce more heat (e.g. adrenaline and thyroxine are released to increase metabolism) and to conserve it. Body temperature then returns to normal — see Figure 5 below.

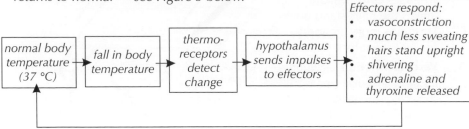

body temperature rises

Figure 5: *Negative feedback mechanism activated by a fall in body temperature.*

Practice Questions — Application

Q1 If a person spends a long time in a hot bath, their skin might appear pink when they get out. Explain the role of the autonomic nervous system in this response.

Q2 When blood glucose concentration gets low, the brain receives signals which stimulate feelings of hunger. Assuming activity levels are the same, is a person likely to feel hungry more quickly in a hot or cold external environment? Explain your answer.

Q3 The effects of some sympathomimetic drugs, such as cocaine, include vasoconstriction and an increase in muscular activity. In hot weather people who have taken cocaine are at risk of hyperthermia (their internal body temperature becomes dangerously high). Suggest why this occurs.

Practice Questions — Fact Recall

Q1 How is body temperature controlled in:
 a) an ectotherm?
 b) an endotherm?

Q2 How do the metabolic rates of an ectotherm and an endotherm differ?

Q3 Explain how sweat glands are important for controlling body temperature.

Q4 Describe two mechanisms that the body uses to increase heat production and explain how they work.

Q5 Describe how arterioles near the skin surface respond when low temperatures are detected by thermoreceptors.

Q6 What part of a mammal's brain controls body temperature?

Q7 Describe how the brain receives information about the external temperature of the body.

Q8 Briefly describe how the autonomic nervous system returns internal body temperature to normal following a fall in body temperature.

3. Control of Blood Glucose Concentration

Blood glucose concentration is under tight control by a hormonal system. If this control system doesn't work properly it may result in diabetes.

Glucose concentration in the blood

All cells need a constant energy supply to work — so blood glucose concentration must be carefully controlled. The concentration of glucose in the blood is normally around 90 mg per 100 cm^3 of blood. It's monitored by cells in the **pancreas**. Blood glucose concentration rises after eating food containing carbohydrate. It falls after exercise, as more glucose is used in respiration to release energy.

Hormonal control of blood glucose concentration

The hormonal system (see p. 114) controls blood glucose concentration using two hormones called insulin and glucagon. They're both secreted by clusters of cells in the pancreas called the **islets of Langerhans**.

The islets of Langerhans contain **beta (β) cells** and **alpha (α) cells** (see Figure 1). β cells secrete insulin into the blood. α cells secrete glucagon into the blood. Insulin and glucagon act on effectors, which respond to restore the blood glucose concentration to the normal level.

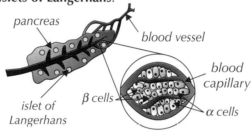

Figure 1: The location of α and β cells in the islets of Langerhans.

Insulin

Insulin lowers blood glucose concentration when it's too high. It binds to specific receptors on the cell membranes of liver cells and muscle cells and increases the permeability of cell membranes to glucose, so the cells take up more glucose.

Insulin also activates enzymes that convert glucose into glycogen. Liver and muscle cells are able to store glycogen in their cytoplasm, as an energy source. The process of forming glycogen from glucose is called **glycogenesis** (see Figure 2). Insulin also increases the rate of respiration of glucose, especially in muscle cells.

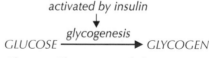

Figure 2: The process of glycogenesis.

Glucagon

Glucagon raises blood glucose concentration when it's too low. It binds to specific receptors on the cell membranes of liver cells and activates enzymes that break down glycogen into glucose. The process of breaking down glycogen is called **glycogenolysis**.

Glucagon also promotes the formation of glucose from glycerol and amino acids. The process of forming glucose from non-carbohydrates is called **gluconeogenesis** (see Figure 4 on the next page). Glucagon also decreases the rate of respiration of glucose in cells.

Learning Objectives:

- Know the factors that influence blood glucose concentration.
- Understand the role of the liver in glycogenesis and gluconeogenesis.
- Understand the role of insulin and glucagon in controlling the uptake of glucose by cells and activating enzymes needed in the interconversion of glucose and glycogen.
- Understand the effect of adrenaline on the breakdown and synthesis of glucagon.
- Know the second messenger model of adrenaline and glucagon action.
- Understand what causes Type I and Type II diabetes and know how they can be controlled by insulin and changes to the diet.

Specification Reference 3.5.4

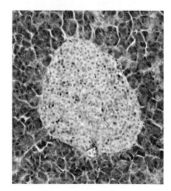

Figure 3: Islet of Langerhans (white) in the pancreas containing α cells and β cells.

Tip: Liver cells are also called hepatocytes.

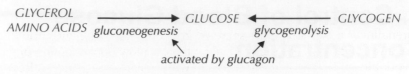

Figure 4: The processes of glycogenolysis and gluconeogenesis.

Negative feedback mechanisms and glucose concentration

Negative feedback mechanisms keep blood glucose concentration normal.

Rise in blood glucose concentration

When the pancreas detects blood glucose concentration is too high, the β cells secrete insulin and the α cells stop secreting glucagon. Insulin then binds to receptors on liver and muscle cells (the effectors). The liver and muscle cells respond to decrease the blood glucose concentration, e.g. glycogenesis is activated (see previous page). Blood glucose concentration then returns to normal.

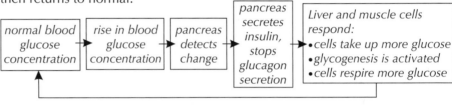

Figure 5: Negative feedback mechanism activated by a rise in blood glucose.

Fall in blood glucose concentration

When the pancreas detects blood glucose is too low, the α cells secrete glucagon and the β cells stop secreting insulin. Glucagon then binds to receptors on liver cells (the effectors). The liver cells respond to increase the blood glucose concentration, e.g. glycogenolysis is activated (see previous page). Blood glucose concentration then returns to normal.

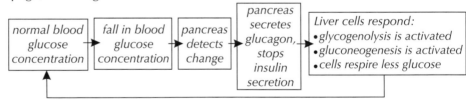

Figure 6: Negative feedback mechanism activated by a fall in blood glucose.

Practice Questions — Application

Q1 After eating a big bowl of pasta describe how a person's blood glucose concentration will change and explain how their body returns it back to normal.

Q2 Von Gierke's disease is a glycogen storage disease. It's caused by an enzyme deficiency, which means the processes of glycogenolysis and gluconeogenesis can't work properly. Explain why someone with von Gierke's disease might suffer from hypoglycaemia if they don't eat regularly.

Adrenaline

Adrenaline is a hormone that's secreted from your adrenal glands (found just above your kidneys). It's secreted when there's a low concentration of glucose in your blood, when you're stressed and when you're exercising. Adrenaline binds to receptors in the cell membrane of liver cells and does these things to increase blood glucose concentration:

- It activates glycogenolysis (the breakdown of glycogen to glucose).
- It inhibits glycogenesis (the synthesis of glycogen from glucose).

It also activates glucagon secretion and inhibits insulin secretion, which increases glucose concentration. Adrenaline gets the body ready for action by making more glucose available for muscles to respire.

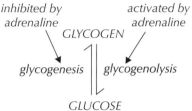

Figure 7: The effect of adrenaline on glycogenesis and glycogenolysis.

Second messengers

Both adrenaline and glucagon can activate glycogenolysis inside a cell even though they bind to receptors on the outside of the cell. They do this by the **second messenger model** — the binding of the hormone to cell receptors activates an enzyme on the inside of the cell membrane, which then produces a chemical known as a second messenger. The second messenger activates other enzymes in the cell to bring about a response.

To activate glycogenolysis, adrenaline and glucagon bind to their specific receptors on the cell surface membrane, which causes an enzyme called **adenylate cyclase** to be activated inside the cell. Activated adenylate cyclase converts ATP into a chemical called **cyclic AMP** (**cAMP**), which is a second messenger. cAMP activates a cascade (a chain of reactions) that break down glycogen into glucose (glycogenolysis) — see Figure 8.

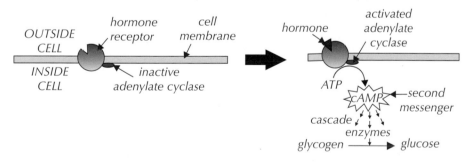

Figure 8: Second messenger model of adrenaline and glucagon action.

Summary of blood glucose control

Process	Converts	Activated by	Inhibited by
Glycogenesis	Glucose to glycogen	Insulin	Adrenaline
Glycogenolysis	Glycogen to glucose	Glucagon and adrenaline	—
Gluconeogenesis	Glycerol / amino acids to glucose	Glucagon	—

Diabetes

Diabetes mellitus is a condition where blood glucose concentration can't be controlled properly. There are two types:

Type I

In Type I diabetes, the β cells in the islets of Langerhans don't produce any insulin. After eating, the blood glucose level rises and stays high — this is called hyperglycaemia and can result in death if left untreated. The kidneys can't reabsorb all this glucose, so some of it's excreted in the urine. Type I diabetes can be treated by regular injections of insulin (see page 157). But this has to be carefully controlled because too much can produce a dangerous drop in blood glucose levels — this is called hypoglycaemia. Eating regularly and controlling simple carbohydrate intake (sugars) helps to avoid a sudden rise in glucose.

Type II

Type II diabetes is usually acquired later in life than Type I, and it's often linked with obesity. It occurs when the β cells don't produce enough insulin or when the body's cells don't respond properly to insulin. Cells don't respond properly because the insulin receptors on their membranes don't work properly, so the cells don't take up enough glucose. This means the blood glucose concentration is higher than normal. It can be treated by controlling simple carbohydrate intake and losing weight. Glucose-lowering tablets can be taken if diet and weight loss can't control it.

Tip: Simple carbohydrates are more easily broken down to glucose, which is then absorbed by the digestive system, than complex carbohydrates.

Practice Questions — Application

The table below shows the blood glucose concentration of a person with Type I diabetes taken at various times throughout the day. The person controls her diabetes with insulin injections after meals and aims to keep her blood glucose concentration between 4 and 7 mmol/l.

	Before lunch	One hour after lunch	Before evening meal
Day 1	4.2 mmol/l	8.7 mmol/l	5.0 mmol/l
Day 2	3.5 mmol/l	7.3 mmol/l	6.7 mmol/l

Q1 a) On which day do you think the person ate a lunch with the highest proportion of simple carbohydrates? Explain your answer.

　　b) Give one assumption that you have made in your answer to a) about the insulin injections.

Q2 From the data in the table, when would you expect the blood concentration of adrenaline to be highest? Explain your answer.

Practice Questions — Fact Recall

Q1 Where are insulin and glucagon secreted from?

Q2 Give three ways in which insulin reduces blood glucose concentration.

Q3 Name the process that converts glucose to glycogen.

Q4 Name and describe two processes activated by glucagon.

Q5 Describe the negative feedback mechanism that is activated by a fall in blood glucose concentration.

Q6 Explain how adrenaline brings about glycogenolysis when blood glucose concentration is low.

Q7 Describe how Type II diabetes can be controlled.

4. Control of the Menstrual Cycle

Learning Objectives:

- Understand how FSH, LH, oestrogen and progesterone control the menstrual cycle of a mammal.

- Understand how negative and positive feedback mechanisms control the secretion of FSH, LH, oestrogen and progesterone.

- Be able to interpret graphs showing the blood concentrations of FSH, LH, oestrogen and progesterone during a menstrual cycle.

Specification Reference 3.5.5

The menstrual cycle — lots of hormones, lots of feedback mechanisms, lots of fun. You might want to take a deep breath first though, there's a lot going on...

The human menstrual cycle

The human **menstrual cycle** (also called the oestrous cycle) lasts about 28 days. It is a cycle of physiological changes in which the female body prepares for reproduction. The menstrual cycle involves:

- A follicle (an egg and its surrounding protective cells) developing in the ovary.

- Ovulation — an egg being released.

- The uterus lining becoming thicker so that a fertilised egg can implant.

- A structure called a corpus luteum developing from the remains of the follicle.

If there's no fertilisation, the uterus lining breaks down and leaves the body through the vagina. This is known as menstruation, which marks the end of one cycle and the start of another.

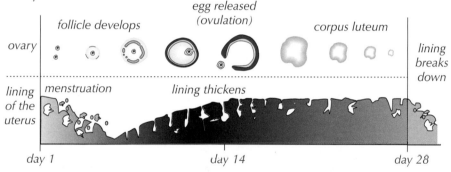

Figure 1: *Diagram showing body changes in the human menstrual cycle.*

Tip: Figure 1 shows you what's going on in the menstrual cycle, but you don't need to memorise every last detail.

Menstrual hormones

The menstrual cycle's controlled by the action of four hormones:

- **Follicle-stimulating hormone (FSH)** — does just what it says, it stimulates the follicle to develop.

- **Luteinising hormone (LH)** — stimulates ovulation and stimulates the corpus luteum to develop.

- **Oestrogen** — stimulates the uterus lining to thicken.

- **Progesterone** — maintains the thick uterus lining, ready for implantation of an embryo.

FSH and LH are secreted by the anterior pituitary gland in the brain. Oestrogen and progesterone are secreted by the ovaries.

Practice Questions — Fact Recall

Q1 Describe the roles of FSH and LH in the menstrual cycle.

Q2 Which hormone:

    a) stimulates the uterus lining to thicken?

    b) maintains a thick uterus lining ready for implantation?

Q3 Which two hormones are released by the:

    a) anterior pituitary gland?   b) ovaries?

Tip: It's a good idea to get your head round what the hormones do and where they're released before the next few pages, which show you how they all work together. It can get a bit tricky if you don't know the basics.

Hormone changes in the menstrual cycle

Hormone concentrations change during different stages of the menstrual cycle — these changes control what happens in the cycle (see Figure 2). The different concentrations of hormones are controlled by feedback loops.

Exam Tip

In the exam you might have to interpret a graph on the menstrual cycle of a different mammal (i.e. not a human). Don't panic — the hormones work in just the same way but the timings may be different, e.g. the menstrual cycle of a rat lasts only 4 to 5 days.

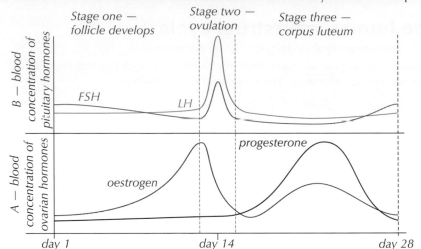

Figure 2: Changes in hormone concentrations throughout the menstrual cycle.

Stage one — high FSH concentration

A high FSH concentration in the blood stimulates follicle development. The follicle releases oestrogen. FSH stimulates the ovaries to release oestrogen. This causes the concentration of oestrogen in the blood to rise, which stimulates the uterus lining to thicken. Oestrogen inhibits FSH being released from the anterior pituitary gland.

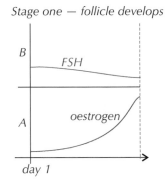

So after FSH has stimulated follicle development, negative feedback (via oestrogen) keeps the FSH concentration low (see Figure 3). This makes sure that no more follicles develop.

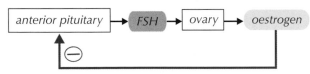

Figure 3: The negative feedback mechanism in the first stage of the menstrual cycle.

Stage two — oestrogen concentration peaks and LH surges

Oestrogen concentration increases to a high level. When oestrogen concentration is high it no longer inhibits FSH release. Instead it stimulates the anterior pituitary gland to release LH and FSH. In turn, LH stimulates the ovaries to release more oestrogen. Oestrogen further stimulates the anterior pituitary gland release more LH, and so on. This causes a surge in LH concentration (it rapidly increases) which stimulates ovulation — the follicle ruptures and the egg is released.

So a high oestrogen concentration triggers a positive feedback mechanism (see Figure 4).

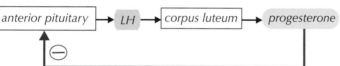

Figure 4: *The positive feedback mechanism in the second stage of the menstrual cycle.*

LH also stimulates the ruptured follicle to turn into a corpus luteum.

Tip: It's a bit weird — oestrogen usually inhibits FSH and LH release, but at really high levels it switches to stimulating their release.

Stage three — progesterone concentration rises

The corpus luteum releases progesterone, so progesterone concentration rises. Progesterone inhibits the release of FSH and LH from the anterior pituitary gland, so the concentrations of these fall. The uterus lining is maintained by progesterone.

So negative feedback makes sure that no more follicles develop when the corpus luteum is developing — see Figure 5.

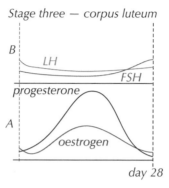

Stage three — corpus luteum

Tip: Here, progesterone prevents the positive feedback effects of oestrogen.

Figure 5: *The negative feedback mechanism in the third stage of the menstrual cycle.*

If no embryo implants, the corpus luteum breaks down and stops releasing progesterone. When progesterone stops being released, FSH and LH concentrations increase because they're no longer inhibited by progesterone. Also the uterus lining isn't maintained so it breaks down — menstruation happens and the cycle starts again.

Tip: An embryo refers to a fertilized egg that's in the early stages of development.

Practice Questions — Application

Q1 The graph below shows the changes in hormone concentrations during the oestrous cycle of a ewe.

a) Explain how the oestrogen concentration between days 10-13 prevents the development of too many follicles.

b) Describe the positive feedback mechanism responsible for the levels of oestrogen and LH between points X and Y.

c) Explain which day you would expect:

i) ovulation to occur.   ii) the corpus luteum to break down.

Tip: A ewe is a female sheep.

Q2 Menopause occurs when a woman's ovaries permanently stop releasing hormones. Explain why blood concentrations of FSH may be high after a woman has experienced menopause.

Q3 Some pig farmers control the menstrual cycle of their livestock by giving all their sows progesterone for 20 days and then stopping it. Explain how this enables the farmers to have all their sows ready for breeding at the same time.

Tip: A sow is a female pig.

Q4 Some fertility tests allow women to know the days when they have the greatest chance of conceiving. They work by detecting a very high level of one of the menstrual hormones. Suggest which hormone the tests detect and how this indicates the best time for conceiving.

Section Summary

Make sure you know:

- That homeostasis involves control systems that maintain a constant internal environment (within certain limits).

- Why it's important to maintain the right internal body temperature and pH (in terms of enzyme action), and the right blood glucose concentration (in terms of water potential and energy transfer).

- That negative feedback mechanisms return levels back to normal and why multiple negative feedback mechanisms give more control.

- That positive feedback amplifies a change and is often involved in the breakdown of control systems.

- How to interpret diagrams showing positive and negative feedback.

- That an ectotherm is an animal that can't control its body temperature internally and an endotherm is an animal that can control its body temperature internally (by homeostasis).

- The mechanisms involved in heat loss (sweating, flat hairs, vasodilation), heat production (shivering, adrenaline and thyroxine release), and heat conservation (less sweat, hairs stand up, vasoconstriction) in mammals.

- How the hypothalamus and the autonomic nervous system maintain a constant body temperature.

- That diet and exercise affect blood glucose concentration.

- That glycogenesis is the conversion of glucose to glycogen, glycogenolysis is the conversion of glycogen to glucose, and gluconeogenesis is the conversion of glycerol or amino acids to glucose.

- That insulin lowers blood glucose level when it's too high by binding to receptors on liver and muscle cells and activating glycogenesis, causing the cells to take up more glucose and causing the cells to respire more glucose.

- That glucagon raises blood glucose level when it's too low by binding to receptors on liver cells and activating glycogenolysis and gluconeogenesis, and causing the cells to respire less glucose.

- How a second messenger allows adrenaline and glucagon to activate glycogenolysis inside a cell.

- The causes of Type I diabetes (no insulin produced) and Type II diabetes (not enough insulin produced or body cells don't respond properly to it) and how they can be controlled (by insulin and changes to the diet).

- How FSH, LH, oestrogen and progesterone control the menstrual cycle of a mammal, and how their levels are controlled by negative and positive feedback mechanisms.

- How to interpret graphs showing the blood concentrations of FSH, LH, oestrogen and progesterone during a menstrual cycle.

Exam-style Questions

1 The activity levels of a squirrel and a tortoise living in the same area were recorded over a 20 hour period. The temperature of the external environment in the test period was also recorded. The results are shown on the graph below.

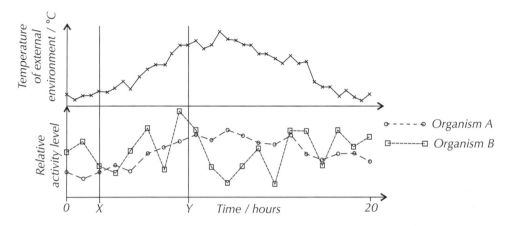

1 (a) Describe the activity levels of the organisms in relation to temperature.

(2 marks)

1 (b) (i) Tortoises are ectotherms, squirrels are endotherms.
     Which organism, A or B, is the tortoise? Explain your answer.

(1 mark)

1 (b) (ii) Squirrels have a much wider geographical range than tortoises.
     Suggest why this is.

(2 marks)

1 (c) (i) It was observed that the hairs on the squirrel were standing up at point X.
     Explain how and why this response came about.

(4 marks)

1 (c) (ii) Describe and explain the mechanisms of heat loss that may
     occur in the squirrel's body at point Y on the graph.

(6 marks)

2 The level of menstrual hormones in the blood affects a woman's fertility.

2 (a) Some women have naturally low levels of FSH. Describe the effect that low levels of FSH would have on a woman's fertility and explain your answer.

(2 marks)

2 (b) The combined pill is a method of contraception containing both oestrogen and progesterone. A woman takes a pill each day for 21 days then has 7 days break. On the days when she takes a pill, oestrogen concentration in the blood is maintained at a level that inhibits FSH release.

2 (b) (i) Apart from the inhibition of FSH release by oestrogen, suggest two other ways in which the pill works as a contraceptive. Explain your answers.

(4 marks)

2 (b) (ii) Suggest what change may occur in the woman's uterus during the 7 days when she doesn't take a pill. Explain your answer.

(2 marks)

2 (c) The blood concentration of hormones not involved in the menstrual cycle affect a woman during pregnancy. For example, during contractions the hormone oxytocin is released into the blood, which causes more contractions.

What type of feedback mechanism is this an example of?

(1 mark)

3 In an experiment, the blood glucose concentrations of a Type II diabetic and a non-diabetic were recorded at regular intervals in a 150 minute time period. 15 minutes into the experiment a glucose drink was given. The normal range for blood glucose concentration in a healthy individual is between 82 and 110 mg/100 cm³. The results of the experiment are shown on the graph below.

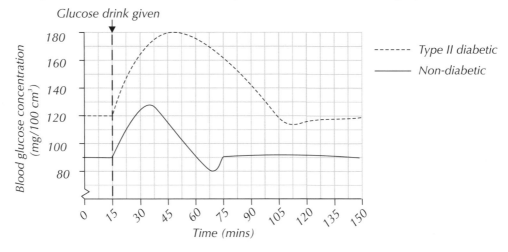

3 (a) (i) Explain why the Type II diabetic's blood glucose concentration takes longer to decrease after they take the glucose drink than the non-diabetic's.

(2 marks)

3 (a) (ii) If the diabetic person had exercised after taking the glucose drink would their blood glucose concentration have decreased more quickly or more slowly? Explain your answer.

(1 mark)

3 (b) Suggest how the blood glucose concentration of a Type I diabetic would differ from the Type II diabetic after having the glucose drink.

(2 marks)

3 (c) (i) Suggest what time insulin is released in the non-diabetic. Explain your answer.

(2 marks)

3 (c) (ii) Blood glucose concentration continues to rise after the release of insulin. Why is this?

(1 mark)

3 (d) Explain how negative feedback works to increase the blood glucose concentration in the non-diabetic between 65 and 75 minutes.

(6 marks)

1. DNA and RNA

You learnt about DNA (deoxyribonucleic acid) and its structure at AS, but you need to cover it again for A2 — mainly so you can compare it to the structure of two other important nucleic acids, mRNA and tRNA.

DNA structure

Remember, DNA is a double helix — it's formed from two separate strands which are coiled around each other to form a spiral (see Figure 1). The strands are polynucleotides. They're made up of lots of nucleotides joined together in a long chain.

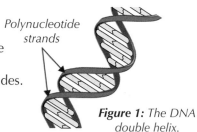

Polynucleotide strands

Figure 1: *The DNA double helix.*

Nucleotide structure

Each nucleotide is made from a phosphate group, a pentose sugar (with 5 carbon atoms) and a nitrogenous base — see Figure 2.

The sugar in DNA nucleotides is a deoxyribose sugar. Each nucleotide has the same sugar and phosphate. The base on each nucleotide can vary though. There are four possible bases — adenine (A), thymine (T), cytosine (C) and guanine (G).

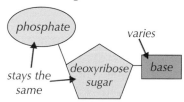

phosphate *varies* *stays the same* *deoxyribose sugar* *base*

Figure 2: *A DNA nucleotide.*

Polynucleotide strands

Many nucleotides join together to form the polynucleotide strands. The nucleotides join up between the phosphate group of one nucleotide and the sugar of another, creating a sugar-phosphate backbone (see Figure 3).

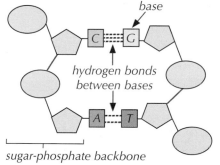

base *hydrogen bonds between bases* *sugar-phosphate backbone*

Figure 3: *A section of a DNA molecule.*

Specific base pairing

Two DNA polynucleotide strands join together by hydrogen bonds between the bases. Each base can only join with one particular partner — this is called specific base pairing. Adenine always pairs with thymine (A - T) and guanine always pairs with cytosine (G - C) — see Figure 3.

Tip: When two strands have bases that pair up, the strands are said to be <u>complementary</u> to each other:

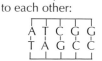

Genes

Genes are sections of DNA. They're found on chromosomes. Genes code for proteins (polypeptides) — they contain the instructions to make them. It's the order of nucleotide bases in a gene that determines the order of amino acids in a particular protein.

Tip: Proteins are made from amino acids. Different proteins have a different number and order of amino acids.

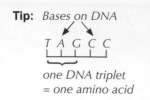

Each amino acid is coded for by a sequence of three bases (called a triplet) in a gene. A DNA triplet is also called a base triplet or a codon. Different sequences of bases code for different amino acids. This is the genetic code — see page 174 for more. So the sequence of bases in a section of DNA is a template that's used to make a protein during protein synthesis.

DNA and protein synthesis

DNA molecules are found in the nucleus of the cell. The organelles that assemble proteins are called **ribosomes** — they're found in the cytoplasm. DNA is too large to move out of the nucleus, so a section is copied into a molecule called **mRNA** (a type of RNA, see below). This process is called **transcription**. The mRNA leaves the nucleus and joins with a ribosome in the cytoplasm, where it can be used to synthesise a protein. This process is called **translation**. Figure 4 summarises this.

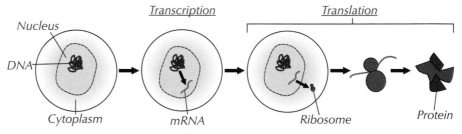

Figure 4: Making a protein from DNA.

RNA

Like DNA, RNA is a type of nucleic acid. It's made of nucleotides that contain one of four different bases. The nucleotides also form a polynucleotide strand with a sugar-phosphate backbone. But RNA differs from DNA in these ways:

- The sugar in RNA nucleotides is a **ribose** sugar (not deoxyribose).
- The nucleotides form a single polynucleotide strand (not a double one).
- **Uracil** (U) replaces thymine as a base. Uracil always pairs with adenine during protein synthesis.

You need to know about the structure and composition of two different types of RNA — messenger RNA (mRNA) and transfer RNA (tRNA).

Messenger RNA (mRNA)

mRNA is a single polynucleotide strand (see Figure 5). It's made in the nucleus during transcription. mRNA carries the genetic code from the DNA in the nucleus to the cytoplasm, where it's used to make a protein during translation. In mRNA, groups of three adjacent bases are usually called **codons** (they're sometimes called triplets or base triplets).

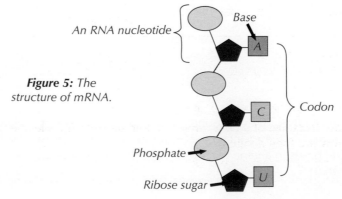

Figure 5: The structure of mRNA.

Tip: Bases on DNA

one DNA triplet
= one amino acid

Tip: There's more on transcription and translation on p. 170-173.

Tip: mRNA is able to leave the nucleus through nuclear pores because it's a much smaller molecule than DNA.

Tip: RNA stands for ribonucleic acid.

Tip: There are actually several different types of RNA, each with a different function. One of the other types, siRNA, is covered on page 179.

Tip: mRNA acts as a messenger by carrying genetic information between DNA and the cytoplasm — that's how it gets its name.

Tip: mRNA is copied from DNA — so its sequence is complementary to the DNA sequence. See page 170 for more.

Transfer RNA (tRNA)

tRNA is a single polynucleotide strand that's folded into a clover shape (see Figure 6). Hydrogen bonds between specific base pairs hold the molecule in this shape.

Every tRNA molecule has a specific sequence of three bases at one end called an **anticodon**. They also have an amino acid binding site at the other end. tRNA is found in the cytoplasm where it's involved in translation. It carries the amino acids that are used to make proteins to the ribosomes.

Tip: Transfer RNA is so called because it transfers amino acids to the ribosomes. There's more about this on page 172.

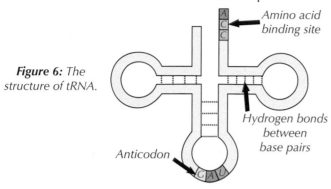

Figure 6: The structure of tRNA.

Amino acid binding site

Hydrogen bonds between base pairs

Anticodon

DNA, mRNA and tRNA comparison

You need to know the structure and composition of DNA, mRNA and tRNA really well — you could be asked to compare them in your exam. The table below outlines the main differences between them:

	DNA	mRNA	tRNA
Shape	Double-stranded — twisted into a double helix and held together by hydrogen bonds.	Single-stranded	Single-stranded — folded into a clover shape and held together by hydrogen bonds.
Sugar	Deoxyribose sugar	Ribose sugar	Ribose sugar
Bases	A, T, C, G	A, U, C, G	A, U, C, G
Other features	Three adjacent bases called a triplet (sometimes a base triplet or codon).	Three adjacent bases called a codon (sometimes a triplet or a base triplet).	Each tRNA molecule has a specific sequence of three bases called an anticodon and an amino acid binding site.

Exam Tip
Questions that ask you to compare the structures of DNA, mRNA and tRNA should be easy marks in the exam — make sure you can answer them.

Practice Questions — Fact Recall

Q1 Name the sugar in RNA.

Q2 Name the bases in: a) DNA, b) mRNA, c) tRNA.

Q3 How are the structures of a DNA molecule and an mRNA molecule similar? How are they different?

Q4 Describe in detail the structure of tRNA.

Learning Objectives:

- Know that transcription is the production of mRNA from DNA.
- Understand the role of RNA polymerase in transcription.
- Know that pre-mRNA is spliced to form mRNA in eukaryotic cells.
- Know that translation is the production of polypeptides from the sequence of codons carried by mRNA.
- Understand the role of ribosomes and tRNA in translation.

Specification Reference 3.5.6

2. Protein Synthesis

Proteins are synthesised (made) using the instructions in DNA.
Protein synthesis involves two main stages: transcription and translation.

Transcription

Transcription is the first stage of protein synthesis. During transcription an mRNA copy of a gene (a section of DNA) is made in the nucleus. Here's how:

1. RNA polymerase attaches to the DNA

Transcription starts when **RNA polymerase** (an enzyme) attaches to the DNA double helix at the beginning of a gene.
The hydrogen bonds between the two DNA strands in the gene break, separating the strands, and the DNA molecule uncoils at that point. One of the strands is then used as a template to make an mRNA copy — see Figure 1.

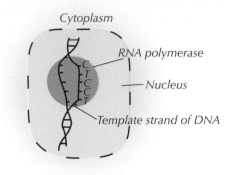

Figure 1: *RNA polymerase attaches to the DNA double helix.*

Tip: When RNA polymerase attaches to the DNA double helix, it binds to a specific DNA sequence called a <u>promoter</u> (see page 178). There's a promoter near the beginning of each gene.

Tip: Free RNA nucleotides aren't bound to anything in the nucleus — they're just floating freely.

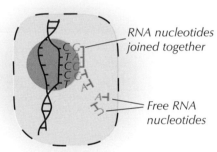

Figure 2: *A complementary mRNA molecule starts to form.*

2. Complementary mRNA is formed

The RNA polymerase lines up free RNA nucleotides alongside the template strand. Specific base pairing means that the mRNA strand ends up being a **complementary copy** of the DNA template strand (except the base T is replaced by U in RNA). Once the RNA nucleotides have paired up with their specific bases on the DNA strand they're joined together, forming an mRNA molecule — see Figure 2.

3. RNA polymerase moves down the DNA strand

The RNA polymerase moves along the DNA, separating the strands and assembling the mRNA strand. The hydrogen bonds between the uncoiled strands of DNA re-form once the RNA polymerase has passed by and the strands coil back into a double helix — see Figure 3.

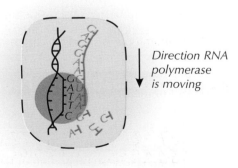

Figure 3: *RNA polymerase moves down the DNA strand.*

4. mRNA leaves the nucleus

When RNA polymerase reaches a particular sequence of DNA called a **stop signal**, it stops making mRNA and detaches from the DNA. The mRNA moves out of the nucleus through a nuclear pore and attaches to a ribosome in the cytoplasm, where the next stage of protein synthesis takes place (see next page).

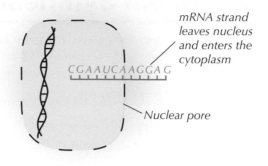

mRNA strand leaves nucleus and enters the cytoplasm

CGAAUCAAGGAG

Nuclear pore

Figure 4: *mRNA leaves the nucleus.*

Tip: Stop signals are particular base triplets, see page 174 for more.

Editing mRNA

mRNA in eukaryotic cells is edited — that's because genes in eukaryotic DNA contain sections that don't code for amino acids. These sections of DNA are called **introns**. All the bits that do code for amino acids are called **exons**.

During transcription the introns and exons are both copied into mRNA. mRNA strands containing introns and exons are called **pre-mRNA**. Introns are removed from pre-mRNA strands by a process called **splicing** — introns are removed and the exons are joined together to form an mRNA strand (see Figure 5). This takes place in the nucleus. The mRNA then leaves the nucleus for the next stage of protein synthesis (translation).

Tip: You've already come across introns and exons at AS, but you need to know them in a bit more detail for A2.

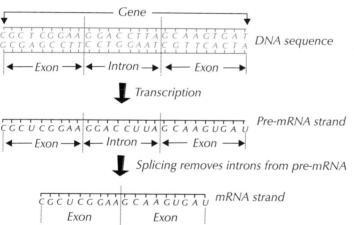

Figure 5: *Pre-mRNA is spliced to produce mRNA.*

Tip: The pre-mRNA strand shown here is complementary to the bottom strand of the DNA sequence (the DNA template strand):

C G C U C ...
G C G A G ...

Practice Questions — Application

Q1 α–amanitin is a deadly toxin produced by some mushrooms. It works by inhibiting RNA polymerase. What effect will this have on protein synthesis? Explain your answer.

Q2 Part of the DNA sequence of a gene is shown below.

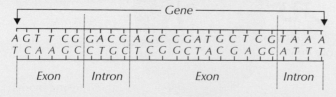

Tip: Q2 continues on the next page.

a) A molecule of pre-mRNA is transcribed using the blue strand as a template. Write down the sequence of this pre-mRNA molecule.

b) The pre-mRNA molecule is spliced to produce mRNA. Write down the sequence of the mRNA strand.

c) How many amino acids would this mRNA strand code for?

Translation

Translation is the second stage of protein synthesis. It takes place at the ribosomes in the cytoplasm. During translation, amino acids are joined together by a ribosome to make a polypeptide chain (protein), following the sequence of codons carried by the mRNA. Here's how it works:

The mRNA attaches itself to a ribosome and transfer RNA (tRNA) molecules carry amino acids to the ribosome.

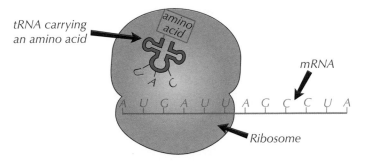

Figure 6: mRNA (turquoise) attached to a bacterial ribosome.

A tRNA molecule, with an anticodon that's complementary to the first codon on the mRNA, attaches itself to the mRNA by specific base pairing. A second tRNA molecule attaches itself to the next codon on the mRNA in the same way.

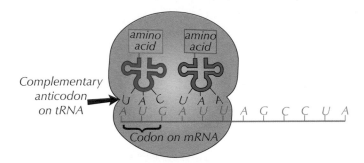

The two amino acids attached to the tRNA molecules are joined by a peptide bond. The first tRNA molecule moves away, leaving its amino acid behind.

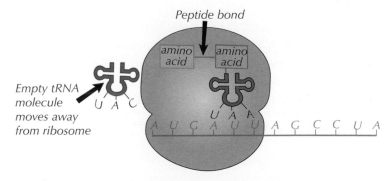

A third tRNA molecule binds to the next codon on the mRNA. Its amino acid binds to the first two and the second tRNA molecule moves away.
This process continues, producing a chain of linked amino acids (a polypeptide chain), until there's a stop signal on the mRNA molecule.

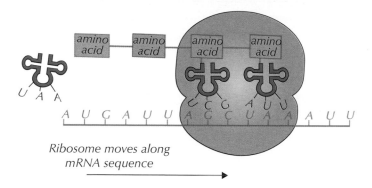

Ribosome moves along
mRNA sequence

The polypeptide chain (protein) then moves away from the ribosome and translation is complete.

Polypeptide
chain

Practice Questions — Application

Q1 Diamond-Blackfan anaemia is an inherited condition caused by one of several gene mutations. The mutations can affect the function of the proteins that make up ribosomes. What effect could this have on protein synthesis? Explain your answer.

Q2 An error occurs during transcription that accidentally inserts a stop signal into the middle of an mRNA sequence. What effect could this have on the protein that is eventually produced? Explain your answer.

> **Tip:** A mutation is any change to the DNA base sequence. See page 184 for more.

Practice Questions — Fact Recall

Q1 Name the two stages of protein synthesis and state where each one takes place.

Q2 a) What is RNA polymerase?
    b) In which stage of protein synthesis is it involved?
    c) Describe the role of RNA polymerase.

Q3 Why is the mRNA that's produced from a DNA template always a complementary copy of the DNA?

Q4 Explain why eukaryotic mRNA gets spliced.

Q5 Describe the function of tRNA.

Q6 Explain how tRNA molecules pair up with mRNA during protein synthesis.

Q7 What type of bond joins two amino acids together?

> **Tip:** Don't get confused between mRNA and tRNA... revisit the lovely table on page 169 if you need to refresh your memory.

Learning Objectives:

- Know that the genetic code is the base triplets in mRNA which code for specific amino acids.
- Know that the genetic code is universal, non-overlapping and degenerate.
- Be able to show an understanding of how the base sequences of nucleic acids relate to the amino acid sequence of polypeptides, when provided with suitable data.
- Be able to interpret data from experimental work investigating the role of nucleic acids.

(Recall of specific codons and the amino acids for which they code, and of specific experiments, will not be tested.)

Specification Reference 3.5.6

3. The Genetic Code and Nucleic Acids

The genetic code is pretty important — it encodes the information in genes and these determine what we look like, how we develop and much, much more. Which is probably why the examiners expect you to know all about the genetic code...

What is the genetic code?

The genetic code is the sequence of base triplets (codons) in mRNA which code for specific amino acids. In the genetic code, each base triplet is read in sequence, separate from the triplet before it and after it. Base triplets don't share their bases — the code is **non-overlapping**.

┌ Examples ─────────

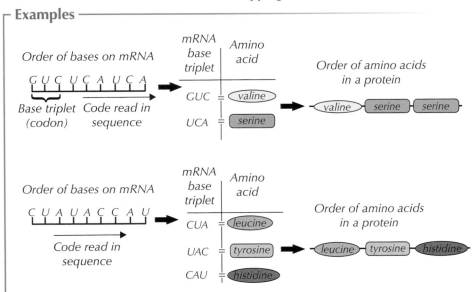

Figure 1: *Examples to explain how the non-overlapping genetic code works.*

The genetic code is also **degenerate** — there are more possible combinations of triplets than there are amino acids (20 amino acids but 64 possible triplets). This means that some amino acids are coded for by more than one base triplet, e.g. tyrosine can be coded for by UAU or UAC. Not all triplets code for amino acids though. Some triplets are used to tell the cell when to start and stop production of the protein — these are called start and stop signals (or codons). They're found at the beginning and end of the mRNA. E.g. UAG is a stop signal.

The genetic code is also **universal** — the same specific base triplets code for the same amino acids in all living things. E.g. UAU codes for tyrosine in all organisms.

Interpreting data on nucleic acids

You might have to interpret information on nucleic acids in the exam. The examples on the next page show you the sorts of data you might get given and the things you might be asked to do.

Examples

The mRNA codons for some amino acids are given in the table on the right.

mRNA codon	Amino Acid
UCU	Serine
CUA	Leucine
UAU	Tyrosine
GUG	Valine
GCA	Alanine
CGC	Arginine

Exam Tip
You don't need to learn any of these codons or the amino acids they code for — all the information you need to answer any questions will be given to you in the exam.

You might be asked to give the DNA sequence for amino acids...

Because mRNA is a complementary copy of the DNA template, the DNA sequence for each amino acid is made up of bases that would pair with the mRNA sequence. The DNA sequence is shown in the table below.

mRNA codon	Amino Acid	DNA sequence
UCU	Serine	AGA
CUA	Leucine	GAT
UAU	Tyrosine	ATA
GUG	Valine	CAC
GCA	Alanine	CGT
CGC	Arginine	GCG

Tip: When interpreting data on nucleic acids remember that DNA contains T and RNA contains U.

Tip: You could also be asked to work out the amino acids from a given DNA sequence and a table.

...or to give the tRNA anticodons from mRNA codons...

tRNA anticodons are complementary copies of mRNA codons, so you can work out the tRNA anticodon from the mRNA codon:

mRNA codon	tRNA anticodon
UCU	AGA
CUA	GAU
UAU	AUA
GUG	CAC
GCA	CGU
CGC	GCG

Tip: You might be asked to name the amino acid coded for by a tRNA anticodon using a table like the one at the top of the page.

...or to write the amino acid sequence for a section of mRNA

To work out the sequence of amino acids from some mRNA, you need to break the genetic code into codons and then use the information in the table to work out what amino acid they code for.

mRNA: CUAGUGCGCUAUUCU

Codons: CUA   GUG   CGC   UAU   UCU

Amino acids: Leucine   Valine   Arginine   Tyrosine   Serine

Tip: You might have to work out the sequence of some mRNA from a sequence of amino acids and a table.

The table on the right shows some mRNA codons and the amino acids they code for.

mRNA codon	Amino Acid
UUU	Phe
UAC	Tyr
CAA	Gln
GCG	Ala
AUG	Met
CAU	His
AUA	Ile

Q1 Using the table, give the mRNA codons for the following amino acid sequence:

Tyr - Phe - Gln - Ile - Ala - His

Q2 Give the DNA base sequence that would code for the following amino acid sequence:

Met - Phe - Gln - Gln - Ala - Tyr - Ile

Q3 Give the tRNA anticodons for the following mRNA codons:

AUGCAUAUACAUUUCAA

Q4 Write down the amino acid sequence that would be produced from the following tRNA anticodons:

AAAGUUUAUGUACGCAUG

Q5 The DNA base sequence below codes for the amino acid sequence beneath it. Neither is complete. Fill in the blanks, using the information in the table to help you.

DNA: GTA - __ - __ - AAA - ATG - __ - GTA

Amino acid: His - Ala - Ile - Phe - ____ - Gln - ___

Interpreting experimental data on nucleic acids

HOW SCIENCE WORKS

In the exam you might have to interpret data from experiments done to investigate nucleic acids and their role in protein synthesis.

Example

To investigate how two new drugs affect nucleic acids and their role in protein synthesis, bacteria were grown in normal conditions for a few generations, then moved to media containing the drugs. After a short period of time, the concentration of protein and complete strands of mRNA in the bacteria were analysed. The results are shown in Figure 2.

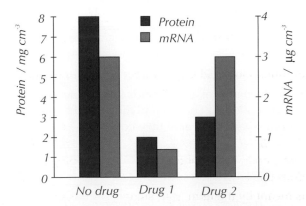

Figure 2: Bar chart to show mRNA and protein concentration in the presence and absence of drugs.

Figure 2 on the previous page shows that both mRNA and protein concentration were lower in the presence of drug 1 compared to the no-drug control. This suggests that drug 1 affects the production of full length mRNA, so there's no mRNA for protein synthesis during translation.

mRNA production in the presence of drug 2 was unaffected, but less protein was produced — 3 mg cm^{-3} compared to 8 mg cm^{-3}. This suggests that drug 2 interferes with translation. mRNA was produced, but less protein was translated from it.

Further tests to establish the nature of the two drugs were carried out. Drug 1 was found to be a ribonuclease (an enzyme that digests RNA). This could explain the results of the first experiment — any strands of mRNA produced by the cell would be digested by drug 1, so couldn't be used in translation to make proteins.

Drug 2 was found to be a single-stranded, clover-shaped molecule capable of binding to the ribosome. Again, this helps to explain the results from the first experiment — drug 2 could work by binding to the ribosome, blocking tRNAs from binding to it and so preventing translation.

Tip: Transcription and translation are on pages 170-173.

Practice Questions —Application

A chemical called puromycin is believed to affect the development of rapid respiration in a freshly cut potato slice, by either affecting the synthesis of proteins or nucleic acids. In an experiment, potato slices were kept in various concentrations of puromycin for 24 hours. Nucleic acid synthesis was monitored by radioactively tagging uracil and then measuring its uptake. Protein synthesis was monitored by radioactively tagging leucine and then measuring its uptake. Afterwards the percentage inhibition of the development of respiration, leucine uptake and uracil uptake were calculated. The results are shown in the table below.

Tip: Leucine is an amino acid.

Puromycin concentration (mol/l)	% inhibition of the development of respiration	% inhibition of leucine uptake	% inhibition of uracil uptake
Control	-	-	-
0.6×10^{-4}	33	32	19
1.0×10^{-4}	49	55	31
2.0×10^{-4}	76	73	55
4.0×10^{-4}	97	93	79

Q1 Suggest why uracil was the only base that was radioactively tagged.

Q2 Describe the results shown in the table for the four different concentrations of puromycin used.

Q3 Do the results show that puromycin has a greater effect on nucleic acid synthesis or protein synthesis?

Practice Questions — Fact Recall

Q1 The genetic code is described as 'non-overlapping'. What does this mean?

Q2 What is meant by the term 'start signal' in mRNA?

Q3 The same base triplets code for the same amino acids in all living things. What word is used to describe this feature of the genetic code?

- Know that the transcription of target genes is stimulated only when specific transcriptional factors move from the cytoplasm into the nucleus.

- Understand the effect of oestrogen on gene transcription.

- Know that small interfering RNA (siRNA) is a short, double-strand of RNA that interferes with the expression of a specific gene.

- Be able to interpret data provided from investigations into gene expression.

Specification Reference 3.5.7

Tip: Transcription and translation are covered on pages 170-173.

4. Regulation of Transcription and Translation

Every cell in an organism contains the same DNA, but not all the proteins it codes for are made. This is because transcription and translation are controlled.

Controlling transcription

All the cells in an organism carry the same genes (DNA) but the structure and function of different cells varies. This is because not all the genes in a cell are expressed (transcribed and used to make a protein). Because different genes are expressed, different proteins are made and these proteins modify the cell (see page 192). The transcription of genes is controlled by protein molecules called **transcription factors**.

The role of transcription factors

Transcription factors move from the cytoplasm to the nucleus. In the nucleus they bind to specific DNA sites called **promoters**, which are found near the start of their target genes — the genes they control the expression of. Transcription factors control expression by controlling the rate of transcription.

Some transcription factors, called **activators**, increase the rate of transcription — e.g. they help RNA polymerase bind to the start of the target gene and activate transcription. Other transcription factors, called **repressors**, decrease the rate of transcription — e.g. they bind to the start of the target gene, preventing RNA polymerase from binding, stopping transcription. Figure 1 shows activators and repressors at work.

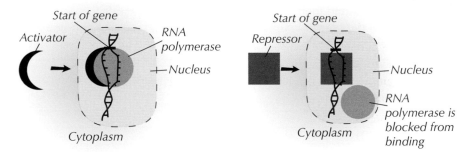

Figure 1: *An activator (left) and a repressor (right) can control the rate of transcription by affecting RNA polymerase.*

Tip: Not all cell types have oestrogen receptors — so not all cells are affected by oestrogen.

Oestrogen

The expression of genes can also be affected by other molecules in the cell, e.g. oestrogen. Oestrogen is a hormone that can affect transcription by binding to a transcription factor called an oestrogen receptor, forming an oestrogen-oestrogen receptor complex.

The complex moves from the cytoplasm into the nucleus where it binds to specific DNA sites near the start of the target gene. The complex can either act as an activator, e.g. helping RNA polymerase, or as a repressor, e.g. blocking RNA polymerase.

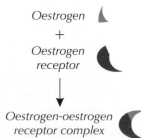

Whether the complex acts as a repressor or activator depends on the type of cell and the target gene — see Figure 2 on the next page. So, the level of oestrogen in a particular cell affects the rate of transcription of target genes.

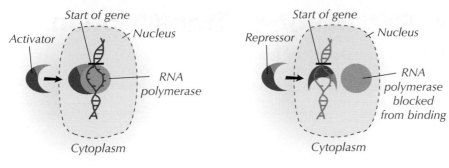

Figure 2: An oestrogen-oestrogen receptor complex can control transcription by acting as an activator (left) or as a repressor (right).

Tip: Remember, transcription factors can repress (prevent) transcription as well as activating it.

siRNA

Gene expression is also affected by a type of RNA called **small interfering RNA** (siRNA). siRNA molecules are short, double-stranded RNA molecules that can interfere with the expression of specific genes. Their bases are complementary to specific sections of a target gene and the mRNA that's formed from it — see Figure 3.

Tip: Unlike mRNA and tRNA, siRNA is double-stranded. For more on the different types of RNA, see pages 168-169.

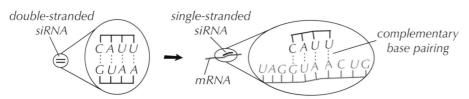

Figure 3: siRNA bases are complementary to a section of mRNA.

Tip: Double-stranded siRNA is unwound into two single-stranded siRNA molecules by an enzyme.

RNA interference

siRNA can interfere with both the transcription and translation of genes. siRNA affects translation through a mechanism called RNA interference:

Tip: siRNA is actually about 20-25 nucleotides long (this diagram just shows a short section).

- In the cytoplasm, siRNA and associated proteins bind to the target mRNA.

- The proteins cut up the mRNA into sections so it can no longer be translated (see Figure 4).

- So, the siRNA prevents the expression of the specific gene as its protein can no longer be made during translation.

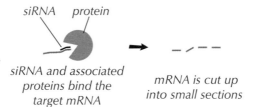

siRNA and associated proteins bind the target mRNA

mRNA is cut up into small sections

Figure 4: siRNA affects gene expression by cutting up target mRNA.

Tip: siRNA has a potential use in treating genetic disorders, for example stopping a known harmful gene from being expressed.

Practice Questions — Application

Q1 Rett syndrome is a neuro-developmental disorder caused by a mutation in the MECP2 gene. The protein produced by the gene is a transcription factor which acts as a repressor and is needed for normal functioning of nerve cells. Mutations in the gene often result in reduced production of the protein. Suggest how a mutation in the MECP2 gene causes Rett syndrome.

Q2 AMD is a medical condition which results in loss of vision because of damage to the retina. It is caused by the expression of multiple genes and by environmental factors. A treatment is being developed using siRNA. Suggest how siRNA could be used to treat AMD.

Interpreting data on gene expression

You could get a question in the exam where you have to interpret data about gene expression. It could be on anything you've learnt on pages 178-179, e.g. transcription factors, oestrogen or siRNAs. Below is an example of a gene expression system in bacteria and an experiment that investigates how it works.

┌─ **Example** ─────────────

The *lac* repressor

E. coli is a bacterium that respires glucose, but it can use lactose if glucose isn't available. If lactose is present, *E. coli* makes an enzyme (β-galactosidase) to digest it. But if there's no lactose, it doesn't waste energy making an enzyme it doesn't need.

The enzyme's gene is only expressed when lactose is present. The production of the enzyme is controlled by a transcription factor — the *lac* repressor. When there's no lactose, the *lac* repressor binds to the DNA at the start of the gene, stopping transcription. When lactose is present it binds to the *lac* repressor, stopping it binding to the DNA, so the gene is transcribed (see Figure 5).

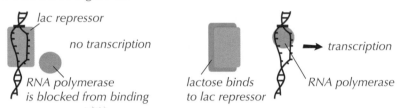

Figure 5: Lactose can activate transcription by stopping the lac repressor from binding to the DNA, so that RNA polymerase can bind instead.

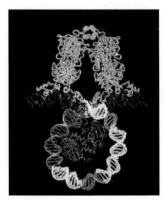

Figure 6: Molecular model of the lac repressor (pink) binding to DNA.

The experiment

Different *E. coli* mutants were isolated and grown in different media, e.g. with lactose or glucose. The mutants have mutations (changes in their DNA bases, see page 184) that mean they act differently from normal *E. coli*, e.g. they produce β-galactosidase when grown with glucose.

To detect whether active (working) β-galactosidase was produced, a chemical that turns yellow in the presence of active β-galactosidase was added to the medium. The production of mRNA that codes for β-galactosidase was also measured. The results are shown in the table.

Medium	Mutant	mRNA	Colour
Glucose	Normal	No	No yellow
Lactose	Normal	Yes	Yellow
Glucose	Mutant 1	Yes	Yellow
Lactose	Mutant 1	Yes	Yellow
Glucose	Mutant 2	No	No yellow
Lactose	Mutant 2	Yes	No yellow

In mutant 1, mRNA and active β-galactosidase were produced even when they were grown with only glucose — the gene is always being expressed. This suggests that mutant 1 has a faulty *lac* repressor, e.g. in the absence of lactose the repressor isn't able to bind DNA, so transcription can occur and mRNA and active β-galactosidase are produced.

In mutant 2, mRNA is produced but active β-galactosidase isn't when lactose is present — the gene is being transcribed but it isn't producing active β-galactosidase. This suggests mutant 2 is producing faulty β-galactosidase, e.g. because a mutation has affected its active site.

Practice Questions — Application

The production of tryptophan in bacteria is controlled by a repressor. When tryptophan is present in the bacterial cell it binds to the repressor, allowing it to bind to promoters near its target genes.

A team of scientists have studied the activity of normal bacteria and bacteria that have a mutation in the tryptophan repressor gene, by measuring the amount of tryptophan mRNA present in the bacteria. Their results are shown in the table below.

Starter culture	Target mRNA (arbitrary units)
Normal bacteria in the presence of tryptophan.	0.13
Normal bacteria without tryptophan present.	9.30
Mutant bacteria in the presence of tryptophan.	9.28
Mutant bacteria without tryptophan present.	9.33

Q1 Suggest three factors that should be controlled in this experiment.

Q2 In normal bacteria, the presence of tryptophan prevents the production of more tryptophan.

a) Use evidence from the table to explain how the presence of tryptophan prevents the production of more tryptophan in normal bacteria.

b) Suggest why it is beneficial for bacteria to be able to control their tryptophan production.

Q3 Describe the results for the mutant bacteria, and suggest an explanation.

Practice Questions — Fact Recall

Q1 What are transcription factors?

Q2 What is:

a) an activator?   b) a repressor?

Q3 Explain why not all cells are affected by oestrogen.

Q4 Give two factors that determine whether oestrogen acts as an activator or as a repressor.

Q5 What is siRNA?

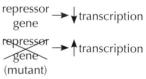

Exam-style Questions

1   A genus of bacteria that produce many important antibiotics is being investigated. One species produces a blue-coloured antibiotic. Production of the antibiotic is controlled by a transcription factor that binds to the start region of the antibiotic gene.

1 (a)   Describe the process of transcription in detail.

(6 marks)

1 (b)   Part of the DNA sequence for the transcription factor gene is shown below.

T C G C C A A C A A C A C T C G

1 (b) (i)   Give the mRNA sequence for the DNA shown above.

(1 mark)

1 (b) (ii)   The mRNA for the transcription factor is the same length as its DNA. Explain why this might be different for a eukaryotic gene.

(3 marks)

1 (c)   Scientists have produced a mutant strain of the bacteria where the same part of the transcription factor gene as given above has the following DNA sequence:

T G C C A A C A A C A C T C G

mRNA codon	Amino acid
GAA	Glutamic acid
GUG	Valine
GUU	Valine
GCG	Alanine
AGC	Serine
ACG	Threonine
UCG	Serine
UUG	Leucine

1 (c) (i)   Name the type of mutation in the sequence above.

(1 mark)

1 (c) (ii)   Using the table provided, give the mRNA and amino acid sequences for the mutant DNA sequence.

(2 marks)

1 (d)   The scientists investigated how the amounts of the transcription factor protein, antibiotic mRNA and the antibiotic itself were affected in the mutant. Their results are shown below.

Bacteria	Transcription factor protein (arbitrary units)	Antibiotic mRNA (arbitrary units)
Normal	7.9	8.2
Mutant	7.7	0.9

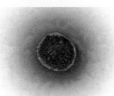 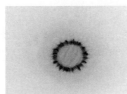

Figure 1: Antibiotic production in normal bacteria (left) and mutant bacteria (right).

1 (d) Is the transcription factor an activator or a repressor? Use the evidence provided on the previous page to explain your answer.

(4 marks)

2 Researchers have been studying the genetic code of a gene with the aim of developing a treatment for a particular genetic disease.

2 (a) (i) What is the genetic code?

(1 mark)

2 (a) (ii) The genetic code is described as universal, non-overlapping and degenerate. Explain what this means.

(3 marks)

2 (b) The genetic disease is caused by the production of a specific enzyme. Part of the enzyme's amino acid sequence is shown below. The table shows the DNA sequence for some amino acids.

Glycine — Histidine — Alanine — Proline — Histidine

Amino acid	DNA sequence
Valine	CAG
Proline	GGA
Glutamine	GTT
Histidine	GTG
Glycine	CCT
Serine	TCG
Alanine	CGT

2 (b) (i) Use the table provided to give the tRNA anticodons for the amino acid sequence shown above.

(2 marks)

2 (b) (ii) Describe how the structure of tRNA differs from mRNA.

(3 marks)

2 (c) The researchers are exploring a possible treatment for the genetic disease that would involve disrupting the process of translation.

2 (c) (i) Name the organelle that mRNA attaches to for translation to take place.

(1 mark)

(c) (ii) Give a detailed description of tRNA's role in translation.

(5 marks)

2 (d) The researchers decide to develop a treatment for the genetic disease using siRNA. Explain how siRNA works to disrupt the expression of genes.

(4 marks)

Tip: When more than two amino acids join together, they form a polypeptide chain. The sequence of amino acids in a polypeptide chain forms the primary structure of protein. The final folding of the polypeptide chain forms the tertiary structure.

5. Mutations

Genes are pretty awesome, but they're not always perfect. Their base sequence can mutate, sometimes changing the protein that gets produced.

What is a mutation?

Any change to the base sequence of DNA is called a mutation. Mutations can be caused by errors during DNA replication. They can also be caused by mutagenic agents (see next page). The types of errors that can occur include:

- **Substitution** — one base is substituted with another, e.g. ATGCCT becomes ATTCCT (G is swapped for T).

- **Deletion** — one base is deleted, e.g. ATGCCT becomes ATCCT (G is deleted).

- **Addition** or **insertion** — one or more bases are added in, e.g. ATGCCT becomes ATGACCT (A is inserted).

The order of DNA bases in a gene determines the order of amino acids in a particular protein (see p. 167). If a mutation occurs in a gene, the sequence of amino acids that it codes for could be altered.

Example

In this example, the mutation changes the sequence of amino acids.

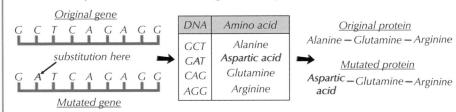

If the sequence of amino acids in a protein is altered, this may affect the protein's **tertiary structure** (its overall 3D shape). If the tertiary structure changes, the protein might not function the way it's supposed to or at all.

Mutations and proteins

Not all mutations affect the order of amino acids in a protein. The degenerate nature of the genetic code (see page 174) means that some amino acids are coded for by more than one DNA triplet (e.g. tyrosine can be coded for by TAT or TAC in DNA).

This means that not all substitution mutations will result in a change to the amino acid sequence of the protein — some substitutions will still code for the same amino acid.

Example

In this example, the mutated protein is the same as the original protein, despite the base substitution.

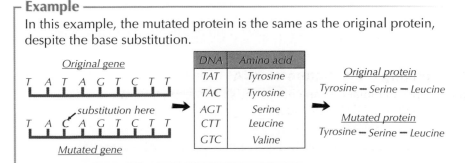

Substitution mutations won't always lead to changes in the amino acid sequence, but deletions and insertions will — deleting or inserting a base will change the number of bases present, which will cause a shift in all the base triplets after it.

Tip: Mutations that cause a shift in all the base triplets are known as frame shift mutations.

Examples

In these examples, deleting or inserting a base changes the way the base triplets are read. This means the mutated protein is different to the original protein.

Original gene

T A T A G T C T T

deletion here

T A T G T C T T

Mutated gene

DNA	Amino acid
TAT	Tyrosine
TAC	Tyrosine
AGT	Serine
CTT	Leucine
GTC	Valine

Original protein
Tyrosine — Serine — Leucine

Mutated protein
Tyrosine — Valine

Original gene

T A T A G T C T T

insertion here

T A T G A G T C T

Mutated gene

DNA	Amino acid
TAT	Tyrosine
GAG	Glutamic acid
AGT	Serine
TCT	Serine
CTT	Leucine

Original protein
Tyrosine — Serine — Leucine

Mutated protein
Tyrosine — Glutamic — Serine
acid

Exam Tip
If you get given a type of mutation you haven't seen before in the exam, don't panic — you'll be given all the information you need to answer the question. Just take your time working out the new order of triplets and amino acids.

Tip: Mutations that change a protein are often bad news (see next page). But some mutations can result in a protein that works better than the original one. If the genes that code for beneficial mutations occur in the gametes, the mutations can become more common in the population by natural selection.

Mutagenic agents

Mutations occur spontaneously, e.g. when DNA is misread during replication. But some things can cause an increase in the rate of mutations — these are called **mutagenic agents**. Ultraviolet radiation, ionising radiation, some chemicals and some viruses are examples of mutagenic agents. They can increase the rate of mutations by:

1. Acting as a base

Chemicals called base analogs can substitute for a base during DNA replication, changing the base sequence in the new DNA.

Example

5-bromouracil is a base analog that can substitute for thymine. It can pair with guanine (instead of adenine), causing a substitution mutation in the new DNA.

Tip: Remember, DNA replicates itself every time a cell divides.

2. Altering bases

Some chemicals can delete or alter bases.

Example

Alkylating agents can add an alkyl group to guanine, which changes the structure so that it pairs with thymine (instead of cytosine).

3. Changing the structure of DNA

Some types of radiation can change the structure of DNA, which causes problems during DNA replication.

Example

UV radiation can cause adjacent thymine bases to pair up together.

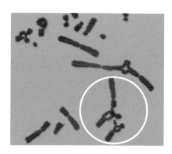

Figure 1: *The circled chromosomes have been damaged by exposure to an alkylating agent.*

Hereditary and acquired mutations

Mutations can be hereditary (you inherit them from your parents) or acquired (you develop them during your lifetime). Hereditary mutations are present in the gametes, so if a gamete is fertilised the fetus will have the mutation. Acquired mutations occur in individual cells after fertilisation (e.g. in adulthood).

Some hereditary mutations can cause **genetic disorders** — these are inherited disorders caused by abnormal genes or chromosomes, e.g. cystic fibrosis. Other hereditary mutations can increase the likelihood of developing certain **cancers**, e.g. mutations of the gene BRCA1 can increase the chances of developing breast cancer. Acquired mutations can also cause cancer. For more on how hereditary and acquired mutations cause cancer, see next page.

Tip: Make sure you understand the difference between hereditary and acquired mutations — you'll come across them again later in the section.

Tip: A hereditary mutation in the BRCA1 gene might significantly increase your chances of developing breast cancer — but it doesn't mean you definitely will develop breast cancer.

Tip: 'Asp', 'His', 'Ile', etc are just abbreviated names of amino acids, e.g. 'Asp' is short for aspartic acid.

Practice Questions — Application

The table the below shows some amino acids and the base triplets that code for them.

Base Triplet(s)	Amino Acid
GAT	Asp
CAT	His
ATA	Ile
CTT/CTC	Leu
ATG	Met
ACA	Thr
TAT	Tyr

The following letters represent part of the DNA base sequence of a gene:

CTTCATGATACA

Look at the four mutations below.

Mutation A (a base substitution): CT**C**CATGATACA

Mutation B (also a base substitution): CTTCAT**C**ATACA

Mutation C (a base deletion): CTT(-)ATGATACA

Mutation D (a base inversion): CT**CT**ATGATACA

For each of the mutations:

Q1 Give the amino acid sequence coded for by the mutated gene.

Q2 Explain what effect (if any) this may have on the protein coded for by the gene.

Tip: A base inversion is where the order of bases in a section of DNA is reversed. For example, a base inversion mutation of AT**GCAT** could give the amino acid sequence AT**TACG**.

Practice Questions — Fact Recall

Q1 What is a mutation?

Q2 Do mutations always affect the protein coded for by a gene? Explain your answer.

Q3 When might a mutation occur spontaneously?

Q4 What is a mutagenic agent?

Q5 Give an example of a mutagenic agent.

Q6 Explain the difference between hereditary and acquired mutations.

6. Mutations and Cancer

If a mutation occurs in a gene that controls cell division it can cause cancer.

Cell division and cancer

There are two types of gene that control cell division — **tumour suppressor genes** and **proto-oncogenes**. If mutations occur in these genes, it can cause uncontrolled cell division. If a cell divides uncontrollably the result is a **tumour** — a mass of abnormal cells. Tumours that invade and destroy surrounding tissue are called cancers.

Tumour suppressor genes

When functioning normally, tumour suppressor genes slow cell division by producing proteins that stop cells dividing or cause them to self-destruct (apoptosis) — see Figure 1.

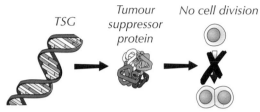

Figure 1: Action of a normal tumour suppressor gene (TSG).

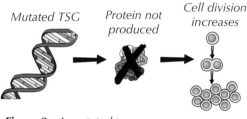

Figure 2: A mutated tumour suppressor gene (TSG) results in uncontrolled cell division.

If a mutation occurs in a tumour suppressor gene, the gene will be inactivated. The protein it codes for isn't produced and the cells divide uncontrollably (the rate of division increases) resulting in a tumour — see Figure 2.

Proto-oncogenes

When functioning normally, proto-oncogenes stimulate cell division by producing proteins that make cells divide — see Figure 3.

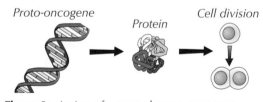

Figure 3: Action of a normal proto-oncogene.

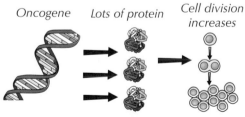

Figure 4: A mutated proto-oncogene stimulates uncontrolled cell division.

If a mutation occurs in a proto-oncogene, the gene can become overactive. This stimulates the cells to divide uncontrollably (the rate of division increases) resulting in a tumour — see Figure 4. A mutated proto-oncogene is called an **oncogene**.

Practice Questions — Application

p53 is a tumour suppressor gene. Mutations in p53 are found in over half of all cancers.

Q1 Suggest how p53 normally functions.

Q2 Suggest how mutations in p53 could lead to cancer.

Learning Objectives:

- Know that the rate of cell division is controlled by tumour suppressor genes that slow cell division and proto-oncogenes that stimulate cell division.
- Know that a mutated tumour suppressor gene is inactivated, allowing the rate of cell division to increase.
- Know that a mutated proto-oncogene, called an oncogene, stimulates cells to divide too quickly.

Specification Reference 3.5.6

Tip: Apoptosis is a type of programmed cell death. It's where cells that are infected, damaged or have reached the end of their functional life are destroyed.

Tip: Mutations in tumour suppressor genes and proto-oncogenes are often acquired (see previous page), but some are inherited.

Tip: If you're struggling to remember which gene does what, the clue is in the name. Tumour <u>suppressor</u> genes <u>suppress</u> the growth of tumours — so they're the ones that slow down cell division.

Cancer and most genetic disorders are caused by mutations (see previous two pages). Knowing whether a disorder is caused by an acquired or inherited mutation affects the prevention and diagnosis of the disorder. Identifying the specific mutation that causes a disorder in an individual affects the prevention, diagnosis and treatment. The next few pages cover some examples for each type of disorder...

Cancer caused by acquired mutations

Prevention

Knowing that cancer can be caused by acquired mutations affects prevention. If you know that acquired mutations are caused by mutagenic agents you can try to prevent cancer developing by reducing your exposure to mutagenic agents. Here are three ways mutagenic agents can be avoided:

Tip: Acquired mutations can occur spontaneously or be caused by exposure to mutagenic agents (see page 185).

Examples
- Protective clothing — people who work with mutagenic agents should wear protective clothing.
- Sunscreen — this should be worn when the skin is exposed to the Sun (UV radiation).
- Vaccination — some acquired cancers are caused by viruses, e.g. HPV (human papillomavirus) has been linked to cervical cancer. A vaccine is available that should protect women from around 80% of the viruses linked to cervical cancer. This greatly reduces the risk of developing this type of cancer.

Diagnosis

Knowing that cancer is caused by acquired mutations also affects diagnosis. Normally cancer would be diagnosed after symptoms had appeared. But by knowing the cause is an acquired mutation, high-risk individuals can be screened for cancers that the general population aren't normally screened for — or they can be screened earlier and more frequently if screening is carried out. This can lead to earlier diagnosis of cancer (before symptoms appear), which increases the chances of recovery.

Tip: See pages 221-222 for how to screen for mutations.

Examples
- People who have Crohn's disease are at a higher risk of getting colon cancer and so are screened for colon cancer.
- As women get older their risk of developing breast cancer increases. So women in high risk groups (between 50 and 70 years of age) are routinely screened for breast cancer in the UK.

Some types of cancer are often caused by a particular mutation. Knowing which specific mutation a type of cancer is usually caused by can affect diagnosis. For example, more sensitive tests can be developed, which can lead to earlier and more accurate diagnosis, improving the chances of recovery.

Example
There's a mutation in the RAS proto-oncogene in around half of all bowel cancers. Bowel cancer can be detected early by looking for RAS mutations in the DNA of bowel cells.

Treatment

Individuals diagnosed with cancer can also have the DNA from the cancerous cells analysed to see which mutation has caused it. Knowing which specific mutation the cancer is caused by affects treatment.

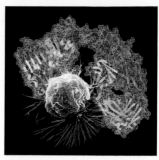

Examples

- Breast cancer caused by mutation of the HER2 proto-oncogene can be treated with a drug called Herceptin®. This drug binds specifically to the altered HER2 protein receptor and suppresses cell division and tumour growth. Breast cancer caused by other mutations is not treated with this drug as it doesn't work.

- Skin cancer caused by a mutation of the B-RAF proto-oncogene can be treated with the drug ZELBORAF™. ZELBORAF™ inhibits the mutated B-RAF enzyme — this stops cells that express the mutant from growing. Skin cancers caused by other mutations can't be treated this way.

Figure 2: *Molecular model of Herceptin® (green) and a breast cancer cell (pink).*

The aggressiveness of the treatment can also differ depending on the mutation. For example, if the mutation is known to cause an aggressive (fast-growing) cancer it may be treated with higher doses of radiotherapy or by removing larger areas of the tumour and surrounding tissue during surgery.

If the specific mutation is known, **gene therapy** may be able to treat it. For example, if you know it's caused by inactivated tumour suppressor genes (see page 187), gene therapy could be used to provide working versions of the genes.

Tip: Gene therapy involves altering the defective genes inside cells to treat genetic disorders or cancer (see page 224). Currently, gene therapy has only been used to treat cancer in clinical trials.

Cancer caused by hereditary mutations

Cancer caused by hereditary mutations usually results in a family history of a certain type of cancer. If an individual has a family history of cancer, things can be done to prevent it developing and diagnose it earlier if it does.

Prevention

Most cancers are caused by mutations in multiple genes. So people with a family history of cancer should avoid gaining extra acquired mutations by reducing exposure to mutagenic agents.

Tip: Hereditary mutations aren't usually enough to cause cancer by themselves — additional acquired mutations are also needed.

Examples

- Those with a family history of lung cancer shouldn't smoke.
- Those with a family history of skin cancer should be especially careful in the Sun to avoid getting sunburnt.

Individuals with a family history of cancer can have their DNA analysed to see if they carry the specific mutation. Knowing which specific mutation the cancer is caused by may affect its prevention. For example, if the mutation causes a very high risk of cancer, preventative surgery may be carried out — removing the organ the cancer is likely to affect before cancer develops.

Example

Women with a mutation in BRAC1 sometimes choose to have a mastectomy (removal of one or both breasts) to prevent breast cancer from developing.

Tip: It's very rare that such an extreme measure (like removing a breast) is taken, but a mutation in BRAC1 gives an extremely high (50-65%) chance of breast cancer developing.

Diagnosis

Screening, or increased and earlier screening, if there's a family history can lead to early detection (i.e. before symptoms appear) and increased chances of recovery.

Tip: A colonoscopy involves attaching a camera onto a long tube and passing it through the colon.

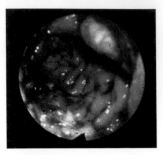

Figure 3: *Colonoscopic view of a human colon with colon cancer. Tumours appear bright red.*

Examples

- More frequent breast examinations if there's a family history of breast cancer.
- Frequent colonoscopies for those with a mutated APC gene to diagnose hereditary colon cancer earlier.

Treatment

Treatment is similar to treating cancer caused by acquired mutations (see previous page). E.g. the treatment depends on the particular mutation. But cancer caused by hereditary mutations is often diagnosed earlier, which can change the treatment used. New treatments are also being developed that are tailored to cancers caused by hereditary mutations in specific genes.

Example

Research is being conducted into a treatment for breast, pancreatic and cervical cancers caused by a faulty BRCA gene. This involves using small molecules which block an enzyme involved in repairing DNA. The molecules may be able to prevent the DNA repair in cancerous cells containing a faulty BRCA gene. This kills the cancer cells and so could provide a targeted treatment for cancers caused by BRCA mutations.

Genetic disorders

Diagnosis

Tip: A carrier has a faulty recessive allele but doesn't have any symptoms of the disorder.

Genetic disorders are caused by hereditary mutations. If a person has a family history of a genetic disorder they can have their DNA analysed to see if they have the mutation that causes it or if they are a carrier. If they're tested and diagnosed before symptoms develop, any treatment available can begin earlier.

Example

If sickle cell anaemia is diagnosed at birth, treatments that relieve symptoms and work to avoid complications can be given straight away.

Tip: Sickle cell anaemia is caused by a mutation in the haemoglobin gene. See page 221 for more.

Also, if people know they have the disorder or are a carrier, it can help to figure out if any children they have (or might have) are at risk.

Treatment

Gene therapy (see page 224) may be able to treat some genetic disorders.

Example

Cystic fibrosis is a genetic disorder caused by a mutation in the CFTR gene. Scientists have shown it's possible to treat symptoms of cystic fibrosis by inserting a normal copy of the mutated CFTR gene into a sufferer's lungs.

The treatment of genetic disorders can also be different for different mutations.

Example

The mutation that causes Huntington's disease results in an abnormally high number of CAG repeats in the HTT gene. The number of repeats varies and can affect when someone will start to display symptoms. Because of this, the exact mutation for Huntington's disease affects symptom treatment options.

Prevention

Carriers or sufferers of genetic disorders can undergo preimplantation genetic diagnosis during *in-vitro* fertilisation (IVF) to prevent any offspring having the disease. Embryos are produced by IVF and screened for the mutation. Only embryos without the mutation are implanted in the womb.

┌─ **Example** ───────────────────────────────────

Embryos produced by IVF can be screened for cystic fibrosis to make sure that only embryos without a mutation in the CFTR gene are implanted in the womb.

Tip: Preimplantation genetic diagnosis is also called embryo screening.

Practice Questions — Application

Q1 Retinoblastoma is a rare form of childhood cancer, characterised by tumours in one or both eyes. It is caused by a mutation in the RB1 tumour suppressor gene, which codes for the pRB protein.

   a) The RB1 gene has two alleles. A mutation has to occur in both RB1 alleles for retinoblastoma to develop. Suggest why this is the case.

   b) Some children with retinoblastoma inherit a mutation in one of their RB1 alleles. These children are more likely to develop further tumours than children who acquire a mutation in early childhood.

     Explain how genetic testing to determine whether a child has inherited an RB1 mutation may be beneficial.

Tip: You need to know how tumour suppressor genes and proto-oncogenes work to answer some of these questions. Take a look back at page 187 if you get stuck.

Tip: An allele is a version of a gene.

Q2 Imatinib is an anti-cancer drug that inhibits the function of CD117, a receptor protein produced by the KIT oncogene.

   a) The KIT oncogene is responsible for some gastrointestinal tumours. Suggest why a doctor will biopsy one of these tumours and test it for the presence of CD117 before deciding on a course of treatment.

   b) There are many anti-cancer drugs available that target oncogenes. They work by inhibiting the function of the oncogene protein. Developing a drug against mutated tumour suppressor genes can be more difficult. Suggest why this might be the case.

Tip: When doctors biopsy a tumour they take a small sample of cells from it to test and examine under a microscope.

Q3 Huntington's disease is an inherited disorder caused by a dominant mutation in the HTT gene. Symptoms don't usually appear until middle-age. Suggest one benefit to a person of being tested for a HTT mutation if they have a family history of Huntington's disease.

Tip: Characteristics of dominant alleles always appear in the phenotype (see page 92).

Q4 Phenylketonuria (PKU) is an inherited disorder caused by a single gene mutation. The mutation prevents the enzyme that converts phenylalanine into other substances from functioning.

Phenylalanine is an amino acid found in meat and dairy products. High levels of phenylalanine in the body can cause seizures and problems with brain development.

   a) Suggest how PKU could be treated.

   b) All babies in the UK are screened for PKU shortly after birth using the heel prick test (a blood sample is taken from the baby's heel and tested, see Figure 4).

     Suggest why this is beneficial for sufferers of PKU.

Figure 4: *The heel prick test being carried out on a new born baby.*

8. Stem Cells

Learning Objectives:

- Know that totipotent cells are cells that can mature into any body cell.

- Know that totipotent cells occur only for a limited time in mammalian embryos.

- Know that multipotent cells are found in mature mammals and that they can divide to form only a limited number of different cell types.

- Understand that during development, totipotent cells translate only part of their DNA, resulting in cell specialisation.

- Know that in mature plants, many cells remain totipotent and that they have the ability to develop *in vitro* into whole plants or into plant organs when given the correct conditions.

- Be able to interpret data relating to tissue culture of plants from samples of totipotent cells.

Specification Reference 3.5.7

All multicellular organisms stem from, err, stem cells. Every cell in your body was produced from a stem cell. So was every cell in every other multicellular organism's body. So they're pretty important.

What are stem cells?

Multicellular organisms are made up from many different cell types that are specialised for their function, e.g. liver cells, muscle cells, white blood cells. All these specialised cell types originally came from stem cells. Stem cells are unspecialised cells that can develop into other types of cell. Stem cells divide to become new cells, which then become specialised. Stem cells are also capable of dividing to produce more stem cells — this is called self-renewal.

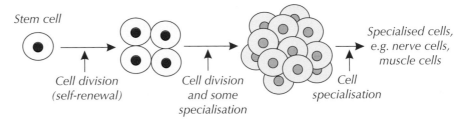

Figure 1: *Diagram showing stem cell division.*

Where are stem cells found?

All multicellular organisms have some form of stem cell. Stem cells are found in the embryo (where they become all the specialised cells needed to form a fetus) and in some adult tissues (where they become specialised cells that need to be replaced, e.g. stem cells in the bone marrow can become red blood cells).

Stem cells that can mature (develop) into any type of body cell in an organism are called **totipotent** cells. Totipotent stem cells in humans are only present in the early life of an embryo. After this point the embryonic stem cells lose their ability to specialise into all types of cells. The few stem cells that remain in mature animals are called **multipotent** stem cells. They can only develop into a few types of cells.

Becoming specialised

Stem cells become specialised because during their development they only transcribe and translate part of their DNA. Stem cells all contain the same genes — but during development not all of them are transcribed and translated (expressed). Under one set of conditions, certain genes are expressed and others are switched off. Under different conditions, different genes are expressed and others are switched off.

Genes that are expressed get transcribed into mRNA, which is then translated into proteins. These proteins modify the cell — they determine the cell structure and control cell processes (including the expression of more genes, which produces more proteins).

Changes to the cell produced by these proteins cause the cell to become specialised. These changes are difficult to reverse, so once a cell has specialised it stays specialised. This is summarised in Figure 3 on the next page.

Figure 2: *A cluster of human embryonic stem cells.*

Tip: See pages 170-173 for more on transcription and translation.

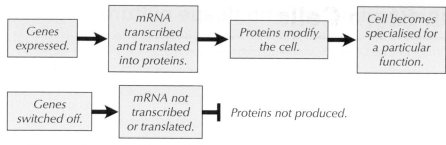

Figure 3: *Summary of how cells become specialised through gene expression.*

Tip: The process of cells becoming specialised is known as differentiation.

Tip: It's a mix of some genes being switched on and other genes being switched off that causes specialisation.

Example 1 — red blood cells

Red blood cells contain lots of haemoglobin and have no nucleus (to make room for more haemoglobin). They are produced from a type of stem cell in the bone marrow. The stem cell produces a new cell in which the genes for haemoglobin production are expressed. Other genes, such as those involved in removing the nucleus, are expressed too. Many other genes are expressed or switched off, resulting in a specialised red blood cell.

Example 2 — nerve cells

Nerve cells have long axons and dendrites (branches), which connect them to other nerve cells. They're produced from stem cells in the neural tube. The stem cells produce new cells in which the genes that direct the axon to extend outwards are expressed. Genes that direct the dendrites to form are also expressed. Many other genes are switched off.

Stem cells in plants

Mature plants also have stem cells — they're found in areas where the plant is growing, e.g. the roots and shoots. These areas are called **meristems**. Unlike in mammals (such as humans), all stem cells in plants are totipotent — they can mature into any cell type. This means they can be used to grow plant organs (e.g. roots) or whole new plants *in vitro* (artificially). Growing plant tissue artificially is called tissue culture.

Tissue culture

Here's how plant tissue culture works:

- A single totipotent stem cell is taken from a meristem.

- The cell is placed in some growth medium (e.g. agar) that contains nutrients and growth factors. The growth medium is sterile, so microorganisms can't grow and compete with the plant cells.

- The plant stem cell will grow and divide into a mass of unspecialised cells. If the conditions are suitable (e.g. the plant cells are given the right growth factors), the cells will mature (develop) into specialised cells.

- The cells grow and specialise to form a plant organ or an entire plant depending on the growth factors used.

Figure 4: *Red blood cells (top) and nerve cells (bottom) are both types of specialised cell.*

Tip: Plants produced by tissue culture are clones — they're genetically identical to the original stem cell.

Tip: See page 142 for more on growth factors.

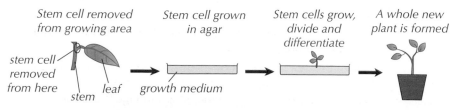

Stem cell removed from growing area — Stem cell grown in agar — Stem cells grow, divide and differentiate — A whole new plant is formed

stem cell removed from here — stem — leaf — growth medium

Figure 5: *The process of plant tissue culture.*

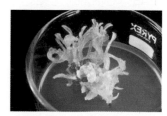

Figure 6: *Tobacco plant grown via tissue culture.*

Interpreting data on tissue culture

You might have to interpret data on tissue culture in the exam. This is the sort of thing you might get:

Exam Tip
It's not just growth factors that affect plant tissue culture — things like pH and temperature do too. You could get data involving any of these conditions in the exam — the important thing is that you're able to describe and explain it.

Example

The table below shows the results of a tissue culture experiment — samples of plant tissue were taken from a shoot and grown on media with varying ratios of the growth factors auxin and cytokinin.

Growth medium	Ratio of auxin : cytokinin	Growth after two months
1	1 : 1	Growth, but no specialised cells
2	1 : 25	Shoot formation
3	25 : 1	Root formation

- Growth medium 1 showed no specialised cell growth — so an equal ratio (1 : 1) of auxin : cytokinin promotes unspecialised cell growth.

- Growth medium 2 showed shoot formation — so a high cytokinin : auxin ratio (25 : 1) promotes the growth of specialised shoot cells.

- Growth medium 3 showed root formation — so a high auxin : cytokinin ratio (25 : 1) promotes the growth of specialised root cells.

The results of this experiment show that the ratio of these growth factors helps to control the specialisation of different tissues in this plant.

Practice Questions — Application

Gibberellin is a plant hormone associated with plant growth and stem elongation. An investigation was carried out in which equal concentrations of gibberellin were added to tissue cultures of five different plant species. These test cultures and control cultures of the same species (which were not given gibberellin) were left to grow in the same conditions for two weeks. The results are shown below.

Q1 Describe the results shown in the graph.

Q2 Based on the results, what effects does gibberellin have on plant growth in tissue culture? Suggest a possible explanation for these effects.

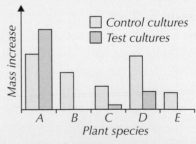

Practice Questions — Fact Recall

Q1 Give two properties of stem cells.

Q2 Where are stem cells found in mammals?

Q3 Explain the difference between totipotent and multipotent stem cells.

Q4 Describe how stem cells become specialised.

Q5 What's special about stem cells in mature plants compared to stem cells in adult mammals?

Q6 Describe how plants can be grown *in vitro* via tissue culture.

Tip: Make sure you're clear about the difference between totipotent and multipotent stem cells — even if it's not asked directly in the exam, you could need to know the difference to be able to answer other questions.

9. Stem Cells in Medicine

Stem cells can be used in medicine to treat or cure various diseases. Some stem cell therapies are already being used, others are still being developed.

Learning Objectives:

- Understand that totipotent and multipotent stem cells can be used in treating some genetic disorders.

- Be able to evaluate the use of stem cells in treating human disorders.

Specification Reference 3.5.7

Stem cell therapies in existence

Stem cells can divide into other cell types, so they could be used to replace cells damaged by illness or injury. Some stem cell therapies already exist for some diseases affecting the blood and immune system.

Bone marrow transplants

Bone marrow contains stem cells that can become specialised to form any type of blood cell. Bone marrow transplants can be used to replace the faulty bone marrow in patients that produce abnormal blood cells. The stem cells in the transplanted bone marrow divide and specialise to produce healthy blood cells.

This technique has been used successfully to treat leukaemia (a cancer of the blood or bone marrow) and lymphoma (a cancer of the lymphatic system). It has also been used to treat some genetic disorders, such as sickle-cell anaemia and severe combined immunodeficiency (SCID).

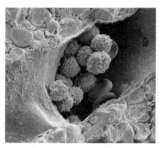

Figure 1: *Bone marrow with developing white blood cells (blue).*

> **Example — SCID**
>
> Severe combined immunodeficiency (SCID) is a genetic disorder that affects the immune system. People with SCID have a poorly functioning immune system as their white blood cells (made in the bone marrow from stem cells) are defective. This means they can't defend the body against infections by identifying and destroying microorganisms. So SCID sufferers are extremely susceptible to infections.
>
> Treatment with a bone marrow transplant replaces the faulty bone marrow with donor bone marrow that contains stem cells without the faulty genes that cause SCID. These then differentiate to produce functional white blood cells. These cells can identify and destroy invading pathogens, so the immune system functions properly.

Stem cell therapies of the future

As stem cells can divide into specialised cell types, scientists think they could be used to replace damaged tissues in a range of diseases. Scientists are researching the use of stem cells as treatment for lots of conditions, including:

- Spinal cord injuries — stem cells could be used to replace damaged nerve tissue.

- Heart disease and damage caused by heart attacks — stem cells could be used to replace damaged heart tissue.

- Bladder conditions — stem cells could be used to grow whole bladders, which are then implanted in patients to replace diseased ones.

- Respiratory diseases — donated windpipes can be stripped down to their simple collagen structure and then covered with tissue generated by stem cells. This can then be transplanted into patients.

- Organ transplants — organs could be grown from stem cells to provide new organs for people on donor waiting lists.

Tip: These treatments aren't available yet, although some of them are at the clinical trial stage of testing.

Sources of stem cells

To use stem cells scientists have to get them from somewhere.
There are two potential sources of human stem cells.

1. Adult stem cells

These are obtained from the body tissues of an adult. For example, adult stem cells are found in bone marrow. They can be obtained in a relatively simple operation — with very little risk involved, but quite a lot of discomfort. Adult stem cells aren't as flexible as embryonic stem cells (see below) — they can only specialise into a limited range of cells, not all body cell types (they're multipotent). Although scientists are trying to find ways to make adult stem cells specialise into any cell type.

2. Embryonic stem cells

These are obtained from embryos at an early stage of development. Embryos are created in a laboratory using *in vitro* fertilisation (IVF) — egg cells are fertilised by sperm outside the womb. Once the embryos are approximately 4 to 5 days old, stem cells are removed from them and the rest of the embryo is destroyed. Embryonic stem cells can develop into all types of specialised cells (they're totipotent).

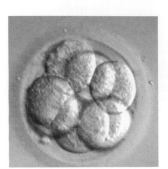

Figure 2: *A pre-implantation IVF embryo.*

Tip: Embryos in the normal sense are made when a sperm fertilises an egg. But it is possible to create an embryo by artificially stimulating an unfertilised egg cell to divide.

Exam Tip
You might have to evaluate the use of stem cells in treating human disorders in the exam. Make sure you consider both sides of the argument and balance the benefits against the possible risks.

Ethical considerations

Obtaining stem cells from embryos created by IVF raises ethical issues because the procedure results in the destruction of an embryo that could become a fetus if placed in a womb. Some people believe that at the moment of fertilisation an individual is formed that has the right to life — so they believe that it's wrong to destroy embryos.

HOW SCIENCE WORKS

Some people have fewer objections to stem cells being obtained from unfertilised embryos — embryos made from egg cells that haven't been fertilised by sperm. This is because the embryos couldn't survive past a few days and wouldn't produce a fetus if placed in a womb.

Some people think that scientists should only use adult stem cells because their production doesn't destroy an embryo. But adult stem cells can't develop into all the specialised cell types that embryonic stem cells can.

The decision makers in society have to take into account everyone's views when making decisions about important scientific work like stem cell research and its use to treat human disorders.

Tip: Rejection of transplants occurs quite often and is caused by the patient's immune system recognising the tissue as foreign and attacking it.

Tip: Adult stem cells taken from the patient's own tissues are also less likely to be rejected by the patient's body as they won't be seen as foreign.

Benefits of stem cell therapy

People who make decisions about the use of stem cells to treat human disorders have to consider the potential benefits of stem cell therapies:

- They could save many lives — e.g. many people waiting for organ transplants die before a donor organ becomes available. Stem cells could be used to grow organs for those people awaiting transplants.
- It might even be possible to make stem cells genetically identical to a patient's own cells. These could then be used to grow some new tissue or an organ that the patient's body wouldn't reject.
- They could improve the quality of life for many people — e.g. stem cells could be used to replace damaged cells in the eyes of people who are blind.

Q1 Sickle cell anaemia is an inherited disorder caused by a mutation in the haemoglobin protein. The mutated protein causes red blood cells to 'sickle' (twist into a crescent shape). The sickled cells then clump together, blocking capillaries and restricting blood flow.

All blood cells are produced from multipotent cells in the bone marrow. Describe how a bone marrow transplant could be used to cure sickle cell anaemia.

Q2 The cornea is the front part of the eye. Together with the lens, it refracts light into the eye and enables us to see.

Scientists have been able to restore loss of vision caused by damage to the cornea using stem cells taken from healthy corneas.

a) Suggest why stem cells are able to restore loss of vision in these circumstances.

b) Patients with loss of vision in one eye are treated with stem cells taken from their other, healthy eye. Suggest two benefits of this.

Q3 A team of scientists is investigating the use of embryonic stem cells in spinal cord injuries. Spinal cord injuries can cause paralysis, and patients can require long-term medical care and can have a lower quality of life. The team inject patients with embryonic stem cells taken from donated embryos left over from fertility treatment that would otherwise be discarded. If this injection works it could potentially allow for movement in the patients. There are also other treatments being developed by different teams of scientists that don't use embryonic stem cells.

Discuss the use of embryonic stem cells in this investigation.

Exam Tip
If you're asked to discuss the use of stem cells in the exam, you need to make your answer specific to the question asked to get full marks — don't just give general advantages and disadvantages.

Section Summary

Make sure you know...

- That DNA is made up of two nucleotide strands wound together forming a double helix, that mRNA (messenger RNA) is made of a single nucleotide strand and that tRNA (transfer RNA) is made of a single nucleotide strand folded into a clover shape.
- The differences in the sugar, bases and other features between DNA, mRNA and tRNA.
- That transcription is the first stage of protein synthesis and involves the production of an mRNA copy of a gene in the nucleus.
- That during transcription DNA strands separate and the enzyme RNA polymerase lines up free RNA nucleotides and assembles the mRNA strand.
- That pre-mRNA contains introns (sections of DNA that don't code for amino acids) and exons (sections of DNA that do code for amino acids). The introns are removed by splicing to form mRNA.
- That translation is the second stage of protein synthesis in which amino acids are joined together by ribosomes to make a polypeptide strand (protein) based on the order of codons in mRNA.
- That tRNA molecules carry amino acids to the ribosomes during translation.
- That the genetic code is the sequence of base triplets (codons) in mRNA which code for specific amino acids.
- That the genetic code is universal (the same base pairs code for the same amino acids in all living things), non-overlapping (codons do not share triplets) and degenerate (there are more possible combinations of triplets than there are amino acids).
- How to interpret data relating to nucleic acids and the expression of genes.
- How transcription and translation are regulated by transcription factors and siRNA.
- That oestrogen can affect translation by binding to a transcription factor.
- That mutations are changes to the base sequence of DNA, e.g. base deletions and substitutions.
- That some mutations can change the order of amino acids in a protein.
- That not all mutations change the amino acid sequence because the genetic code is degenerate.
- That mutations can occur spontaneously, e.g. if mistakes are made during DNA replication, but can also be caused by mutagenic agents (such as UV radiation, ionising radiation and certain chemicals).
- That tumour suppressor genes slow down cell division and proto-oncogenes stimulate cell division.
- That mutated tumour suppressor genes can be inactivated and fail to stop cell division. This allows cells to divide uncontrollably and may lead to cancer.
- That mutated proto-oncogenes (called oncogenes) stimulate cells to divide uncontrollably, which can lead to cancer.
- How to interpret information about proto-oncogenes and tumour suppressor genes in relation to the prevention, treatment and diagnosis of cancers.
- How to evaluate the effect on diagnosis and treatment of disorders caused by acquired mutations (including cancers) and those caused by hereditary mutations (including cancers and genetic disorders).
- That totipotent stem cells are cells that can mature (develop) into any type of body cell, but that multipotent stem cells can only mature into a few types of cells.
- That stem cells become specialised during their development by only expressing some of their genes.
- That stem cells in plants are totipotent and that tissue culture can be used to develop a whole new plant or plant organs.
- How to interpret data relating to the tissue culture of plants from samples of totipotent cells.
- That stem cells can be used in medicine to treat genetic disorders, cancer and other human disorders.
- That the two potential sources of human stem cells are adult stem cells (which are multipotent) and embryonic stem cells (which are totipotent).
- That there are many benefits to stem cell therapy, but that there are also ethical issues to consider.

Exam-style Questions

1   A mutation in the APC gene is found in the majority of colon cancers.
A smaller number have a mutation in the gene which codes for ß-catenin.

         The APC protein helps to mark ß-catenin for destruction in the cytoplasm.
This prevents ß-catenin from moving to the nucleus and activating the transcription
of genes needed for cell division. Mutations in the APC gene prevent the protein
produced from carrying out its function.

1 (a) (i)   Of the two genes described above, which is a tumour suppressor gene
and which is a proto-oncogene? Explain your answer.

(2 marks)

1 (a) (ii)   Suggest how a mutation in each of these genes could lead to cancer.

(2 marks)

1 (b)   Mutations that result in a non-functioning APC protein are usually caused
by base deletions. Explain how a deletion of one or more bases could result
in a non-functioning APC protein.

(3 marks)

1 (c)   People with a hereditary mutation in the APC gene have a condition called FAP.
FAP sufferers will almost certainly develop colon cancer by the age of forty if
preventative measures are not taken.

         Suggest one way in which knowing you have a hereditary APC mutation
could help in the prevention, diagnosis or treatment of colon cancer.

(1 mark)

2   Ethidium bromide is an intercalating agent. This means that it is capable of
inserting itself between DNA base pairs.

2 (a)   Ethidium bromide can act as a mutagenic agent.
What is a 'mutagenic agent'?

(1 mark)

2 (b)   The DNA sequence below is a short section of a gene.

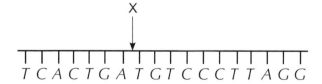

         If a molecule of ethidium bromide were to insert itself into the gene at point X,
what effect could this have on the amino acid sequence coded for by the gene?
Explain your answer.

(2 marks)

2 (c)   Some intercalating agents are used as anti-cancer drugs.
Suggest how they might work when used for this purpose.

(3 marks)

3 Alkaloids are chemicals produced by plants. They are widely used in the pharmaceutical industry. Alkaloids can be harvested from plants grown by tissue culture.

An investigation was carried out into the best time to harvest alkaloids produced via tissue culture. Alkaloids were collected from five different cultures of the same plant species. The cells in each tissue culture were at a different stage of specialisation. The results are shown in the graph below.

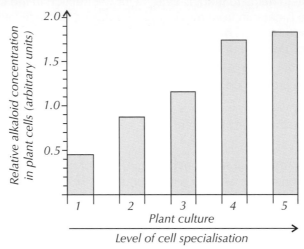

3 (a) (i) Describe the results shown in the graph.

(1 mark)

3 (a) (ii) How much higher was the alkaloid concentration in culture 5 compared to culture 1? Give your answer as a percentage.

(2 marks)

3 (b) Auxins promote cell growth and division, but high concentrations of auxins can reduce cell specialisation.

3 (b) (i) When plants are grown via tissue culture for alkaloid production, auxins are often added to the growth medium during the early stages, but removed later on. Suggest why this is the case.

(2 marks)

3 (b) (ii) Auxins can affect whether or not certain genes are expressed. Describe and explain how this could affect cell specialisation.

(5 marks)

3 (c) The density of cells in the tissue culture also affects alkaloid yield.

A separate investigation recorded the concentration of alkaloid produced by tissue cultures with cell densities of between 20 g/dm³ and 80 g/dm³. The results are shown in the table.

Cell density (g/dm³)	20	40	60	80
Concentration of alkaloid produced (arbitrary units).	0.7	1.1	1.3	1.0

What does this tell you about the effect of cell density on alkaloid production in this particular tissue culture?

(2 marks)

1. Making DNA Fragments

Gene technology allows us to study and alter genes. The first step in gene technology is often making a DNA fragment — a bit of DNA containing a gene.

Gene technology

Gene technology is basically all the techniques that can be used to study and alter genes and their function. Examples include:

- The polymerase chain reaction (PCR) — produces lots of identical copies of a specific gene (see next page).
- *In vivo* gene cloning — also produces lots of copies of a gene (see p. 205).
- DNA probes — used to identify specific genes (see page 216).

Scientists use these techniques to do many things (as well as study genes), for example, genetic engineering (see p. 209), DNA fingerprinting (see p. 212), diagnosing diseases (see p. 221) and treating genetic disorders (see p. 224).

Methods for making DNA fragments

As gene technology is all about studying genes, a good place to start is getting a copy of the DNA fragment containing the gene you're interested in (the target gene). There are three ways that DNA fragments can be produced:

Method 1 — using reverse transcriptase

Many cells only contain two copies of each gene, making it difficult to obtain a DNA fragment containing the target gene. But they can contain many mRNA molecules (see p. 168) complementary to the gene, so mRNA is often easier to obtain. The mRNA molecules can be used as templates to make lots of DNA. The enzyme **reverse transcriptase** makes DNA from an RNA template. The DNA produced is called **complementary DNA** (cDNA).

Tip: The cDNA is a complementary copy of the mRNA because of specific base pairing (except that it replaces the U in mRNA with a T) — look at p. 168 for a quick reminder.

> **Example** ────────────
> Pancreatic cells produce the protein insulin. They have loads of mRNA molecules for insulin, but only two copies of the gene itself. So reverse transcriptase could be used to make cDNA from the insulin mRNA.

To make cDNA, mRNA is first isolated from cells. Then it's mixed with free DNA nucleotides and reverse transcriptase. The reverse transcriptase uses the mRNA as a template to synthesise new strands of cDNA — see Figure 1.

Tip: You might wonder why you can't just use the mRNA copy of the gene. Well gene technology normally needs DNA as DNA is the genetic material of most organisms. Also RNA is much more unstable than DNA, which makes it a pain to work with.

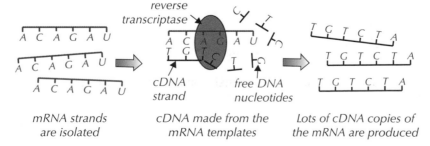

| mRNA strands are isolated | cDNA made from the mRNA templates | Lots of cDNA copies of the mRNA are produced |

Figure 1: *cDNA synthesis using reverse transcriptase.*

Method 2 — using the Polymerase Chain Reaction (PCR)

The polymerase chain reaction (PCR) can be used to make millions of copies of a fragment of DNA in just a few hours. PCR has several stages and is repeated over and over to make lots of copies — see Figure 2.

Step 1

A reaction mixture is set up that contains the DNA sample, free nucleotides, **primers** and **DNA polymerase**. Primers are short pieces of DNA that are complementary to the bases at the start of the fragment you want. DNA polymerase is an enzyme that creates new DNA strands.

Step 2

The DNA mixture is heated to 95 °C to break the hydrogen bonds between the two strands of DNA. The mixture is then cooled to 50-65 °C so that the primers can bind (anneal) to the strands.

Step 3

The reaction mixture is heated to 72 °C, so DNA polymerase can work. The DNA polymerase lines up free DNA nucleotides alongside each template strand. Specific base pairing means new complementary strands are formed.

Step 4

Two new copies of the fragment of DNA are formed and one cycle of PCR is complete. The cycle starts again — the mixture is heated to 95 °C and this time all four strands (two original and two new) are used as templates.

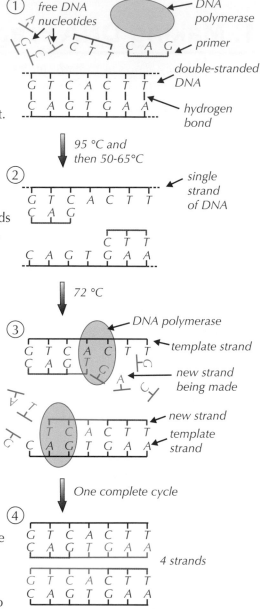

Figure 2: One cycle of the polymerase chain reaction (PCR).

Figure 3: Scientist using a programmable PCR machine.

As shown below, each PCR cycle doubles the amount of DNA, e.g. 1st cycle = 2 × 2 = 4 DNA fragments, 2nd cycle = 4 × 2 = 8 DNA fragments and so on.

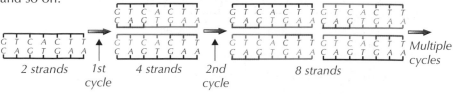

Method 3 — using restriction endonuclease enzymes

Some sections of DNA have **palindromic sequences** of nucleotides. These sequences consist of antiparallel base pairs (base pairs that read the same in opposite directions) — see Figure 4.

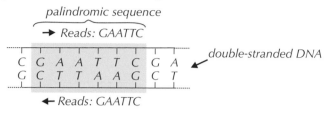

Figure 4: A palindromic DNA sequence.

Restriction endonucleases are enzymes that recognise specific palindromic sequences (known as recognition sequences) and cut (digest) the DNA at these places. Different restriction endonucleases cut at different specific recognition sequences, because the shape of the recognition sequence is complementary to an enzyme's active site.

Examples

- The restriction endonuclease *Eco*RI cuts at GAATTC.
- The restriction endonuclease *Hind*III cuts at AAGCTT.

If recognition sequences are present at either side of the DNA fragment you want, you can use restriction endonucleases to separate it from the rest of the DNA — see Figure 5. The DNA sample is incubated with the specific restriction endonuclease, which cuts the DNA fragment via a hydrolysis reaction. Sometimes the cut leaves **sticky ends** — small tails of unpaired bases at each end of the fragment. Sticky ends can be used to bind (anneal) the DNA fragment to another piece of DNA that has sticky ends with complementary sequences (there's more about this on p. 205).

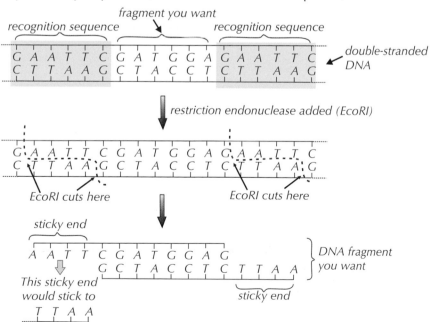

Figure 5: Using a restriction endonuclease enzyme to cut DNA.

Tip: Methods 2 and 3 will produce fragments of the whole bit of DNA you want, introns and all (see p. 171). But method 1 uses mRNA to make DNA, so you only get the coding part (exons).

Tip: Remember, the active site is where an enzyme's substrate binds. In this case, the recognition sequence is the substrate molecule.

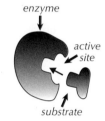

Exam Tip
Make sure you use the right words to describe these processes in the exam e.g. complementary shape not 'the same shape'.

Tip: You won't always find the same restriction enzyme site either side of the fragment you want. E.g. you might get an *Eco*RI site on one side and a *Hind*III on the other, so you'd have to incubate the DNA sample with both enzymes to cut the piece you're after.

Practice Questions — Application

Q1 A scientist wants to produce DNA copies of a gene using some mRNA as a starting template. What enzyme will she need to do this?

Q2 The following DNA fragment is being copied using PCR. The arrows mark the start of each DNA strand.

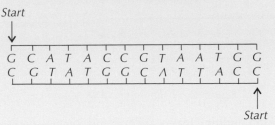

Start

G C A T A C C G T A A T G G
C G T A T G G C A T T A C C

Start

a) The scientist carrying out the PCR uses primers that are four bases long. Give the sequences of the primers he will need to use to copy the DNA fragment.

b) The scientist carries out six cycles of PCR. How many single strands of DNA will he have once the six cycles are complete?

Q3 Using information from the table below, describe and explain how restriction endonucleases could be used to cut this DNA sequence:

CAGGATCCTCCTTACATAGTGAATTCATGC

Restriction endonuclease	Recognition sequence
BamHI	*GGATCC*
HindIII	*AAGCTT*
EcoRI	*GAATTC*

Tip: Restriction endonuclease enzymes are used a lot in gene technology to cut DNA fragments, so make sure you can answer Q3 — they'll pop up again, I promise.

Exam Tip
You could easily get asked about a restriction endonuclease you haven't heard of before in the exam — but don't panic. They all work in the same basic way, so just apply what you know to the question.

Practice Questions — Fact Recall

Q1 a) What is cDNA?

b) Describe how cDNA can be made from mRNA.

c) Give one reason why cDNA is made in this way.

Q2 What does PCR stand for?

Q3 Explain what is meant by the term 'palindromic sequence'.

Q4 What are sticky ends? Why are they useful?

2. Gene Cloning

Once you've got a fragment of DNA using one of the methods on pages 201-203, you'll probably want to make more copies of it. This is done using gene cloning.

In vitro and *in vivo* gene cloning

Gene cloning is all about making loads of identical copies of a gene. This can be done using two different techniques:

- *In vitro* cloning — where the gene copies are made outside of a living organism using PCR (see page 202).

- *In vivo* cloning — where the gene copies are made within a living organism. As the organism grows and divides, it replicates its DNA, creating multiple copies of the gene (see below).

The different types of cloning are used for different reasons — these are covered on page 207.

In vivo cloning

Once you've got the DNA fragment containing the target gene you can use it for *in vivo* cloning:

Part 1 — Making recombinant DNA

The first step in *in vivo* cloning is to insert the DNA fragment into a **vector's DNA** — a vector is something that's used to transfer DNA into a cell. Vectors can be plasmids (small, circular molecules of DNA in bacteria) or bacteriophages (viruses that infect bacteria). The vector DNA is isolated and then restriction endonucleases and DNA **ligase** (an enzyme) are used to stick the DNA fragment and vector DNA together — see Figure 1.
Here's how it works:

Step 1

The vector DNA is isolated.

Step 2

The vector DNA is cut open using the same restriction endonuclease that was used to isolate the DNA fragment containing the target gene (see p. 203). This means that the sticky ends of the vector DNA are complementary to the sticky ends of the DNA fragment containing the gene.

Step 3

The vector DNA and DNA fragment are mixed together with DNA ligase. DNA ligase joins the sticky ends of the DNA fragment to the sticky ends of the vector DNA. This process is called **ligation**.

Step 4

The new combination of bases in the DNA (vector DNA + DNA fragment) is called **recombinant DNA**.

① A T C G A A T T C G A T ← *Vector DNA*
  T A G C T T A A G C T A

↓ *restriction endonuclease*

② *sticky end*
  A T C G   A A T T C G A T
  T A G C T T A A   G C T A
    sticky end

③ *sticky end*   +   *DNA fragment containing gene*
  A A T T C G A T G
        G C T A C T T A A
          sticky end

↓ *DNA ligase*

④   *Recombinant DNA*
  A T C G A A T T C G A T G A A T T C G A T
  T A G C T T A A G C T A C T T A A G C T A

Figure 1: *In vivo cloning part 1 — making recombinant DNA.*

Learning Objectives:

- Know that fragments of DNA can be used to clone genes by *in vivo* and *in vitro* techniques.

- Understand that *in vitro* cloning uses the polymerase chain reaction (PCR) to clone directly.

- Understand that *in vivo* cloning involves the use of restriction endonucleases and ligases to insert a gene into vectors, which are then transferred into host cells.

- Understand that *in vivo* cloning involves the identification and growth of transformed host cells to clone the desired DNA fragments.

- Understand the importance of "sticky ends" in *in vivo* cloning.

- Know the relative advantages of *in vivo* and *in vitro* cloning.

Specification Reference 3.5.8

Tip: If the DNA fragment was made from mRNA or PCR you'd need to incubate it with restriction enzymes to get sticky ends.

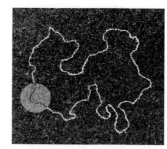

Figure 2: *Recombinant plasmid DNA. The DNA fragment containing the target gene is highlighted red.*

Part 2 — Transforming cells

The vector with the recombinant DNA is used to transfer the gene into cells (called **host cells**). Host cells that take up the vectors containing the gene of interest are said to be **transformed**. If a plasmid vector is used, host cells have to be persuaded to take in the plasmid vector and its DNA.

Example

Host bacterial cells are placed into ice-cold calcium chloride solution to make their cell walls more permeable. The plasmids are added and the mixture is heat-shocked (heated to around 42 °C for 1-2 minutes), which encourages the cells to take in the plasmids.

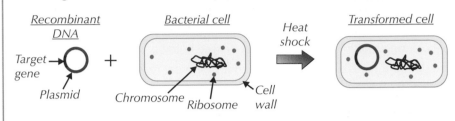

With a bacteriophage vector, the bacteriophage will infect the host bacterium by injecting its DNA into it — see Figure 3. The phage DNA (with the target gene in it) then integrates into the bacterial DNA.

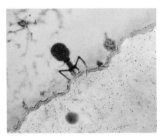

Figure 3: This isn't an alien spaceship — it's actually a bacteriophage (orange) injecting its viral DNA into an E. coli *bacterium (blue).*

Part 3 — Identifying transformed cells

Not all host cells will have taken up the vector and its DNA.
Marker genes can be used to identify the transformed cells (see Figure 5):

Step 1

Marker genes can be inserted into vectors at the same time as the gene to be cloned. This means any transformed host cells will contain the gene to be cloned and the marker gene.

Step 2

Host cells are grown on agar plates and each cell divides and replicates its DNA, creating a colony of cloned cells. Transformed cells will produce colonies where all the cells contain the cloned gene and the marker gene.

The marker gene can code for antibiotic resistance — if the host cells are grown on agar plates containing the specific antibiotic, only transformed cells that have the marker gene will survive and grow. Marker genes can also code for fluorescence — when the agar plate is placed under a UV light only transformed cells will fluoresce.

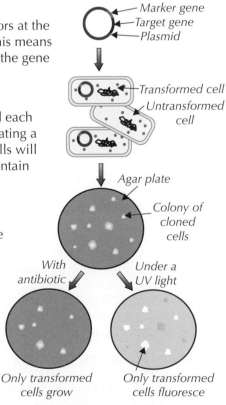

Figure 5: In vivo cloning part 3 — identifying transformed cells.

Step 3

Identified transformed cells are allowed to grow more, producing lots and lots of copies of the cloned gene.

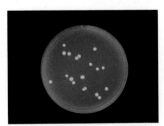

Figure 4: Fluorescing transformed bacteria colonies containing the commonly used marker gene for GFP (green florescent protein).

The advantages and disadvantages of gene cloning

Depending on the reason why you want to clone a gene, you can choose to do it either by *in vivo* cloning or *in vitro* cloning. Both techniques have advantages and disadvantages:

Tip: *In vitro* is Latin for within glass. *In vivo* is Latin for within the living. (It's because they're Latin that they're written in italics.)

In vivo cloning: the advantages

- Cloning *in vivo* can produce mRNA and protein as well as DNA because it's done in a living cell (which has the ribosomes and all the enzymes needed to produce them).

- Cloning *in vivo* can also produce modified DNA, modified mRNA or modified protein — they have modifications added to them, e.g. sugar or methyl ($-CH_3$) groups.

- Large fragments of DNA can be cloned using *in vivo* cloning, e.g. between 20 to 45 kilobases of DNA can be inserted into some plasmids and bacteriophages.

- *In vivo* cloning can be a relatively cheap method, depending on how much DNA you want to produce.

Tip: A kilobase is 1000 nucleotide bases. It's often shortened to kb.

In vivo cloning: the disadvantages

In vivo cloning also has disadvantages — the DNA fragment has to be isolated from other cell components, you may not want modified DNA, and it can be quite a slow process (because some types of bacteria grow quite slowly).

In vitro cloning (PCR): the advantages

- *In vitro* cloning can be used to produce lots of DNA (but not mRNA or protein).

- The DNA produced isn't modified (see above). This is an advantage if you don't want it to be modified.

- This technique only replicates the DNA fragment of interest (e.g. the target gene). This means that you don't have to isolate the DNA fragment from host DNA or cell components.

- *In vitro* cloning is a fast process. PCR can clone millions of copies of DNA in just a few hours.

Tip: It can be easy to think of all the techniques in this section as stand-alone, but don't. Scientists can combine them in different ways to get exactly what they want.

In vitro cloning (PCR): the disadvantages

In vitro cloning also has disadvantages — it can only replicate a small DNA fragment (compared to *in vivo*), you may want a modified product, mRNA and protein aren't made as well, and it can be expensive if you want to produce a lot of DNA.

Practice Questions — Application

Q1 A scientist is studying the role of a protein in cancer progression. He used *in vivo* cloning to transform some *E. coli* cells with recombinant DNA containing the gene that codes for the protein. He then grew the cells on an agar plate containing penicillin.

a) Suggest why the scientist didn't use *in vitro* cloning.

b) A DNA fragment containing the target gene is made using restriction endonucleases. Describe and explain how the recombinant DNA is produced using this fragment.

c) Explain why you think the cells have been grown on an agar plate containing penicillin.

Exam Tip
Because the techniques in this section can be combined in weird and whacky ways make sure you really understand why each one is used and all the details involved. Then you shouldn't be thrown in the exam if a technique is used in a context not mentioned here or in class.

Q2 Read the passage below and answer the questions that follow.

The LacZ gene is found in *E.coli*. It codes for an enzyme called β-galactosidase. β-galactosidase breaks down the colourless substance X-gal into a blue pigment.

LacZα and LacZΩ are mutated versions of the LacZ gene. Each one codes for a protein that forms part of the β-galactosidase enzyme. When the two proteins are produced in the same cell, they assemble to form a fully-functional β-galactosidase enzyme. Neither protein works as the enzyme by itself.

LacZα and LacZΩ can be used as marker genes to test whether *E.coli* have taken up recombinant DNA. The target gene is inserted into the middle of a LacZα gene on bacterial plasmids (see diagram on the right). The plasmids also contain a gene for ampicillin-resistance.

Ampicillin-resistance gene

LacZα gene

Target gene inserted into LacZα gene

Plasmid

The plasmids are taken up by *E.coli* containing a copy of the LacZΩ gene. The *E.coli* are then cultured on agar plates containing X-gal and ampicillin.

a) What is the role of the bacterial plasmids?

b) Explain why the plasmids contain an ampicillin-resistance gene.

c) *E.coli* that have taken up plasmids containing the target gene will be white. *E.coli* containing plasmids without the target gene will be blue. Explain why this is the case.

Practice Questions — Fact Recall

Q1 Name the process that *in vitro* cloning uses.

Q2 How is *in vivo* cloning different to *in vitro* cloning?

Q3 Explain what is meant by the term, 'vector'.

Q4 Give an example of a vector used in *in vivo* cloning.

Q5 What type of enzyme is used to cut DNA to give sticky ends?

Q6 Describe the role of ligases in *in vivo* cloning.

Q7 In *in vivo* cloning, what is a host cell?

Q8 What does it mean when a cell is described as being 'transformed'?

Q9 Explain the importance of identifying transformed cells in *in vivo* cloning.

Q10 What are marker genes are used for?

Q11 Give two disadvantages of *in vivo* cloning over *in vitro* cloning.

3. Genetic Engineering

This topic is important for your exams, but it's important in everyday life too — you get stories on genetically engineered crops and food popping up a lot in newspapers. Lets start with what genetic engineering really is.

What is genetic engineering?

Genetic engineering is the manipulation of an organism's DNA. It is also known as **recombinant DNA technology**. Organisms that have had their DNA altered by genetic engineering are called **transformed organisms**. These organisms have recombinant DNA — DNA formed by joining together DNA from different sources.

Microorganisms, plants and animals can all be genetically engineered to benefit humans. Transformed microorganisms can be made using the same technology as *in vivo* cloning (see page 205).

Example

Foreign DNA can be inserted into microorganisms to produce the protein insulin. Here's how:

The DNA fragment containing the insulin gene is isolated using a technique from p. 201-203.	The DNA fragment is inserted into a plasmid vector (p. 205).	The plasmid containing the recombinant DNA is transferred into a bacterium (p. 206).

AATTCCATG / GCTACTTAA

←*DNA fragment*

The insulin produced from the cloned gene is extracted and purified.

Transformed bacteria are identified and grown (see p. 206).

Transformed plants can also be produced — a gene that codes for a desirable characteristic is inserted into a plasmid. The plasmid is added to a bacterium and the bacterium is used as a vector to get the gene into the plant cells. The transformed plant will have the desirable characteristic coded for by that gene. For example, genes could be added to an important crop so that it can tolerate drought conditions.

Transformed animals can be produced too — a gene that codes for a desirable characteristic is inserted into an animal embryo. The transformed animal will have the desirable characteristic coded for by that gene. E.g. genes could be added to mosquitos to make them resistant to malaria.

The genetic engineering debate

Some people have concerns about transformed organisms (see next two pages). But producing transformed organisms can benefit humans in lots of ways (see next page). You need to understand both sides of the genetic engineering debate — then in the exam, and in everyday life, you can give a balanced opinion and make informed decisions knowing all the facts.

Learning Objectives:

- Understand how recombinant DNA technology is used to produce transformed organisms that benefit humans.

- Be able to interpret information relating to the use of recombinant DNA technology.

- Be able to evaluate the ethical, moral and social issues associated with the use of recombinant technology in agriculture, in industry and in medicine.

- Be able to balance the humanitarian aspects of recombinant DNA technology with the opposition from environmentalists and anti-globalisation activists.

Specification Reference 3.5.8

Tip: Transformed organisms are also known as genetically engineered or genetically modified (GM) organisms.

Figure 1: *Genetically engineered mice. The jellyfish gene that codes for green fluorescent protein has been inserted into the mice so they fluoresce.*

The benefits of transformed organisms

Humanitarians believe that using recombinant technology will benefit people in lots of different ways:

In agriculture

Agricultural crops can be transformed so that they give higher yields or are more nutritious. This means these plants can be used to reduce the risk of famine and malnutrition.

> **Example**
>
> Golden Rice is a variety of transformed rice. It contains one gene from maize and one gene from a soil bacterium, which together enable the rice to produce beta-carotene. The beta-carotene is used by our bodies to produce vitamin A. Golden Rice is being developed to reduce vitamin A deficiency in areas where there's a shortage of dietary vitamin A, e.g. south Asia, Africa. Vitamin A deficiency is a big problem in these areas (up to 500 000 children per year worldwide go blind due to vitamin A deficiency).

Crops can also be transformed to have resistance to pests or droughts. Pest-resistant crops need fewer pesticides, which reduces costs and any environmental problems associated with using the chemicals. Drought-resistant crops can survive in drought-prone areas with little water.

In industry

Industrial processes often use biological catalysts (enzymes). These enzymes can be produced from transformed organisms, so they can be produced in large quantities for less money, reducing costs.

> **Example**
>
> Chymosin (or rennin) is an enzyme used in cheese-making. It used to be made from rennet (a substance produced in the stomach of cows), but it can now be produced by transformed organisms. This means it can be made in large quantities, relatively cheaply and without killing any cows, making some cheese suitable for vegetarians.

In medicine

Many drugs and vaccines are produced by transformed organisms using recombinant DNA technology.

> **Example**
>
> Insulin is used to treat Type 1 diabetes and used to come from animals (cow, horse or pig pancreases). This insulin wasn't human insulin though, so it didn't work quite as well. Human insulin is now made from transformed microorganisms, using a cloned human insulin gene (see previous page).

Drugs made using recombinant DNA technology can be produced quickly, cheaply and in large quantities. This could make them more affordable and so available to more people.

The concerns about transformed organisms

Some people have ethical, moral and social concerns about the use of recombinant DNA technology (see the next page). These people include anti-globalisation activists (who oppose globalisation, e.g. the growth of large multinational companies at the expense of smaller ones.) Some environmentalists also have concerns about the possible environmental effects of the technology.

Tip: How transformed organisms can be made was covered on the previous page.

Figure 2: *Genetically engineered (transformed) Golden Rice (right) compared to normal white rice (left).*

Exam Tip
You don't need to learn these examples, but knowing them means you could quote them in an exam question about the benefits of genetic engineering.

Tip: Transformed crops could be used to make vaccines in areas where refrigeration isn't available (vaccines usually need to be stored in fridges). This would make the vaccines available to more people.

In agriculture

Farmers might plant only one type of transformed crop (this is called monoculture). This could make the whole crop vulnerable to disease because the plants are genetically identical. It could also damage the environment by reducing biodiversity.

Some people are also concerned about the possibility of 'superweeds' — weeds that are resistant to herbicides. These could occur if transformed crops interbreed with wild plants. The spreading of recombinant DNA in this way could have unknown consequences for the environment.

In industry

Without proper labelling, some people think they won't have a choice about whether to consume food made using genetically engineered organisms. Some people are worried that the process used to purify proteins (from genetically engineered organisms) could lead to the introduction of toxins into the food industry.

In medicine

Companies who own genetic engineering technologies may limit the use of technologies that could be saving lives. Also, some people worry that this technology could be used unethically, e.g. to make designer babies (babies that have characteristics chosen by their parents). This is currently illegal though.

Globally

A few, large biotechnology companies control some forms of genetic engineering. As the use of this technology increases, these companies get bigger and more powerful. This may force smaller companies out of business, e.g. by making it harder for them to compete. Anti-globalisation activists are against this.

Tip: Biodiversity describes the variety of living organisms in an area. Monoculture reduces biodiversity by reducing the number of plant species in an area. This in turn reduces the number of other species, e.g. insects, that the area can support.

Exam Tip
It can't be said enough — if you're asked about issues involved in genetic engineering, make sure you think about both sides of the debate. That means talking about the pros and cons, pluses and negatives, benefits and concerns.

Practice Questions — Application

A large agricultural company's research and development department have created transformed soybean plants that are resistant to a certain herbicide. The resistance gene was isolated from bacteria.

Q1 Explain how the transformed soybean plant could have been created.

Q2 Suggest how the transformed soybean plant may benefit humans.

Q3 Why might some people oppose the use of this transformed plant?

4. Genetic Fingerprinting

On to some gene technologies that fire the imagination (and a number of television shows). First up is genetic fingerprinting...

The principles of genetic fingerprinting

Not all of an organism's genome (all the genetic material in an organism) codes for proteins. Some of the genome consists of repetitive, non-coding base sequences — base sequences that don't code for proteins and repeat next to each other over and over (sometimes thousands of times), e.g. CATGCATGCATG is a repeat of the non-coding base sequence CATG.

The number of times these sequences are repeated differs from person to person, so the length of these sequences in nucleotides differs too. E.g. a four nucleotide sequence might be repeated 12 times in one person giving 48 nucleotides (12 × 4), but repeated 16 times in another person giving 64 nucleotides (16 × 4).

The repeated sequences occur in lots of places in the genome. The number of times a sequence is repeated (and so the number of nucleotides) at different, specific places (loci) in the genome can be compared between individuals — this is called **genetic fingerprinting**. The probability of two individuals having the same genetic fingerprint is very low because the chance of two individuals having the same number of sequence repeats at each locus in DNA is very low.

Producing genetic fingerprints

So genetic fingerprints can be compared between different individuals. Now you need to know how one is made.

Step 1 — PCR is used to make DNA fragments

A sample of DNA is obtained, e.g. from a person's blood, saliva etc. PCR (see page 202) is used to make many copies of the areas of DNA that contain the repeated sequences — see Figure 1. Primers are used that bind to either side of these repeats and so the whole repeat is amplified (copied many times). Different primers are used for each locus under investigation. You end up with DNA fragments where the length (in nucleotides) corresponds to the number of repeats the person has at each specific locus, e.g. one person may have 80 nucleotides, another person 120. A fluorescent tag is added to all the DNA fragments (usually to the primers) so they can be viewed under UV light (see next page).

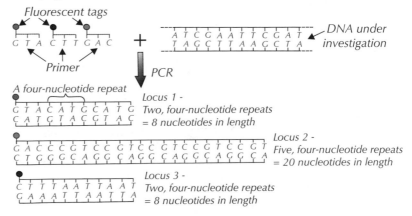

Figure 1: DNA fragments are made for fingerprint analysis by PCR.

Learning Objectives:

- Know that an organism's genome contains many repetitive, non-coding base sequences.

- Know that the probability of two individuals having the same repetitive sequences is very low.

- Understand the technique of genetic fingerprinting in analysing DNA fragments that have been cloned by PCR, and its use in determining genetic relationships and in determining the genetic variability within a population.

- Be able to explain the biological principles that underpin genetic fingerprinting techniques.

- Be able to interpret data showing the results of gel electrophoresis to separate DNA fragments.

- Be able to explain why scientists might use genetic fingerprints in the fields of forensic science, medical diagnosis and animal and plant breeding.

Specification Reference 3.5.8

Tip: A locus (plural, loci) is the fixed position of a gene on a chromosome (see p. 91).

Step 2 — Separation of the DNA fragments by gel electrophoresis

To separate out DNA fragments, the DNA mixture is placed into a well in a slab of gel and covered in a buffer solution that conducts electricity — see Figure 2 (Side view). An electrical current is passed through the gel — DNA fragments are negatively charged, so they move towards the positive electrode at the far end of the gel. Shorter DNA fragments move faster and travel further through the gel, so the DNA fragments separate according to length. This produces a pattern of bands — see Figure 2 (View of gel from above).

Tip: Fragments move through the gel in order of length, so longer fragments stay towards the top (-ve) end and shorter fragments move further down (towards the +ve end).

Tip: The positive electrode is called the anode and the negative electrode is called the cathode.

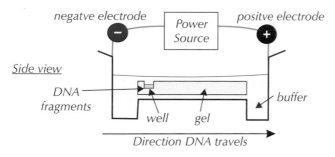

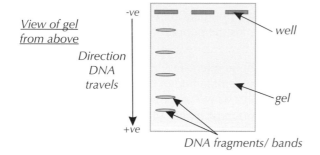

Figure 2: DNA fragments are separated by gel electrophoresis.

Step 3 — Analysis of the genetic fingerprints

After the gel has been running long enough, the equipment is turned off and the gel is placed under a UV light. Under the UV light the DNA fragments can be seen as bands. These bands make up the genetic fingerprint — see Figure 4. A ladder may have been added to one well — this is a mixture of DNA fragments of known length that allows you to work out the length of the other bands on the gel. Two genetic fingerprints can be compared, e.g. if both fingerprints have a band at the same location on the gel it means they have the same number of nucleotides and so the same number of sequence repeats at that place — it's a match.

Figure 3: A scientist loading a DNA sample into a gel.

Tip: Gels are also used to separate RNA by length or proteins according to size. (And they can be run vertically in slightly different equipment too.)

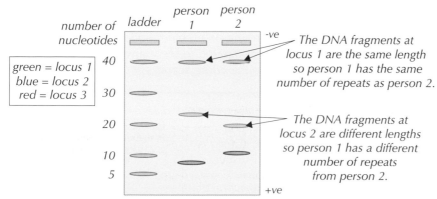

Figure 4: Diagram showing a genetic fingerprint.

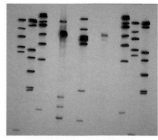

Figure 5: A genetic fingerprint.

Uses of genetic fingerprinting

1. Determining genetic relationships

We inherit the repetitive, non-coding base sequences from our parents. Roughly half of the sequences come from each parent. This means the more bands on a genetic fingerprint that match, the more closely related (genetically similar) two people are.

> **Tip:** Roughly half the bands will match in a paternity test as we inherit half our DNA from our mum and half from our dad.

Example

Paternity tests are used to determine the biological father of a child by comparing genetic fingerprints. If lots of bands match, then that person is most probably the child's father. The higher the number of places in the genome compared, the more accurate the test result. The gel on the right shows that Adult 2 is most likely the father, as six out of ten bands match.

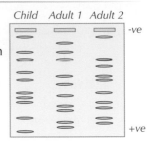

Genetic fingerprinting can also be used to look at much wider ranging genetic relationships, e.g. to see if a population of black bears found in Virginia is descended from a population in Canada or Alaska. The idea is still the same — the more bands the populations have in common, the more closely related they are.

Sometimes you might be interested in tracing only the male or female line of descent. To look at the female line of descent you need to look at DNA in mitochondria (the organelles where aerobic respiration takes place). This is because in humans and most other organisms, mitochondrial DNA (mtDNA) is only inherited from your mum. If you're after the male side, you need to look at Y chromosome DNA, as only men have a Y chromosome.

> **Tip:** Comparing mtDNA to see how closely related species are is used a lot in phylogenetics (the study of the evolution of organisms).

2. Determining genetic variability within a population

The greater the number of bands that don't match on a genetic fingerprint, the more genetically different people are. This means you can compare the number of repeats at several places in the genome for a population to find out how genetically varied that population is. E.g. the more the number of repeats varies at several places, the greater the genetic variability within a population.

3. In forensic science

Forensic scientists use genetic fingerprinting to compare samples of DNA collected from crime scenes (e.g. DNA from blood, semen, skin cells, saliva, hair etc.) to samples of DNA from possible suspects, to link them to crime scenes. The DNA is isolated from all the collected samples (from the crime scene and from the suspects). Each sample is replicated using PCR (see p. 202). The PCR products are run on an electrophoresis gel and the genetic fingerprints produced are compared to see if any match. If the samples match, it links a person to the crime scene.

> **Tip:** PCR is used to amplify the areas of DNA that contain the repeated sequences, so enough is produced for them to be seen on the gel.

> **Tip:** In fingerprint analysis in the UK, the results from ten different loci (plural for locus) are analysed. The chances of two fingerprints matching by chance is at least 1 in 1000 million.

Example

This gel shows that the genetic fingerprint from suspect C matches that from the crime scene, linking them to the crime scene. All four bands match, so suspect C has the same number of repeats (nucleotides) at four different places.

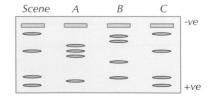

4. For medical diagnosis

In medical diagnosis, a genetic fingerprint can refer to a unique pattern of several alleles. It can be used to diagnose genetic disorders and cancer. It's useful when the specific mutation isn't known or where several mutations could have caused the disorder, because it identifies a broader, altered genetic pattern.

Example 1

Preimplantation genetic haplotyping (PGH) screens embryos created by IVF for genetic disorders before they're implanted into the uterus. The faulty regions of the parents' DNA are used to produce genetic fingerprints, which are compared to the genetic fingerprint of the embryo. If the fingerprints match, the embryo has inherited the disorder. It can be used to screen for cystic fibrosis, Huntington's disease etc.

Example 2

Genetic fingerprinting can be used to diagnose sarcomas (types of tumour). Conventional methods of identifying a tumour (e.g. biopsies) only show the physical differences between tumours. Now the genetic fingerprint of a known sarcoma (e.g. the different mutated alleles) can be compared to the genetic fingerprint of a patient's tumour. If there's a match, (i.e. the mutated alleles are the same) the sarcoma can be specifically diagnosed and the treatment can be targeted to that specific type (see pages 189-190).

5. In animal and plant breeding

Genetic fingerprinting can be used on animals and plants to prevent inbreeding, which causes health, productivity and reproductive problems. Inbreeding decreases the gene pool (the number of different alleles in a population), which can lead to an increased risk of genetic disorders, leading to health problems, etc. Since genetic fingerprinting can be used to identify how closely-related individuals are (see previous page), it can be used to identify the least related individuals in a population so that we can breed them together.

Genetic fingerprinting can also be used by animal breeders to prove pedigree (who an animal's parents and other descendents are). Animals with a good pedigree will sell for more money. E.g. the offspring of Crufts or Grand National winners can sell for a lot of money if you can prove their pedigree.

Tip: The type of genetic fingerprinting used in medical diagnosis is slightly different to the one described on pages 213-215, but don't worry — you just need to know why genetic fingerprinting is important for medical diagnosis.

Tip: Genetic disorders and cancer are both caused by mutations in DNA — see page 186 for more.

Tip: A specific mutation can be found using gene probes and sequencing (see p. 216-219).

Practice Questions — Application

A young woman has come forward claiming to be the long lost daughter of a wealthy diplomat. Scientists have used genetic fingerprinting to produce the gel shown below.

Q1 Explain how the structure of an organism's genome allows a genetic fingerprint to be made.

Q2 For what purpose during the genetic fingerprinting procedure would the scientists have used the following:

a) PCR,

b) gel electrophoresis?

Q3 Do you believe the woman is the daughter of the diplomat? Explain your answer.

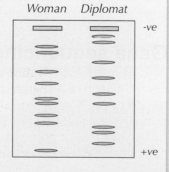

Exam Tip
In the exam, you could get a question about genetic fingerprinting in any of a huge range of contexts. So make sure you understand and can explain how it works, and are able to describe all its possible uses.

5. Locating and Sequencing Genes

Gene sequencing means finding out the order of bases in a gene. But before you can sequence a gene, you need to be able to locate it...

Locating genes using DNA probes

DNA probes can be used to locate genes (e.g. on chromosomes) or see if a person's DNA contains a mutated gene (e.g. a gene that causes a genetic disorder). DNA (gene) probes are short single strands of DNA — see Figure 1. They have a specific base sequence that's complementary to the base sequence of part of a target gene (the gene you're looking for, e.g. a gene that causes a genetic disorder). This means a DNA probe will **hybridise** (bind) to the target gene if it's present in a sample of DNA.

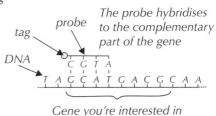

Figure 1: A DNA probe.

A DNA probe also has a label attached, so that it can be detected. The two most common labels are a radioactive label (detected using X-ray film) or a fluorescent label (detected using UV light). Figure 2 and the text below explain how fluorescently labelled probes are used:

Step 1

A sample of DNA is digested into fragments using restriction enzymes (see page 203) and separated using electrophoresis (see page 213).

Step 2

The separated DNA fragments are then transferred to a nylon membrane and incubated with a fluorescently labelled DNA probe. If the gene is present, the DNA probe will hybridise (bind) to it.

Step 3

The membrane is then exposed to UV light and if the gene is present there will be a fluorescent band. E.g. the DNA in fragment X contains the target gene.

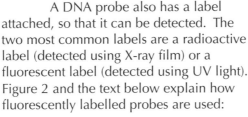

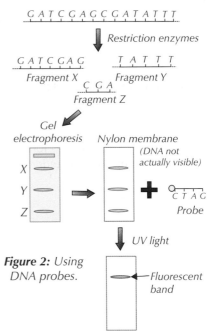

Figure 2: Using DNA probes.

Figure 3: Human chromosomes (red) with DNA probes (yellow) hybridised to complementary base sequences.

Gene sequencing techniques

Once you've located a gene you can get on with sequencing it. Most genes are too long to be sequenced all in one go though, so they're cut into smaller sections using restriction enzymes. The smaller sections are then sequenced using DNA sequencing (see pages 218-219) and put back in the correct order, so the entire gene sequence can be read in the right order. Restriction mapping is the technique used to do this (see next page).

Restriction mapping

Different restriction endonuclease enzymes are used to cut labelled DNA into fragments. The DNA fragments are then separated by electrophoresis (see page 213). The lengths of the fragments produced are used to determine the relative locations of cut sites. Once these are known, a **restriction map** of the original DNA can be made — this is a diagram of the piece of DNA showing the different cut sites, and so where the recognition sites of the restriction enzymes used to cut the DNA are found.

Tip: There's more on restriction endonucleases and recognition sites on page 203.

Example 1

Some DNA, 6 kilobases long, was radioactively labelled. The DNA was digested using the restriction enzyme *Eco*RI, and the digested fragments were separated using electrophoresis — see Figure 4. The information in the gel was used to draw a restriction enzyme map of the DNA.

The gel shows that the DNA was cut into two fragments (one 4 kb long and one 2 kb long), so there's a *Eco*RI recognition sequence in one of two places:

Figure 4: Gel electrophoresis diagram.

Exam Tip
Don't be confused if a gel looks different in the exam to the diagrams in this book. The principles are all still the same.

From the radioactive lane in the gel, you can see that only the 4 kb piece is radioactive. This means that the tag must be on the 4 kb piece. So the *Eco*RI recognition site must be 4 kb from the tag and the restriction map must be:

Tip: Remember, kb means kilobase (1000 nucleotide bases).

Example 2

Some DNA, 10 kilobases long, was radioactively labelled. The DNA was digested using two restriction enzymes, *Hind*III and *Eco*RI, and the digested fragments were separated using electrophoresis. The gel was used to build up a restriction map of the original DNA.

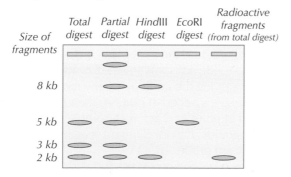

Tip: The total and partial digest columns are explained on the next page.

The gel shows that the DNA was cut into two fragments by *Hind*III, so there's one *Hind*III recognition sequence in one of two places. But because the 2 kb piece is radioactive, the label must be on the 2 kb piece. So the *Hind*III site must be 2 kb from the label.

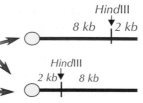

Tip: Example 2 is quite hard, so get out a piece of paper and draw out the different combinations yourself as you read through it. Sometimes scribbling different possible combinations on a piece of paper is the only way to work out restriction maps.

The gel also shows that the DNA was cut into two fragments both 5 kb long by EcoRI, so there's one EcoRI recognition sequence in the middle of the piece.

Finally, putting both of these together, the complete restriction map must be:

Take a look back at the gel on the previous page. You can see that the restriction map matches the fragments of the total digest (where both the enzymes are present and the DNA is cut at all of the recognition sites) — the radioactive label is on the 2 kb HindIII piece.

The partial digest (where the restriction enzymes haven't been left long enough to cut all of their recognition sequences) also matches. E.g. if EcoRI doesn't cut there'll be an 8 kb fragment produced.

DNA base sequencing

DNA base sequencing can be used to determine the order of bases in a section of DNA — so it can be used to sequence fragments of genes. It can be carried out by the **chain termination method**, which lets you sequence small fragments of DNA, up to 750 base pairs. Here's how it works:

Step 1

A mixture of the following is added to four separate tubes:

- A single-stranded DNA template — the DNA to be sequenced.
- DNA polymerase — the enzyme that joins DNA nucleotides together.
- Lots of DNA primer — short pieces of DNA (see p. 202).
- Free nucleotides — lots of free A, T, C and G nucleotides.
- A fluorescently-labelled modified nucleotide — like a regular nucleotide, but once it's added to a DNA strand, no more bases are added after it. A different modified nucleotide is added to each tube (these are called A*, T*, C*, G*).

Step 2

The tubes undergo PCR, which produces many strands of DNA.
The strands are different lengths because each one terminates at a different point depending on where the modified nucleotide was added.
For example look at Figure 5 on the next page — in tube A (with the modified adenine nucleotide A*) sometimes A* is added to the DNA at point 4 instead of A, stopping the addition of any more bases (the strand is terminated). Sometimes A is added at point 4, then A* is added at point 5. Sometimes A is added at point 4, A again at point 5, G at point 6 and A* is added at point 7. So strands of three different lengths (4 bases, 5 bases and 7 bases) all ending in A* are produced.

Step 3

The DNA fragments in each tube are separated by electrophoresis and visualised under UV light (because of the fluorescent label).
The complementary base sequence can be read from the gel (see Figure 5). The smallest nucleotide (e.g. one base) is at the bottom of the gel. Each band after this represents one more base added. So by reading the bands from the bottom of the gel upwards, you can build up the DNA sequence one base at a time.

Tip: Restriction mapping has lots of other uses too. E.g. you can work out if a piece of vector DNA contains your added DNA fragment (see p. 205). Vector DNA containing your DNA fragment will produce a different restriction map to vector DNA that doesn't contain the fragment.

Tip: You should be able to see where restriction mapping comes into this now. You've got a gene, say 5 kb in length to sequence. You cut it up using restriction enzymes, sequence each chunk, and then stick the sequence back in the right order using the restriction map.

Tip: It's just random chance whether the nucleotide (e.g. A) or the modified nucleotide (e.g. A*) gets added at a particular point.

Tip: Remember, the smallest DNA fragments travel the furthest through the gel — towards the positive electrode.

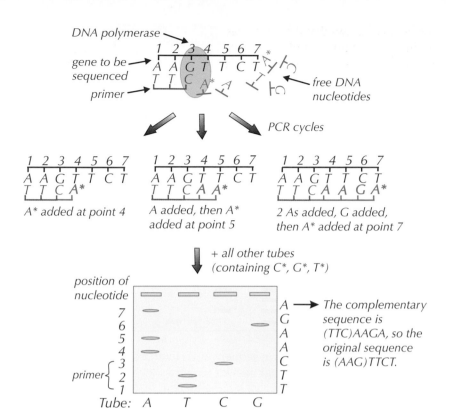

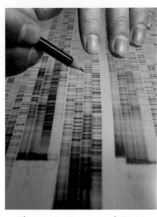

Figure 6: *An actual DNA sequencing gel.*

Figure 5: *DNA sequencing example showing what happens in Tube A (see previous page which contains A*.*

Modern DNA base sequencing

Nowadays sequencing is done altogether in one tube in an automated DNA sequencer. The tube contains all the modified nucleotides, each with a different coloured fluorescent label, and a machine reads the sequence for you. So instead of running a gel and determining the sequence from that, you get a computer read-out that looks a bit like Figure 7 (right hand diagram).

Exam Tip
The techniques described over the previous four pages can be used together to locate, restriction map and sequence a gene, or they can be used separately for lots of different reasons. So don't be put off if you get asked about them in a different context in the exam. Just remember what you've learnt about each process.

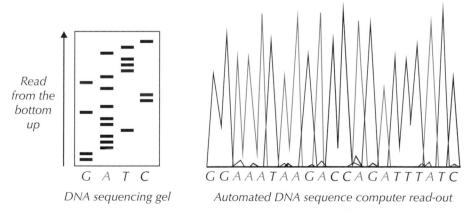

DNA sequencing gel   Automated DNA sequence computer read-out

Figure 7: *Example of a DNA sequencing gel and an automated computer read out of the same sequence.*

This means DNA sequencing is now much quicker and cheaper to carry out, which allows whole genomes to be sequenced for relatively little time and money.

Q1 A 14 kb DNA fragment is digested using restriction enzymes and the products produced run on a gel. The radioactive fragments from the total digest, partial digest, *Hind*III digest and *Bam*HI digest are shown in the radioactive fragments lane.

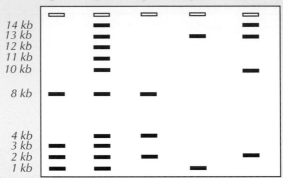

Tip: Q1b) is quite tricky, but go through it one step at a time. When you've got your answer, don't forget to double check it against the fragments in the total and partial digest lanes.

a) How many recognition sequences in total are there in the DNA fragment? Explain your answer.

b) Produce a complete restriction map of the fragment.

Q2 A species of bacteria produces a clinically useful antibiotic. Some scientists use a DNA probe to see if two other species produce similar antibiotics.
The scientists expose their nylon membrane to UV light and the results are shown in the diagram on the right.

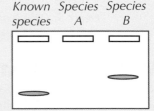

a) Explain how they carried out the experiment.
b) Do either of A or B produce a similar antibiotic?

Q1 What are DNA probes?

Q2 How can a fluorescently labelled DNA probe be used to locate a specific gene?

Q3 What is a restriction map?

Q4 Name the type of enzymes involved in restriction mapping.

Q5 In restriction mapping, what is: a) a total digest, b) a partial digest?

Q6 What is DNA base sequencing?

Q7 Describe the process of DNA base sequencing.

6. DNA Probes in Medical Diagnosis

You've learnt a bunch of interesting techniques, but you don't just need to know about them for the exam. They're useful in real life — particularly in medicine.

Medical applications of gene technology

The results from digests, cloning, mapping and sequencing genes have a wide range of uses, including medical diagnosis and treatment. For example, some disorders are caused by mutated genes (see below). If we know the sequence a gene should be and what the mutated versions are, then we can use this information to screen people for a genetic disorder. Screening basically means analysing a person's DNA to see if they have any mutations.

Mutated genes and genetic disorders

Some mutated genes can cause diseases such as genetic disorders and cancer (see page 186). Some mutated genes are useful in some situations but not in others. You need to know this example:

Example

Sickle-cell anaemia is a recessive genetic disorder caused by a mutation in the haemoglobin gene. The mutation causes an altered haemoglobin protein to be produced, which makes red blood cells sickle-shaped (crescent-shaped). The sickle red blood cells block capillaries and restrict blood flow, causing organ damage and periods of acute pain.

Some people are carriers of the disease — they have one normal and one mutated copy of the haemoglobin gene. Sickle-cell carriers are partially protected from malaria. This advantageous effect has caused an increase in the frequency of the sickle-cell allele (the mutated version of the gene) in areas where malaria is common (e.g. parts of Africa). However, this also increases the likelihood of people in those areas inheriting two copies of the sickle-cell allele, which means more people will suffer from the disease sickle-cell anaemia in these areas.

Screening for mutated genes

DNA probes (see page 216) can be used to screen for clinically important genes (e.g. the mutated sickle cell gene). To make a probe, the gene that you want to screen for is sequenced. PCR is then used to produce multiple copies of part of the gene — these are the probes. There are two main ways of screening for genes using DNA probes:

Screening for a single gene

The probe can be labelled and used to look for a single gene in a sample of DNA — this was described on page 216.

Example

A DNA sample from each of three patients was digested, separated on a gel and transferred to a nylon membrane. After incubation with a labelled fluorescent probe for a mutated gene sequence, the membrane was placed under UV light, and the results are shown opposite. Sample 3 has a visible band, so patient 3 has the mutated gene.

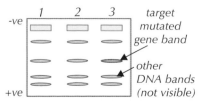

Learning Objectives:

- Know that many human diseases result from mutated genes or from genes that are useful in one context but not in another, e.g. sickle-cell anaemia.

- Know that DNA sequencing and PCR are used to produce DNA probes that can be used to screen patients for clinically important genes.

- Understand the principles of using DNA probes.

- Understand that the methods behind DNA probes are continuously updated and automated.

- Understand that information from genetic screening can be used in genetic counselling, e.g. for parents who are both carriers of defective genes and, in the case of oncogenes, in deciding the best course of treatment for cancers.

Specification Reference 3.5.8

Tip: Sickle-cell anaemia is a recessive disorder. That means you need two copies of the mutated haemoglobin allele to have the disease.

Screening for multiple genes

The probe can be used as part of a DNA **microarray**, which can screen for lots of different genes at the same time.

A DNA microarray is a glass slide (see Figure 1) with microscopic spots of different DNA probes attached to it in rows. A sample of human DNA with fluorescent labels is washed over the array. If the labelled human DNA contains any DNA sequences that match any of the probes, it will stick to the array. So this means you can screen the DNA for lots of different mutated genes at the same time.

The array is washed, to remove any fluorescently labelled DNA that hasn't stuck to it, and then visualised under UV light. Any labelled DNA attached to a probe will show up (fluoresce) — see Figure 2. Any spot that fluoresces means that the person's DNA contains that specific gene. E.g. if the probe is for a mutated gene that causes a genetic disorder, this person has the mutated gene and so has the disorder.

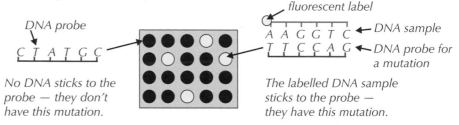

No DNA sticks to the probe — they don't have this mutation.

The labelled DNA sample sticks to the probe — they have this mutation.

Figure 2: Diagram of a DNA microarray.

Development of scientific techniques

In the past, some of the gene technologies you've learnt about in this section were labour-intensive, expensive and could only be done on a small scale. Now these techniques are often automated, more cost-effective and can be done on a large scale.

For example, using a single probe to screen for a single mutated gene (see previous page) is slow and small-scale. Now we have DNA microarrays — they're quick and can screen for thousands of genes at once (see above).

Scientific methods like this are constantly being updated and automated to be faster, cheaper, and more accurate (because there's less human error). This means medical diagnoses become faster and more accurate.

Uses of screening

Genetic screening is used for two main reasons in medicine — diagnosing genetic disorders and deciding treatment options for some disorders and diseases.

Diagnosis and genetic counselling

Genetic counselling is advising patients and their relatives about genetic disorders. It involves advising people about screening (e.g. if there's a family history of cancer) and explaining the results of a screening. Screening can help to identify the carrier of a gene, the type of mutated gene they're carrying (indicating the type of genetic disorder or cancer) and the most effective treatment.

If the results of a screening are positive (an individual has the mutation) then genetic counselling is also used to advise the patient on the options of prevention or treatment available.

Example 1

A woman with a family history of breast cancer may have genetic counselling to help her decide whether or not to be screened for known mutations that can lead to breast cancer, e.g. a mutation in the BRCA1 tumour suppressor gene. If she is screened and the result is positive, genetic counsellors might explain that a woman with the mutated BRCA1 gene has an 85% chance of developing breast cancer before the age of 70. Counselling can also help the woman to decide if she wants to take preventative measures, e.g. a mastectomy, to prevent breast cancer developing.

Tip: There's more on how identifying the mutation can affect treatment on pages 189-190.

Example 2

A couple who are both carriers of the sickle-cell allele (see page 221) may like to have kids. They may undergo genetic counselling to help them understand the chances of them having a child with sickle-cell anaemia (one in four). Genetic counselling also provides unbiased advice on the possibility of having IVF and screening their embryos for the alleles, so embryos without the mutation are implanted in the womb. It could also provide information on the help and drugs available if they have a child with sickle-cell anaemia.

Tip: Couples in this situation may be offered pre-implantation genetic haplotyping (see page 215).

Deciding treatment options

Cancers can be caused by mutations in proto-oncogenes (forming oncogenes) and mutations in tumour suppressor genes (see page 187). Different mutations cause different cancers, which respond to treatment in different ways. Screening using DNA probes for specific mutations can be used to help decide the best course of treatment.

Example

Breast cancer can be caused by a mutation in the HER2 proto-oncogene. If a patient with breast cancer is screened and tests positive for the HER2 oncogene, they can be treated with the drug Herceptin®. This drug binds specifically to the altered HER2 protein receptor and suppresses cell division. Herceptin® is only effective against this type of breast cancer because it only targets the altered HER2 receptor. Studies have shown that targeted treatment like this, alongside less-specific treatment like chemotherapy, can increase survival rate and decrease relapse rate from breast cancer.

Practice Questions — Application

A couple's first child has been born showing symptoms associated with a variety of genetic disorders. Scientists decide to screen the child to determine what specific genetic mutation his DNA contains.

Q1 Describe the process that should be used to screen the child.

Q2 The child is eventually diagnosed with a rare recessive genetic disorder. Explain why the couple might have genetic counselling.

- Understand the use of gene therapy to supplement defective genes.
- Be able to evaluate the effectiveness of gene therapy.

Specification Reference 3.5.8

7. Gene Therapy

There is a chance that in the future we'll be able to treat genetic disorders and some cancers right at the source — using gene therapy to alter the mutations that have caused it.

How does gene therapy work?

Gene therapy involves altering the defective genes (mutated alleles) inside cells to treat genetic disorders and cancer. How you do this depends on whether the disorder is caused by a mutated dominant allele or two mutated recessive alleles.

- If it's caused by two mutated recessive alleles you can add a working dominant allele to make up for them — you 'supplement' the faulty ones.
- If it's caused by a mutated dominant allele you can 'silence' the dominant allele (e.g. by sticking a bit of DNA in the middle of the allele so it doesn't work any more).

You get the 'new' allele (DNA) inside the cell by using vectors (see page 205). A range of different vectors can be used, e.g. altered viruses, plasmids or liposomes (spheres made of lipid).

Tip: If you can't remember the difference between dominant and recessive alleles, check out page 92.

The two types of gene therapy

There are two types of gene therapy:

Somatic therapy

This involves altering the alleles in body cells, particularly the cells that are most affected by the disorder.

Tip: Gene therapy isn't being used to treat people yet, but some gene therapy treatments are undergoing clinical trials.

> ┌ **Example** ─────────────────
> Cystic fibrosis (CF) is a genetic disorder that's very damaging to the respiratory system, so somatic therapy for CF targets the epithelial cells lining the lungs.

Somatic therapy doesn't affect the individual's sex cells (sperm or eggs) though, so any offspring could still inherit the disease.

Germ line therapy

This involves altering the alleles in the sex cells. This means that every cell of any offspring produced from these cells will be affected by the gene therapy and they won't suffer from the disease. Germ line therapy in humans is currently illegal though.

Tip: Sex cells are the gametes — eggs and sperm. Body cells are all the rest, e.g. skin cells, liver cells, heart cells, etc.

Advantages of gene therapy

You need to be able to evaluate gene therapy — this involves discussing the advantages and disadvantages of the technique. Up first the advantages:

- Gene therapy could prolong the lives of people with life threatening genetic disorders and cancer.
- Gene therapy could give people with genetic disorders and cancer a better quality of life if it helps to ease symptoms.
- Germ line therapy would allow the carriers of genetic disorders to conceive a baby without that disorder or risk of cancer.
- Germ line therapy could decrease the number of people that suffer from genetic disorders and cancer, which is beneficial for individuals and society as a whole (as fewer people will require treatment).

Tip: Not all of these advantages apply to both types of gene therapy.

Disadvantages of gene therapy

And now the disadvantages:

- The body could identify vectors as foreign bodies and start an immune response against them.
- An allele could be inserted into the wrong place in the DNA, possibly causing more problems, e.g. cancer.
- An inserted allele could get overexpressed, producing too much of the missing protein, and so causing other problems.
- Disorders caused by multiple genes (e.g. lots of cancers) would be difficult to treat with this technique.
- The effects of the treatment may be short-lived in somatic therapy.
- The patient might have to undergo multiple treatments with somatic therapy.
- It might be difficult to get the allele into specific body cells.

Exam Tip
If you're asked to evaluate anything in the exam you should always try to be unbiased and give both sides of the argument (advantages and disadvantages).

Tip: Gene expression is when genes are transcribed and translated into proteins (see pages 170-173). If a gene is overexpressed, this means that too much of the protein it codes for gets made.

Ethical issues surrounding gene therapy

There are also many ethical issues associated with gene therapy. For example, some people are worried that the technology could be used in ways other than for medical treatment, such as for treating the cosmetic effects of aging. Other people worry that there's the potential to do more harm than good by using the technology (e.g. risk of overexpression of genes — see the disadvantages above).

Interpreting data about the effectiveness of gene therapy (HOW SCIENCE WORKS)

In the exam you could be asked to evaluate the effectiveness of gene therapy. There's an example coming up, but you should also look at the How Science Works section (see pages 1-6) for more information about analysing evidence and drawing conclusions.

   With gene therapy questions, you might also need to think about how society might use any scientific data you're presented with to make decisions (see page 6). For example, some gene therapy might be fairly effective but it could cost an awful lot of money, so society needs to weigh up the advantages and disadvantages of the treatment.

Tip: Remember, it's not scientists who make the decisions — they just provide the information for other people to make the decisions, e.g. people in the government.

Example

Background:

X-linked severe combined immunodeficiency disease (X-linked SCID) is an inherited disorder affecting the immune system. The disorder is caused by a mutation in the IL2RG gene, located on the X chromosome. The IL2RG gene codes for a protein that's essential for the development of some immune system cells, so the sufferer is vulnerable to infectious diseases and many die in infancy.

The study:

A study was designed to investigate the effectiveness of gene therapy in patients with X-linked SCID. Ten patients were treated with a virus vector carrying a correct version of the IL2RG gene. After gene transfer, the patient's immune system was monitored for at least three years and noted as functional (good) or not. Their health was also monitored for the same time.

Figure 1: *A baby who is receiving gene therapy for SCID. The baby is kept isolated in a sterile tent so it doesn't pick up any infections.*

The results:

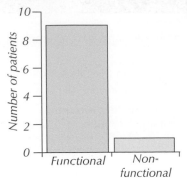

Figure 2a: Bar chart showing the state of the patients' immune systems after gene therapy.

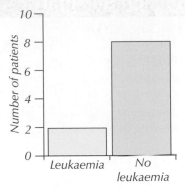

Figure 2b: Bar chart showing the clinical status of the patients within three years of gene therapy.

You might be asked to describe the data...

Figure 2a shows that nine out of the ten patients had a functional immune system after gene therapy. Figure 2b shows that two out of the ten patients developed leukaemia within 3 years of the treatment.

...or draw conclusions...

Gene therapy can be used to correct the symptoms of X-linked SCID, i.e. produce a functioning immune system. However, you can't say gene therapy can cure X-linked SCID as the study doesn't say how long the effects of the treatment lasted for. Two out of the ten patients developed leukaemia after the treatment, so there's a chance it's linked to the gene therapy (e.g. the vector could have inserted the gene into a proto-oncogene or tumour suppressor, see page 187). But you can only suggest a link as other factors may have been involved. For example, the patients could have been more genetically predisposed to develop cancer.

...or evaluate the methodology

The sample size is small — only ten patients were treated. This makes the results less reliable.

Tip: See page 5 for more about drawing conclusions.

Tip: Sample size is the number of samples in the study (e.g. the number of people) — see page 4 for more.

Practice Questions — Application

Haemophilia B is caused by a mutation in the gene for the blood clotting factor IX (FIX). Sufferers usually have FIX levels less than 1% of normal values, causing frequent bleeding and often early death. Increasing levels to greater than 1% can greatly improve patient health. Treatment usually involves FIX injections multiple times a week, which is expensive and inconvenient. A trial has investigated the use of somatic gene therapy to treat haemophilia B. Six patients were injected with a virus carrying the FIX gene. Some results are shown on the right.

Q1 Explain the role of the virus.

Q2 Calculate the average maximum FIX level after gene therapy.

Q3 Was the trial a success? Give evidence to support your answer.

Q4 Describe the possible advantages and disadvantages of this treatment.

Patient	Maximum FIX level (% of normal) after therapy
1	2
2	2
3	3
4	4
5	8
6	12

Section Summary

Make sure you know...

- That fragments of DNA (called cDNA) can be made from mRNA using reverse transcriptase.
- That fragments of DNA can also be made using the polymerase chain reaction (PCR).
- That fragments of DNA can also be isolated using restriction endonuclease enzymes. These enzymes recognise and cut DNA at different, specific palindromic recognition sequences.
- That when some restriction endonuclease enzymes cut DNA they leave sticky ends (tails of unpaired bases) that can be used to bind together DNA fragments with complementary sticky ends.
- That *in vitro* cloning is when copies of genes are made outside of a living organism using PCR.
- That *in vivo* cloning is when copies of genes are made inside a living organism, so that as the organism grows and divides it replicates its DNA, eventually creating lots of copies of the gene.
- That *in vivo* cloning involves: creating recombinant DNA (DNA made by joining together DNA from different sources), producing transformed cells (cells with recombinant DNA), and then identifying and growing transformed cells.
- The relative advantages and disadvantages of both *in vivo* and *in vitro* cloning.
- That genetic engineering (recombinant DNA technology) can be used to produce transformed organisms and the benefits of this for agriculture, industry and medicine.
- Some of the ethical, moral and social concerns about the use of genetic engineering in agriculture, industry and medicine, and be able to evaluate some of these concerns.
- How to interpret information relating to the use of genetic engineering and be able to balance the benefits of genetic engineering with the concerns and opposition from various groups.
- That genomes contain repetitive, non-coding base sequences that are used in genetic fingerprinting.
- That genetic fingerprinting involves: using PCR to make DNA fragments from a sample of DNA, running these fragments on an electrophoresis gel to separate them according to size, and then comparing the length of the fragments against other DNA samples.
- How to analyse genetic fingerprinting gels — by looking at the pattern of bands produced.
- That genetic fingerprinting can be used to determine genetic relationships and the genetic variability within a population, and is also used within the fields of forensic science, medical diagnosis, and animal and plant breeding.
- That DNA probes are short strands of DNA that can be used to locate certain sequences of DNA (e.g. target genes). A DNA probe is complementary to its target gene, so will hybridise (bind) to it.
- That most genes are very long, so in order to sequence them they must first be cut into smaller sections using restriction endonuclease enzymes, and these smaller sections are then put back in order using a restriction map.
- That DNA sequencing is used to determine the order of bases in a section of DNA and that the chain termination method is one way this can be carried out.
- That many human diseases, such as genetic disorders and cancers, can be caused by mutated genes.
- That sickle-cell anaemia is caused by a mutation in the haemoglobin gene. Carriers of this mutation (with one normal and one mutated copy of the gene) are partially protected against malaria.
- That DNA sequencing and PCR can be used to make DNA probes for mutated genes. These probes can be used to screen patients for genetic disorders and cancer mutations, and any information gained can be used in genetic counselling and to decide the best treatment options.
- That gene technologies are continuously updated and automated, so they can be carried out more quickly and on a larger scale, which also makes them more cost-effective.
- That gene therapy involves altering defective genes inside body cells (somatic gene therapy) or sex cells (germ line gene therapy), to treat or cure genetic disorders and cancer.
- How to evaluate the effectiveness of gene therapy.

Exam-style Questions

1   An agricultural company is creating a transformed wheat plant containing a gene for drought resistance. After announcing some early positive results, the company was approached by anti-genetic engineering activists. The company spoke with some of the activists to hear their concerns but continued production of the plant.

1 (a)   Do you agree with the companies decision to continue production?
Explain your answer.

(2 marks)

1 (b)   Scientist at the company produced a restriction map of the drought resistance gene.

1 (b) (i) What are restriction maps used for?

(1 mark)

1 (b) (ii) Describe how a restriction map is produced.

(5 marks)

1 (c)   The scientists used *in vivo* cloning techniques to introduce the gene into some host bacteria. The host bacteria were grown on standard agar plates to produce colonies and the colonies were then transferred to a second set of plates. The first and second sets of plates are shown in the diagram below.

Key:
A — host cells containing no marker gene
B — host cells containing marker gene but no target gene
1-7 — possible transformed cells

First plate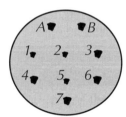

Second plates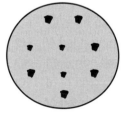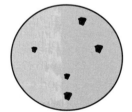

Standard agar   *Standard agar plus 250 mg/ml penicillin*

1 (c) (i) Explain why the colonies of bacteria were transferred to the second set of plates.

(3 marks)

1 (c) (ii) Explain why the bacteria in colony A were added to the plates.

(2 marks)

1 (c) (iii) Suggest one colony for use in further experiments on the transformed wheat plant. Explain your choice.

(1 mark)

2 A prize-winning race horse has been stolen from its stables. Police suspect it has been taken to a stud farm where it has previously gone to breed. The police have obtained DNA samples from four similar-looking horses at the stud farm and used them to produce genetic fingerprints to compare against a genetic fingerprint from the stolen animal. The genetic fingerprints are shown below.

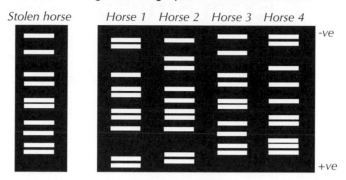

2 (a) Describe and explain how the genetic fingerprints have been produced from the DNA samples.

(5 marks)

2 (b) Use your understanding of the biology behind genetic fingerprint technology to explain why the chances of two genetic fingerprints matching by chance are so small.

(3 marks)

2 (c) Is the stolen animal at the stud farm? Explain your answer.

(1 mark)

2 (d) Compare the genetic fingerprints of horse 4 and the stolen horse. Suggest a reason for these results.

(3 marks)

2 (e) Give one other use for genetic fingerprint technology other than in forensic science.

(1 mark)

3 Scientists are cloning the gene *BtrA* so they can study the effects of the protein it codes for in a species of fish. They start by using PCR to obtain fragments of DNA containing the gene.

3 (a) Describe one other method they could use to obtain a DNA fragment.

(2 marks)

The scientists next incubate the PCR fragments with a restriction enzyme to produce sticky ends, then use *in vivo* cloning techniques to introduce the gene into a bacterial cell along with a fluorescent marker gene.

3 (b) Explain the importance of producing sticky ends for gene cloning.

(2 marks)

3 (c) Describe the *in vivo* cloning techniques used after the production of the sticky ends on the DNA fragments.

(6 marks)

3 (d) Suggest why the scientists used *in vivo* instead of *in vitro* cloning techniques.

(2 marks)

1. Exam Structure

You'll take two exams as part of A2 Biology. Everything you need to know about them is summarised below.

Unit 4 exam — Populations and environment

- There are 75 marks to be had.
- It's 1 hour 30 minutes long (so you've got just over 1 minute per mark).
- There will be 6-9 short answer questions, plus two longer questions. One of the longer questions will be **synoptic** (it'll test you on both AS and A2 material) and cover How Science Works.

Unit 5 exam — Control in cells and in organisms

- There are 100 marks in total.
- It's 2 hours 15 minutes long (again, that's just over 1 minute per mark).
- There will be 8-10 short answer questions, plus two longer questions — both of which will be synoptic. One will test your data handling skills and the other will be an essay question (see next page).

2. Command Words

Command words are just the bits of a question that tell you what to do. You'll find answering exam questions much easier if you understand exactly what they mean, so here's a brief summary table of the most common ones:

Command word:	What to do:
Give / Name / State	Give a brief one or two word answer, or a short sentence.
Define	Give the meaning of a word.
What is meant by...	Give the meaning of a word or phrase.
Describe	Write about what something's like, e.g. describe the structure of fish gills.
Explain	Give reasons for something.
Suggest	Use your scientific knowledge to work out what the answer might be.
Compare	Give the similarities and differences between two things.
Evaluate	Give the arguments both for and against an issue, or the advantages and disadvantages of something. You also need to give an overall judgement.

Some questions will also ask you to answer 'using the information provided' (e.g. a graph, table or passage of text) — if so, you must refer to the information you've been given or you won't get the marks.

Exam Tip
You'll be marked on the quality of your written communication in both exam papers. See the next page for more.

Tip: The Unit 4 exam is worth 16.7% of your A Level and the Unit 5 exam is worth 23.3%. The rest comes from an internal assessment (testing your practical and investigative skills) and from the marks you got for your AS level.

Exam Tip
When you're reading exam questions, underline the command words. That way you'll know exactly what type of answer to give.

Exam Tip
If you're answering a longer 'compare' or 'evaluate' question make a mental list of the similarities and differences or pros and cons first, so you know what you want your answer to include before you start writing.

3. Answering the Essay Question

*Answering the essay question in the Unit 5 exam is a skill in its own right —
so here are some handy hints about what to expect and how to get the marks.*

What's involved

At the end of the Unit 5 exam there's a synoptic essay question worth
25 marks. It's designed to test you on a range of material from both your AS
and A2 courses. You'll be asked to choose one of two possible topics to write
your essay about. You should aim to spend around forty minutes planning and
writing your essay, which should be enough time to write about 3-4 pages.

Getting the marks

You'll be marked on four main things:

- **Scientific content** (up to 16 marks) — this means you'll need to include
  plenty of detailed and accurate scientific facts about the topic you've
  chosen.
- **Breadth of knowledge** (up to 3 marks) — you'll need to cover a balanced
  range of material from both AS and A2.
- **Relevance** (up to 3 marks)— all the material you include must be relevant
  to your chosen topic.
- **Quality of written communication** (up to 3 marks) — you'll get marks
  for your spelling, punctuation and grammar, as well as for using scientific
  terms correctly.

Before you start your essay, it's a good idea to quickly scribble down a rough
plan — this should help you to present your ideas in a clear, logical way.
It should also stop you from repeating yourself or missing out any important
bits. Also, if you run out of time and don't quite manage to finish your essay,
you could still pick up some marks if you've done a good plan.

Exam Tip
Lots of students slip up
on this essay because
they haven't revised the
material they covered at
AS — if you want to get
good marks, AS revision
is essential.

Tip: Remember, you
need to read the essay
question carefully and
answer the question
you're asked — don't
just rehash an old essay
that you happen to have
learnt off by heart.

Exam Tip
If you include material
that's got nothing to do
with the essay title, you
could lose out on marks
for scientific content as
well as for relevance.

4. Answering Data Questions

*You'll get lots of questions about data in the exam, so you need to be a dab
hand at describing the data, drawing conclusions from it and commenting on
its reliability. It's quite a lot to get your head around, but this will help...*

Describing the data

You need to be able to describe any data you're given. The level of detail in
your answer should be appropriate for the number of marks given. Loads of
marks = more detail, few marks = less detail.

Exam Tip
It's easy to get <u>describe</u>
and <u>explain</u> mixed
up. If you're asked to
describe the data, just
state the overall pattern
or trend. If you're asked
to explain the data,
you'll need to <u>give
reasons</u> for the trend
(see next page).

┌─ **Example 1 — Experiment A** ─────────

An experiment was conducted to
investigate the effect of temperature
on the rate of photosynthesis.
The rate of photosynthesis in
Canadian pondweed was measured
at four different temperatures by
measuring the volume of oxygen
produced. All other variables
were kept constant. The results are
shown in the graph on the right.

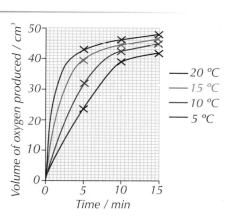

Exam Tip
You'll see data presented
in all sorts of ways in
the exam — scatter
graphs, line graphs, bar
charts, tables... Make
sure you're comfortable
interpreting all of them.

Describing the data (1 mark):
The data shows that the rate of photosynthesis increases with temperature.

Describing the data (3 marks):
The data shows that the rate of photosynthesis increases with temperature from 5 °C up to 20 °C. The pondweed at 20 °C showed the steepest increase in the rate of photosynthesis. Although the rate at all temperatures increases quickly at first, it eventually slows down with time.

Exam Tip
If you need to describe the data in detail, it's a good idea to include numbers from the graph.

Example 2 — Study B

Study B investigated the link between the number of bees in an area and the temperature of the area. The number of bees was estimated at ten 1-acre sites. The temperature was also recorded at each site. The results are shown in the scattergram on the right.

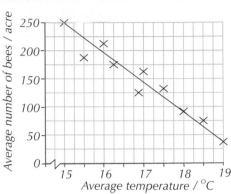

Describing the data (1 mark):
The data shows a negative correlation between the average number of bees and the temperature.

Exam Tip
If a question is only worth 1 mark, don't waste time writing more than you need to.

Tip: See page 5 for more on correlations and causal relationships.

Drawing and checking conclusions

You have to be very careful when drawing conclusions in the exam. For results that show a correlation between the variables, remember that this doesn't prove that a change in one causes a change in the other.

Example — Study B

There's a negative correlation between the average number of bees and temperature. But you can't conclude that the increase in temperature caused the decrease in bees. Other factors may have been involved, e.g. there may have been less food in some areas or more bee predators in others.

The data should always support the conclusion too. This may sound obvious but it's easy to jump to conclusions. Conclusions have to be precise — not make sweeping generalisations.

Example — Experiment A

A science magazine concluded from this data that the optimum temperature for photosynthesis is 20 °C. The data doesn't support this. The rate could be greatest at 22 °C, or 18 °C, but you can't tell from the data because it doesn't go higher than 20 °C and increases of 5 °C at a time were used. The rates of photosynthesis at in-between temperatures weren't measured.

Exam Tip
Data questions are fairly common in the exams. You might be given a conclusion for the data and asked to evaluate it — this just means you have to give reasons why it is (or isn't) a valid conclusion.

Explaining the evidence

You could also be asked to explain the evidence (the data and results) — basically this just means using your knowledge of the subject to give reasons why those results happened.

Example — Experiment A

Temperature increases the rate of photosynthesis because it increases the activity of enzymes involved in photosynthesis, so reactions are catalysed more quickly.

Commenting on reliability

If the data isn't reliable for whatever reason you can't draw a valid conclusion. Here are some of the things you'll need to think about if you're asked to comment on the reliability of an experiment or study in the exam.

1. Size of the data set

For experiments, the more repeats you do, the more reliable the data. The general rule for studies is the larger the sample size, the more reliable the data is.

> **Example — Study B**
>
> Study B is quite small — they only studied ten 1-acre sites. The trend shown by the data may not appear if you studied 50 or 100 sites, or studied them for a longer period of time.

2. Variables

The more variables you control, the more reliable your data is.

> **Example — Study B**
>
> Ideally, all the sites in Study B would have a similar type of land, similar weather, have the same plants growing, etc. Then you could be more sure that the one factor being investigated (temperature) is having an effect on the thing being measured (number of bees).

3. Data collection

Think about all the problems with the method and see if bias has slipped in. The less bias there is, the more reliable the data.

> **Example — Study B**
>
> It's not clear how the sites in study B were selected. If they weren't picked at random (e.g. by using a random number generator and random letter generator to pick the site co-ordinates on a map), then the results might not be representative of the bee population as a whole.

4. Controls

Without controls, it's very difficult to draw valid conclusions.

> **Example — Experiment A**
>
> In experiment A, the negative control would be all the equipment set up as normal but without the pondweed. If no oxygen was produced at any temperature it would show that the variation in the amount of oxygen produced when there was pondweed was due to the effect of temperature on the pondweed, and not the effect of temperature on anything else in the experiment.

5. Repetition by other scientists

For theories to become accepted as 'fact' other scientists need to repeat the work (see page 2). If multiple studies or experiments come to the same conclusion, then that conclusion is more reliable.

> **Example — Study B**
>
> If a second group of scientists repeated Study B and got the same results, the results would be more reliable.

Exam Tip
If you're asked to evaluate the method used in an experiment, you also need to comment on the same things mentioned here.

Tip: Reliability means the results can be consistently reproduced in independent experiments. See pages 3-5 for more info.

Tip: Bias can also come from the people collecting the data. For example, a company testing its own product might report the data in a way that makes it look better than it is.

Tip: There's more on control experiments and control groups on pages 3 and 4.

Exam Tip
You might be asked to evaluate the reliability of an experiment in the exam — or you might be asked to suggest ways to improve its reliability. Either way, keep these five points in mind.

Analysing the data

Sometimes it's easier to compare data by making a few calculations first, e.g. converting raw data into ratios or percentages.

Example

An agricultural scientist investigated the effect of three different pesticides on the number of pests in wheat fields. The number of pests was estimated in each of three fields, using ground traps, before and 1 month after application of one of the pesticides. The number of pests was also estimated in a control field where no pesticide had been applied.
The table shows the results.

Pesticide	Number of pests	
	Before application	1 month after application
1	89	98
2	53	11
3	172	94
Control	70	77

You could be asked to calculate the percentage change (increase or decrease) in the number of pests for each of the pesticides and the control.

Pesticide 1: $(98 - 89) \div 89 = 0.10 \times 100 = 10\%$ increase.

Pesticide 2: $(11 - 53) \div 53 = -0.79 \times 100 = 79\%$ decrease.

Pesticide 3: $(94 - 172) \div 172 = -0.45 \times 100 = 45\%$ decrease.

Control: $(77 - 70) \div 70 = 0.10 \times 100 = 10\%$ increase.

You can then use these values to describe what the data shows:

The percentage increase in pests in the field treated with pesticide 1 was the same as for the control (10% increase). Pesticide 3 reduced pest numbers by 45%, but pesticide 2 reduced the pest numbers the most (79% decrease).

Tip: Remember, ratios and percentages are used so you can <u>compare</u> different sets of data fairly.

Standard deviation

Standard deviation (SD) is a measure of the spread of values about the mean. The smaller the SD the closer all the values are to the mean.

Tip: The mean is the average. To calculate it you add up all the numbers and divide by how many values there are, e.g. for the data set 4, 9, 11 you'd do $(4 + 9 + 11) \div 3 = 8$

SDs can be shown on a graph using **error bars**. The ends of the bars show one SD above and one SD below the mean. Standard deviation can show how reliable the data is — the lower the standard deviation the more reliable it is. For example, data set 1 on the right has a smaller SD than data set 2, so it's more reliable.

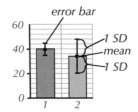

If the error bars overlap (like in the graph above) then the results aren't significantly different. If the error bars don't overlap then it's likely the difference between the results is significant and not due to chance.

Statistical significance

Statistical tests are used to analyse data mathematically. For example, a statistical test might give you a value which tells you that two sets of numbers are correlated. To find out if this correlation is statistically significant (i.e. there's a genuine link between the variables), you need to know the **probability** of the correlation happening by **chance**. If it's less than 5% (or 0.05), then you can be 95% confident that the correlation is significant and not due to chance — which is good enough for most biologists.

Tip: You won't be expected to carry out statistical tests in the exam, but you need to know why they're used.

5. Graph Skills

You should be a dab hand at all things to do with graphs by now, but if you aren't don't worry — here are some tips to help.

Reading values off graphs

If there's a key pay close attention to it — you'll be throwing away easy marks if you don't. If the graph has more than one vertical axis make sure you read off the correct one. Also, always put the units on your answer.

Exam Tip
The x-axis is horizontal, the y-axis is vertical. An easy way to remember this is that 'X' is 'a cross'.

Calculating the gradient of a graph

A little trickier is calculating the gradient of the graph:

$$\text{Gradient} = \frac{\text{Change in Y}}{\text{Change in X}} \qquad \text{Units} = \frac{Y}{X}$$

Tip: Units that are given like 'cm^{3}min^{-1}' can also be given in the form, 'cm^3/min'.

Example

Volume of oxygen produced by Canadian pondweed at 5 °C

Change in X = 5
Change in Y = 23.5

(Graph: Volume of oxygen produced / cm^3 on y-axis (0 to 50), Time / min on x-axis (0 to 15))

If you want to know the rate of this reaction over the first 5 minutes:

Gradient = rate of reaction

$$= \frac{23.5}{5} = 4.7$$

$$\text{Units} = \frac{cm^3}{min} = cm^3min^{-1}$$

So, the answer is 4.7 cm^{3}min^{-1}.

Exam Tip
If the question doesn't say what to use to calculate the gradient (e.g. 'over the first 5 minutes') then use the largest area you can from the straightest part of the graph.

Drawing graphs

Here are a few rules:

- The dependent variable should go on the y-axis (the vertical axis) and the independent on the x-axis (the horizontal axis).

- Always label the axes and include the units.

- If you need to draw a line (or curve) of best fit on a scatter graph, don't just join the points up. Instead, draw the line through or as near to as many points as possible, ignoring any anomalous results.

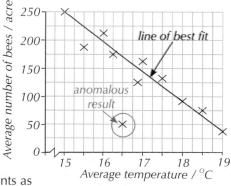

(Graph: Average number of bees / acre on y-axis (0 to 250), Average temperature / °C on x-axis (15 to 19), showing *line of best fit* and an *anomalous result*)

Tip: Repeating the measurements and calculating a mean allows you to draw a more reliable line of best fit.

- To estimate what a result outside the range that you studied might be, just extend the line of best fit then read off the data.

Answers

Unit 4

Section 1: Ecosystems and Populations

1. Ecosystems
Pages 8-9 — Application Questions
Q1 a) abiotic conditions
   The kangaroo rat is adapted to a lack of water in its habitat — which is a non-living feature, and so an abiotic condition.
   b) By producing concentrated urine the kangaroo rat is able to conserve water. This helps it to survive in deserts where there isn't much water available.
Q2 a) The length of their probosci.
   b) The new bee species would compete with the current species with a long proboscis. One species would compete more successfully until only it is left / until it has out-competed the other species.
Q3 a) Species A has a small beak length, with most individuals having a beak length of 5 mm. Species B has a longer beak, with most individuals having a beak length of 15 mm (a difference of 10 mm).
   b) The two bird species occupy different niches. Their beaks are different sizes, which could mean that they eat different sized seeds, so they wouldn't be in competition with each other.

Page 9 — Fact Recall Questions
Q1 All the organisms living in a certain area and all the non-living conditions found there.
Q2 The place where an organism lives within an ecosystem.
Q3 The role of a species within its habitat.
Q4 a) E.g. the organisms a species eats, the organisms a species is eaten by.
   b) E.g. the temperature range an organism can live in, the time of day when an organism is active.
Q5 A feature that increases an organism's chance of survival and reproduction.
Q6 a) Organisms with better adaptations are more likely to survive, reproduce and pass on the alleles for their adaptations, so the adaptations become more common in the population.
   b) natural selection

2. Variation in Population Size
Page 12 — Application Questions
Q1 the number of mice
   Remember, biotic factors are the living things in an ecosystem.
Q2 As the temperature fell, the size of the mouse population decreased. This could have been because the cold weather caused the temperature of the surroundings to fall below the body temperature of the mice. Mice are mammals, so if that had happened the mice would have used up more energy maintaining their body temperature. This would have meant less energy was available for growth and reproduction, causing their population size to fall.

Q3 As the mouse population size increased, there was more food for the owls and so the owl population grew. As the owl population increased, more mice were eaten and so the mice population began to fall. This meant there was less food for the owls, so their population decreased — and so this cycle continued.

Page 12 — Fact Recall Questions
Q1 a) All organisms of one species in a habitat.
   b) All the populations of different species in a habitat.
Q2 Interspecific competition is when organisms of different species compete with each other for the same resources. Intraspecific competition is when organisms of the same species compete with each other for the same resources.

3. Investigating Populations
Page 17 — Application Questions
Q1 a) She could place the quadrat on the ground at random locations across the field and count how much of the quadrat is covered by daisies. A square should be counted if it's more than half-covered.
   b) E.g. the student could divide the field into a grid and use a random number generator to select coordinates. The quadrat could then be placed at these coordinates and the number of daisies in each quadrat counted.
Q2 a) A beating tray could be held under a bush. The bush could then be shaken so that a sample of insects, including ladybirds, falls into it.
   b) E.g. ladybirds are flying insects, so once they landed on the beating tray they could quickly fly away.
   c) E.g. a pooter, which is a jar with a rubber bung sealing the top, and two tubes stuck through the bung. The shorter tube has mesh over the end that's in the jar and the longer tube is open at both ends. If a scientist put the pooter over a ladybird and inhaled through the shorter tube, air would be drawn through the longer tube, and the ladybird below it would be sucked in to the pooter.
Q3 a) i) $\frac{19 \times 14}{3} = 88.67 = 89$ beetles

   ii) $\frac{17 \times 21}{6} = 59.5 = 60$ beetles

   b) No. E.g. the two samples were only taken a day apart, which may not be long enough for the marked beetles to mix back in with the population. Also, the beetles were marked with white paint which might have affected their chances of survival.

Page 18 — Application Question
Q1 a) Any one from, e.g. the bank is steep so investigators should wear footwear with grip/consider changing the investigation site. / The bank may be slippery from the rain, so investigators should wear footwear with grip. / The high levels of rain might have created a risk of flooding, so investigators should check for flood warnings/consider postponing the investigation.
   b) E.g. trampling over the bank during fieldwork could destroy the water voles' burrows. This could affect their ability to survive and impact on their population. If the fieldwork involves capturing the water voles then this may cause distress to the animals, which some people don't agree with.

Page 18 — Fact Recall Questions

Q1 a) The number of individuals of one species in a particular area.

b) Where a particular species is within the area you're investigating.

Q2 Frequency, which is the number of samples a species is recorded in. Percentage cover, which is how much of the area you're investigating is covered by a species.

Q3 a) A square frame divided into a grid of 100 smaller squares by strings attached across the frame.

b) A jar that has a rubber bung sealing the top, and two tubes stuck through the bung. The shorter tube has mesh over the end that's in the jar whereas the longer tube is open at both ends.

c) A steep-sided container that is sunk in a hole in the ground with a partially open top.

Q4

$$\text{Total population size} = \frac{\text{Number caught in 1st sample} \times \text{Number caught in 2nd sample}}{\text{Number marked in 2nd sample}}$$

4. Analysing and Interpreting Distribution Data
Page 20 — Application Questions

Q1 The kite diagram shows that species A is present between 20 and 45 m from the road with a low percentage cover. It's also present between 80-140 m, and is most abundant between 130-140 m. Species B is present between 55-130 m from the road, and is most abundant between 60-85 m. Species C is present between 0-50 m from the road and is most abundant between 0-35 m.
The graph shows that soil salinity is high between 0-30 m from the road, falls sharply between 30-40 m, continues to fall until around 50 m and then remains low.

Q2 Species C, as it is present between 0-50 m from the road and is the most abundant species between 0-30 m from the road, where soil salinity is highest.

Q3 The data shows that at a high soil salinity there is an absence of species B, but this doesn't prove that salt spray from the road is the cause. Species B might be absent for other reasons, e.g. because it is out-competed by species C.

5. Human Populations
Pages 25-26 — Application Questions

Q1 a) Any two from: e.g. the birth rate has fallen because of the use of birth control and family planning. / The death rate has fallen in males because of better health care. / There's been a slight shift towards a greater proportion of males in the population than females because there could have been a social shift towards a desire for male rather than female children.

b) i) population growth rate = birth rate – death rate
= 35.4/1000 – 36.2/1000 = -0.8/1000
(-0.8 ÷ 1000) × 100 = **-0.08%**

ii) population growth rate = birth rate – death rate
= 21.3/1000 – 14.7/1000 = 6.6/1000
(6.6 ÷ 1000) × 100 = **0.66%**

c) i) The Demographic Transition Model — a graph that shows changes in birth rate, death rate and total population size for a human population over a long period of time.

ii) Stage 3, because the birth rate and death rate have fallen and population is increasing at a slow rate.

Q2 a) The population grew slowly between 1850 and 1875, from 15 million people to 20 million people. The population grew more rapidly between 1875 and 1900, from 20 million people to 40 million people. Between 1900 and 1925, the population slightly decreased to about 38 million people.

b) 20 000 000 – 15 000 000 = 5 000 000 people

$$\frac{5\ 000\ 000}{25\ \text{years}} = \textbf{200 000 people per year}$$

c) Between 1900 and 1925, because the population size falls.

Exam-style Questions — pages 27-28

1 a) Their long hind legs with strong muscles allow them to jump long distances and so escape predators *(1 mark)*. Their colour provides camouflage in the grass so they're less likely to be seen and eaten by predators *(1 mark)*.

b) Both species of grasshopper eat all four species of plant *(1 mark)*. Species A mainly eats plant species W and X, whereas species B mainly eats plant species X and Y *(1 mark)*. This suggests that although the two species of grasshopper are similar, they occupy different niches *(1 mark)*.

c) The population sizes of species A and B rise and fall cyclically over the 20 year period *(1 mark)*. The population sizes increase when resources are plentiful but decrease when resources become limited *(1 mark)*. This is because of intraspecific competition / organisms of species A are competing with each other for the same resources, and organisms of species B are competing with each other for the same resources *(1 mark)*.

d) Advantage, e.g. grasshoppers can't jump out of cages once caught/can't escape easily *(1 mark)*.
Disadvantage, e.g. the grasshoppers don't have freedom to move around as much and may become distressed *(1 mark)*.

Even though you haven't learnt specifically about cages, you can still use your common sense and your knowledge of ethical issues to come up with some sensible answers here.

2 a) i) E.g. they could set up a belt transect / place quadrats next to each other along a transect *(1 mark)* leading from the edge of the field that's next to the stream into the middle of the field *(1 mark)*.

ii) They could count how many squares of each quadrat are covered by marsh marigolds by counting a square if it's more than half-covered *(1 mark)*. Measuring percentage cover is a quick way to investigate the abundance of marsh marigolds *(1 mark)* and they wouldn't have to count all the individual marsh marigolds *(1 mark)*.

b) The non-living features of an ecosystem *(1 mark)*.

c) The graphs show that there is a positive correlation between the moisture of the soil and the abundance of marsh marigolds *(1 mark)*. There is also a positive correlation between the soil pH and the abundance of marsh marigolds *(1 mark)*. But you can't conclude from this data that all marsh marigolds will grow better in waterlogged ground, because the results are only taken from an investigation looking at one field *(1 mark)*. The results don't show a causal relationship because it's not clear whether soil moisture or soil pH has the bigger effect on marsh marigold growth *(1 mark)*. Also, there may be other factors involved that increase marsh marigold growth, e.g. fewer predators near the stream *(1 mark)*.

d) E.g. There is risk of flooding, so they should check the weather forecast before doing fieldwork to check for heavy rain which could cause the field to flood *(1 mark)*. There is a risk of falling on the boggy ground, so they should wear suitable footwear such as wellies with good grip *(1 mark)*.

There are two marks available for this question — but it's not enough to just describe two risks, you've got to come up with suggestions about how they can minimise each risk too, to get full marks.

3 a) He could use an appropriate method (e.g. pitfall trap) to capture and count a sample of snails *(1 mark)*. The snails should be marked in a harmless way and released back into their habitat *(1 mark)*. After a week, the same method should be used to collect a second sample of snails from the same population *(1 mark)*. The number of snails in the second sample, and the number in the second sample that are marked, should be counted *(1 mark)*. The population size can be estimated using the equation:

$$\text{Total population size} = \frac{\text{Number caught in 2nd sample} \times \text{Number caught in 1st sample}}{\text{Number marked in 2nd sample}}$$

(1 mark)

Try to use the correct ecological terms in your answers, for example talk about snail habitats (not 'places where snails live').

b)
$$\frac{10 \times 15}{8} = 18.75 = \textbf{19 snails} \textit{ (1 mark)}$$

Section 2: Energy Supply

1. Storing and Releasing Energy
Page 30 — Fact Recall Questions
Q1 Any three from, e.g. photosynthesis / active transport / DNA replication / cell division / protein synthesis.
Q2 A molecule of ATP is made from adenine, a ribose sugar and three phosphate groups.
Q3 a) ADP and P_i
      b) hydrolysis
Q4 Any three from, e.g. ATP stores or releases only a small, manageable amount of energy at a time, so no energy is wasted. / It's a small, soluble molecule so it can be easily transported around the cell. / It's easily broken down, so energy can be easily released. / It can transfer energy to another molecule by transferring one of its phosphate groups. / ATP can't pass out of the cell, so the cell always has an immediate supply of energy.

2. Photosynthesis and the Light-dependent Reaction
Pages 34–35 — Application Questions
Q1 a) i) proton/hydrogen ion/H^+
        ii) Because this forms a proton gradient across the membrane. Protons move down their concentration gradient, into the stroma, via an enzyme called ATP synthase. The energy from this movement combines ADP and inorganic phosphate (P_i) to form ATP.
      b) PSII / photosystem II
      c) D
      d) ATP
Cyclic photophosphorylation doesn't produce any reduced NADP or O_2 — just ATP.

Q2 a) photosystem X = photosystem II/PSII
        photosystem Y = photosystem I/PSI
      b) Light energy absorbed by PSII excites electrons in chlorophyll. This causes the electrons to move to a higher energy level (i.e. they have more energy).
      c) To transport protons into the thylakoid.
In this way a proton gradient is formed across the thylakoid membrane. As the protons move down this concentration gradient, back into the stroma, ATP is formed by ATP synthase.
      d) The electrons are transferred to NADP, along with a proton from the stroma, to form reduced NADP.

Page 35 — Fact Recall Questions
Q1 a) Coloured substances that absorb the light energy needed for photosynthesis.
      b) E.g. chlorophyll a / chlorophyll b / carotene.
Q2 hydrogen
Q3 the thylakoid membranes
Q4 ATP and reduced NADP
Q5 The process of adding phosphate to a molecule using light.
Q6 A chain of proteins through which excited electrons flow.
Q7 a) protons, electrons and oxygen
      b) To replace excited electrons in PSII.
Q8 This energy is used to transport protons into the thylakoid so that the thylakoid has a higher concentration of protons than the stroma. This forms a proton gradient across the membrane. Protons move down their concentration gradient, into the stroma, via an enzyme called ATP synthase. The energy from this movement combines ADP and inorganic phosphate (P_i) to form ATP.
Q9 a) photosystem I/PSI and photosystem II/PSII
      b) photosystem I/PSI
Q10 a) ATP, reduced NADP and oxygen
      b) ATP

3. Light-independent Reaction
Page 38 — Application Questions
Q1 Increasing the speed of rubisco could increase the production rate of glycerate 3-phosphate from ribulose bisphosphate and carbon dioxide, as rubisco catalyses this reaction. The increased production rate of glycerate 3-phosphate would increase the production rate of triose phosphate, which in turn could be converted into organic substances such as glucose more quickly.
Q2 The rate of the light-independent reaction would slow down, because the amount of ribulose bisphosphate that could be regenerated in the Calvin cycle would decrease.

Page 38 — Fact Recall Questions
Q1 a) ribulose bisphosphate (RuBP)
      b) glycerate 3-phosphate (GP)
Q2 a)

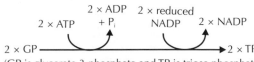

(GP is glycerate 3-phosphate and TP is triose phosphate)
      b) reduction
Q3 In the Calvin cycle ATP is needed for the reduction of glycerate 3-phosphate (GP) to triose phosphate (TP). It's also needed for the regeneration of ribulose bisphophate (RuBP) from triose phosphate.
Q4 five

Q5 a) six
Six turns of the Calvin cycle produces 12 molecules of triose phosphate (TP). Ten of these molecules (5 out of every 6) are used to make ribulose bisphosphate (RuBP) and two are used to make one hexose sugar.
b) 18
Six turns of cycle × 3 ATP molecules per turn = 18 ATP
c) 12
Six turns of cycle × 2 reduced NADP molecules per turn = 12 reduced NADP

Q6 a) Two triose phosphate molecules are joined together to produce a hexose sugar. Large carbohydrates are then made by joining the hexose sugars together.
b) Lipids are made from glycerol and fatty acids. Glycerol is synthesised from triose phosphate, while fatty acids are made from glycerate 3-phosphate.
c) Some amino acids are made from glycerate 3-phosphate, which are joined together to make proteins.

4. Limiting Factors in Photosynthesis
Page 42 — Application Questions
Q1 a) Outside plants week 2 height = 60 cm
(accept 55-65 cm).
Outside plants week 5 height = 150 cm
Difference in plant height = 150 − 60 = 90 cm
% difference in plant height =
(difference ÷ original) × 100 = (90 ÷ 60) × 100 = **150%**
Greenhouse plants week 2 height = 140 cm
(accept 135-145 cm).
Greenhouse plants week 5 height = 225 cm
(accept 220-230 cm).
Difference in plant height = 225 − 140 = 85 cm
% difference in plant height = (85 ÷ 140) × 100 = **60.7%**
b) E.g. the farmer may have increased the carbon dioxide concentration in the greenhouse by burning a small amount of propane in a carbon dioxide generator. / The farmer may have used lamps to provide light at night. / The farmer may have made use of heaters and cooling systems in order to keep a constant optimum temperature.
Q2 a) Plant B. This is because plant A has been under a green light, which is reflected by the plant, reducing the rate of photosynthesis. However, plant B has been under blue light, which is absorbed by photosynthetic pigments, increasing the rate of photosynthesis. This means plant B will have made more glucose and so had more energy for growth.
b) E.g. even though the plant is getting enough light and water, it is exposed to high temperatures of around 40°C. At these temperatures its stomata may close to avoid losing too much water. This means less carbon dioxide can enter the leaf, so photosynthesis will slow right down. In turn, the plant will produce much less glucose, which means it'll have much less energy to carry out all its life processes and may die.

5. Respiration
Page 44 — Application Questions
Q1 a) ATP
b) reduced NAD
c) inorganic phosphate (P_i)
d) triose phosphate
e) H^+ ions/hydrogen ions
Q2 a) phosphorylation
b) oxidation
Q3 The formation of 4ATP from 4ADP + 4P_i in the second part of the reaction.

Q4 a) 10
Two molecules of pyruvate are made for every molecule of glucose that enters glycolysis.
b) 10
Two molecules of reduced NAD are made for every molecule of glucose that enters glycolysis.
c) 10
Four molecules of ATP are produced for each molecule of glucose during glycolysis, but two molecules of ATP are used up in the process. So if five molecules of glucose are used, then 20 molecules of ATP are produced (5 × 4 = 20), but 10 molecules are used up (5 × 2 = 10), so the net gain of ATP molecules is 10.

Page 46 — Application Questions
Q1 a) oxaloacetate = 4C, citrate = 6C
b) Decarboxylation and dehydrogenation occur, producing one molecule of reduced FAD and two of reduced NAD. ATP is produced by substrate level phosphorylation.
Q2 24
Two molecules of carbon dioxide are produced per turn of the Krebs cycle and the Krebs cycle turns twice for each molecule of glucose. So for one molecule of glucose four molecules of carbon dioxide are produced. Therefore if six molecules of glucose were respired, 24 (6 × 4) molecules of carbon dioxide would be produced in the Krebs cycle.
Q3 Acetyl coenzyme A can enter the Krebs cycle, leading to the formation of reduced coenzymes, which are then used in oxidative phosphorylation

Page 47 — Application Question
Q1 a) Carrier 1 will be in a reduced state because it has received electrons from reduced NAD but can't pass them on. Carrier 3 will be in an oxidised state because it has passed its electrons onto oxygen, but hasn't received any more from carrier 2.
If a substance gains electrons it is reduced. If a substance loses electrons it is oxidised.
b) Antimycin A inhibits carrier 2 and so stops electrons moving down the electron transport chain. This means no more energy will be lost from electrons moving down the chain, so H^+ ions will not be transported across the inner mitochondrial membrane and the electrochemical gradient across the membrane won't be maintained. This means the synthesis of ATP by ATP synthase will stop. If a fish can't produce ATP it will die as energy from ATP is needed to fuel all biological processes.

Page 49 — Application Questions
Q1 a) anaerobically
b) two
c)
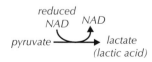
Q2 a) i) lactate/lactic acid
ii) pyruvate
iii) ethanol
b) i) A
ii) B
iii) A
c) two
Q3 Blue, because without oxygen the yeast will have respired anaerobically producing ethanol from pyruvate. This reaction uses hydrogen ions, so Janus Green B will be oxidised.

Page 50 — Fact Recall Questions

Q1 ATP is used to phosphorylate glucose, making triose phosphate.

Q2 In the oxidation of triose phosphate to pyruvate, NAD collects the hydrogen ions from triose phosphate, forming reduced NAD.

Q3 a) Pyruvate is decarboxylated — one carbon atom is removed from pyruvate in the form of carbon dioxide. Then NAD is reduced — it collects hydrogen from pyruvate, changing pyruvate into acetate.
   b) It combines with acetate to form acetyl coenzyme A.
   c) Acetyl coenzyme A enters the Krebs cycle. Reduced NAD is used in oxidative phosphorylation. Carbon dioxide is released as a waste product.

Q4 a) Two molecules of CO_2 are released — one CO_2 is released from the conversion of citrate to a 5-carbon compound and the other CO_2 is released from the conversion of the 5-carbon compound to oxaloacetate.
   b) one

Q5 substrate-level phosphorylation

Q6 a) It is reused in the link reaction.
   b) It is regenerated for use in the next Krebs cycle.

Q7 They lose energy.

Q8 oxygen

Q9 E.g. the conversion of pyruvate to acetate in the link reaction. / The conversion of citrate to the 5-carbon compound in the Krebs cycle. / The conversion of the 5-carbon compound to oxaloacetate in the Krebs cycle. *Every time CO_2 is lost in a reaction, decarboxylation is happening.*

Q10

Substance	Glycolysis	Link reaction	Krebs cycle	Oxidative phosphorylation
ATP	X		X	X
reduced NAD	X	X	X	
reduced FAD			X	
CO_2		X	X	

Exam-style Questions — pages 52-53

1 a) Alcoholic fermentation occurs / pyruvate is converted to ethanol *(1 mark)* which releases CO_2 *(1 mark)*.
   b) The smell of alcohol *(1 mark)*.
   Ethanol is the final product in alcoholic fermentation.
   c) i) The production of ethanol (from ethanal) regenerates NAD *(1 mark)*, which is then used in the reactions of glycolysis *(1 mark)*.
   b) ii) Lactate fermentation occurs / pyruvate is converted to lactate *(1 mark)* and NAD is produced *(1 mark)*.
   d) The second experiment because more ATP is made in aerobic respiration than anaerobic respiration *(1 mark)*.

2 a) i) The oxidation of triose phosphate to pyruvate produces one molecule of reduced NAD *(1 mark)*. The conversion of pyruvate to acetate produces one molecule of reduced NAD *(1 mark)*. The conversion of citrate to a 5-carbon compound in the Krebs cycle produces one molecule of reduced NAD *(1 mark)*. The conversion of this 5-carbon compound to oxaloacetate produces another two molecules of reduced NAD *(1 mark)* and one molecule of reduced FAD *(1 mark)*.
   ii) The electrons move along the electron transport chain *(1 mark)* losing energy at each electron carrier *(1 mark)*. Finally they are passed onto oxygen as it is the final electron acceptor *(1 mark)*.

b) There would be no electrochemical gradient produced across the inner mitochondrial membrane *(1 mark)*. This means there would be no movement of ions across the mitochondrial membrane to drive ATP synthase *(1 mark)* so no ATP would be made *(1 mark)*. The cells would only get ATP from anaerobic respiration *(1 mark)*.
Even though H^+ ions will still be pumped across the inner mitochondrial membrane into the intermembrane space, the uncoupler will be moving them back into the matrix at the same time — so no gradient would be produced.

3 a) In tube B light energy was absorbed by photosystem I in the chloroplasts *(1 mark)* and electrons were excited to a very high energy level *(1 mark)*. Then these excited electrons were transferred to DNIP to produce reduced DNIP *(1 mark)*.
NADP is a coenzyme that can accept from or give hydrogen (and therefore electrons) to another molecule. The question says DNIP is an artificial hydrogen acceptor. This means it can accept hydrogen (and therefore electrons) from other molecules too — it works in the same way as NADP.
   b) Tube A receives no light energy so the light-dependent reaction of photosynthesis can't take place *(1 mark)*. The chloroplasts in test tube C have been boiled, which will have denatured the enzymes in the chloroplast, therefore preventing photosynthesis from taking place *(1 mark)*.
   c) Glycerate 3-phosphate is reduced to triose phosphate *(1 mark)* using hydrogen ions from reduced NADP *(1 mark)*.

4 a) No. The student hasn't taken into account the amount of oxygen that the plant has used for respiration *(1 mark)*.
   b) i) In experiment 1, the rate of photosynthesis increased with increasing light intensity *(1 mark)*. However, after about 200 µmoles/m²/s the rate of photosynthesis levelled off *(1 mark)* because light intensity was no longer the limiting factor *(1 mark)*.
   b) ii) The limiting factor in experiment 2 must be temperature because the graph for experiment 3 levels off at a higher point *(1 mark)* but experiment 3 had the same light intensity and CO_2 concentration as experiment 2 *(1 mark)*.
   c) The level of RuBP will have increased because there would have been less CO_2 to combine with RuBP to form GP *(1 mark)*. The level of TP will have decreased because less GP would have been made and so less converted to TP *(1 mark)*. As TP was made into useful organic substances this will have decreased the level of TP further *(1 mark)*.
If you get a question like this in the exam, make sure you think of the substances before the reactant in the cycle as well as those that come after it.

Section 3: Energy Flow & Nutrient Cycles

1. Energy Transfer and Energy Loss
Page 58 — Application Questions

Q1 a) net productivity = gross productivity – respiratory loss
net productivity = 22 861 – 17 000 = **5861 kJm⁻²yr⁻¹**
   b) % efficiency of energy transfer =
(net productivity of trophic level ÷ net productivity of previous trophic level) × 100
= (627 ÷ 5861) × 100 = **10.7%**

Q2 a) pyramid of energy
   b) respiratory loss = gross productivity – net productivity
      respiratory loss = 8072 – 2073 = **5999 kJm⁻²yr⁻¹**

Don't be thrown by a question that asks you to work out respiratory loss or gross productivity — you should know the net productivity equation off by heart, and all you need to do is rearrange it.

   c) gross productivity = net productivity + respiratory loss
      gross productivity = 119 + 450 = **569 kJm⁻²yr⁻¹**
   d) E.g. because some parts of the small fish aren't eaten so the energy isn't taken in. / Because some parts of the small fish are indigestible and will pass through the large fish and come out as waste.

Some questions like this are tricky to work out — you need to think about what the key phrases, like gross productivity and net productivity, actually mean. Here the question is actually asking you 'Why is the energy absorbed by the large fish less than the energy available to them from the small fish?'

   e) % efficiency of energy transfer =
      (net productivity of trophic level ÷ net productivity of previous trophic level) × 100
      Between plant plankton and animal plankton = (8105 ÷ 31 023) × 100 = **26.1%**
      Between animal plankton and small fish = (2073 ÷ 8105) × 100 = **25.6%**
      Between small fish and large fish = (119 ÷ 2073) × 100 = **5.7%**

Page 58 — Fact Recall Questions
Q1 photosynthesis
Q2 food web
Q3 gross productivity
Q4 The amount of energy lost to the environment when organisms use energy produced from respiration for movement or body heat.
Q5 a) The total amount of energy available to the next trophic level.
   b) net productivity = gross productivity – respiratory loss
Q6 The number of organisms in each trophic level.
Q7 The amount of biomass in each trophic level.
Q8 In some food chains small numbers of big organisms may be fed on by large numbers of smaller organisms which can change the shape of a pyramid of numbers. Food chains based on e.g. plant plankton change the shape of pyramids of biomass because the plankton have a short life span, meaning their biomass is small at any given time. Pyramids of energy are always pyramid shaped because energy is lost at each trophic level.

2. Farming Practices and Productivity
Page 61 — Application Questions
Q1 E.g. the photo appears to show the chickens being kept in warm indoor pens as there is straw on the floor and it's relatively dark. This restricts the chickens' movement so they'll waste less energy moving around and their heat loss will be reduced. The chickens may be fed food that's higher in energy than their natural food. This increases the energy input, so more energy is available for growth.
You're asked to describe and explain — so you need to say what's happening and give reasons why.
Q2 The neonicotinoid pesticide will kill the aphids, so fewer aphids will eat the crop. This means less biomass will be lost from the sweet potato crop, so the crop will grow to be larger and productivity will be greater.
If you've never heard of neonicotinoid pesticides before, don't fret — the question tells you that it's a pesticide and that it kills insects (aphids) so you can work out the answer.

Page 61 — Fact Recall Questions
Q1 They can increase the efficiency of energy conversion, they can remove growth limiting factors and they can increase energy input.
Q2 a) Biological agents include natural predators that eat pest species, parasites that live in or lay their eggs on an insect pest and pathogenic bacteria or viruses that kill pests.
   b) Biological agents may be less cost-effective than chemical pesticides, i.e. they may increase productivity less in the short term for the same amount of money invested.
Q3 An integrated system of pest control is where both chemical pesticides and biological agents are used to kill pest species.
Q4 Natural fertilisers are organic matter, artificial fertilisers are inorganic.
Q5 Farmers need to get the amount of fertiliser they apply just right. Too much and money is wasted as excess fertiliser is washed away. Too little and productivity won't be increased, so less money can be made from selling the crop.
Q6 E.g. some people think the conditions intensively reared animals are kept in cause the animals pain, distress or restricts their natural behaviour, so it shouldn't be done.

3. The Carbon Cycle and Global Warming
Page 63 — Application Questions
Q1 The CO_2 concentration was highest at night because the poppies and other organisms in the field would have been respiring and releasing CO_2, but there was no photosynthesis, so no CO_2 was being used up. The CO_2 concentration was lowest at midday because the poppies and other plants in the field will have been photosynthesising and taking in the CO_2 produced by respiring organisms. Also, in the summer, the light intensity is highest around midday, so the rate of photosynthesis by plants will be greater than their rate of respiration.
Q2 The concentration of CO_2 will be low during the summer (Jun-Aug) because light intensity will be at its greatest, so more photosynthesis will be carried out by the plants, using up the CO_2. The CO_2 concentration will be greater throughout autumn and winter (Sep-April) because less will be removed from the atmosphere, as fewer plants will be photosynthesising.

Page 65 — Application Questions
Q1 No, because this graph doesn't show a global change in atmospheric CO_2 concentration — it shows changes in the atmospheric concentration of CO_2 above two forests. Also, the graph doesn't show data over the last century — it shows data for the last 11 years.
Q2 a) Deforestation was most likely carried out in forest Y in 2007. The atmospheric CO_2 concentration of forest Y increased very steeply in 2007, above the level of CO_2 concentration for forest X. Trees contain a massive amount of CO_2 which is released when they are burnt as part of deforestation.
   b) E.g. the cleared land could have been used for cattle farming because the methane concentration above forest Y increased during and after 2007.
Cattle give off methane as a waste gas.
   c) Deforestation caused average atmospheric CO_2 above the forest to increase. CO_2 is a greenhouse gas which absorbs outgoing energy from the Earth that would be radiated into space, and so keeps the planet warm. Increasing the level of greenhouse gases by activities such as deforestation means too much energy is being absorbed, leading to global warming.

Q1 Carbon is absorbed by plants when they carry out photosynthesis — it becomes carbon compounds in plant tissues. Carbon is passed on through the food chain by feeding. All living organisms die and are broken down by microorganisms called decomposers. Decomposers secrete enzymes onto dead organic material to digest the carbon compounds in them. They then absorb the products of digestion. Carbon is returned to the air (and water) as all living organisms (including the decomposers) carry out respiration, which produces CO_2. If dead organic matter ends up in places where there aren't any decomposers, e.g. deep oceans or bogs, their carbon compounds can be turned into fossil fuels over millions of years (by heat and pressure). The carbon in fossil fuels is released as CO_2 when they're burnt — this is called combustion.

Q2 saprobiontic nutrition

Q3 Respiration occurs during the day and night whereas photosynthesis only occurs during the day, so at night the plants do not remove the CO_2 added to the atmosphere by plants and other organisms respiring.

Q4 An increase in average global temperature over the last century.

Q5 CO_2 is a greenhouse gas, which absorbs outgoing energy from the Earth so less is lost to space. An increase in CO_2 concentration in the atmosphere means more energy is absorbed and re-radiated back to Earth, so the planet warms up.

The greenhouse effect is a natural process which keeps the planet warm — without it the Earth would be a pretty chilly place. The problem is that by increasing the concentration of atmospheric gases like carbon dioxide, we're enhancing the greenhouse effect, and this is what's causing global warming.

Q6 a) E.g. burning fossil fuels / deforestation.
   b) E.g. fossil fuel extraction / cattle farming.

4. The Effects of Global Warming
Page 69 — Application Questions

Q1 a) The abundance of aphids fluctuated between 1960 and 2000, but the general trend was a steady increase from 100 to 400. There were three peaks in the data on aphid abundance — in 1970 at 900, in 1980 at 680 and in 1990 at 1000. The temperature also fluctuated with a generally increasing trend from 7 °C in 1960 to 10 °C in 2000. There were three peaks in the temperature data — in 1970 at 9 °C, in 1980 at 10 °C and in 1990 at 11 °C.

When including data points from the graph in your answer, make sure you've read them off correctly — use a ruler.

   b) E.g. There's a positive correlation between temperature and index of abundance. / As temperature increases so does the index of abundance.

   c) No, the conclusion is not valid because there is no information on the graph to show that more aphid eggs have hatched due to the warmer temperatures. The population spikes could have been caused by more food being available for the aphids, due to the warmer temperatures, so more aphids survived.

When you're asked to evaluate a conclusion based on data, always remember to look at what the data shows and whether it supports the conclusion, and think about any other factors could have caused the change seen.

Q2 a) The data shown in the graph may have led the magazine to draw this conclusion because it suggests that a rise in temperature could lead to increased photosynthesis rates in plants, which would increase their growth. The data suggests that aphids would be less responsive to warning pheromones at warmer temperatures which could mean they become more susceptible to predators, reducing the amount of crops damaged by pests. The data also suggests that at warmer temperatures crops are less susceptible to *P. capsici*, a pathogen which limits plant growth.

   b) E.g. the graph shows laboratory data rather than data collected from farms. You can't evaluate the impact of temperature changes on crop growth, because the graph doesn't show data regarding crop yields. The graph shows the reproduction rates and response to warning pheromones in many aphid species, which may not apply to the species affecting the farmers crops. The data only looks at how temperature directly affects photosynthesis and aphid numbers, but there may be other indirect/secondary factors related to global warming that affect could affect crops, e.g. a rise in temperature could affect the number of predators that eat aphids.

Page 69 — Fact Recall Questions

Q1 CO_2 concentration is a limiting factor for photosynthesis, so increasing global CO_2 concentration could mean crops grow faster, increasing crop yields.

Q2 Any two from, e.g: climate change is affecting the life cycle of some insect pest species. / Some insect pest species are becoming more abundant. / Some insect pest species are becoming less abundant.

Q3 Because species that need warmer temperatures may spread further as the conditions they thrive in exist over a wider area. Species that need cooler temperatures may have smaller ranges as the conditions they thrive in exist over a smaller area.

5. The Nitrogen Cycle and Eutrophication
Page 71 — Fact Recall Questions

Q1 The process of nitrogen gas in the atmosphere being turned into ammonia by bacteria.

Q2 decomposers

Q3 First nitrifying bacteria change ammonium compounds into nitrites. Then other nitrifying bacteria change nitrites into nitrates.

Remember you don't need to know the names of the microorganisms involved in the stages of the nitrogen cycle.

Q4 denitrification

Q5 leaching

Q6 The increased numbers of bacteria reduce the oxygen concentration in the water by carrying out aerobic respiration. Fish and other aquatic organisms die because there isn't enough dissolved oxygen.

Page 73 — Application Questions

Q1 The nitrate concentration of the water increases from 7 mgl⁻¹ to 31 mgl⁻¹ at a distance of 100 m, returns to 7 mgl⁻¹ at 300 m and rises again to 37 mgl⁻¹ at 800 m before falling once more to 7 mgl⁻¹. The algal content of the water increases sharply from 10 000 cells cm⁻³ to 85 000 cells cm⁻³ at a distance of 200 m, returns to 10 000 cells cm⁻³ at 370 m and increases again to 98 000 cells cm⁻³ at 900 m before falling back to 10 000 cells cm⁻³.

Q2 a) 100 m and 800 m, because these sites are where the nitrate concentration increases sharply.

   b) i) $37 - 31 = 6$ mgl^{-1}
      $(6 \div 31) \times 100 = $ **19.4%**
      ii) E.g. the second farm has more land on which crops are grown so more nitrate fertiliser is leached into the river. / The second farm uses a higher concentration of nitrate fertiliser on its land.
      There are lots of possible reasons why the water next to the second farm has a higher nitrogen concentration than the water next to the first farm — you just need to give a sensible answer.

Q3 The control river showed a steady nitrate concentration of 8 mgl^{-1} at all distances and a steady algal content of 10 000 cells cm^{-3} at all distances.

Q4 a) There is a correlation between the nitrate concentration of river A and its algal content. Shortly after the nitrate concentration increases in river A, the algal content increases too.

   b) Nitrates leached from fertilised fields stimulate the growth of algae in rivers, because the algae use nitrogen for growth / to make proteins and nucleic acids.

Exam-style Questions — pages 75-76

1 a) Light / the Sun *(1 mark)*
  b) Photosynthesis *(1 mark)*. E.g. some light energy is the wrong wavelength so plants can't use it *(1 mark)*.
  c) net productivity = gross productivity − respiratory loss
     net productivity = 2143 − 1571 = **572 kJm^{-2}yr^{-1}**
     (1 mark for correct working only, 2 marks for correct answer)
  d) E.g. because some parts of food, e.g. roots or bones, aren't eaten by organisms so the energy isn't taken in *(1 mark)*. Also, some parts of food are indigestible so pass through organisms and come out as waste, e.g. faeces *(1 mark)*.
  e) percentage efficiency of energy transfer −
     (net productivity of trophic level ÷ net productivity of previous trophic level) × 100
     Between the producer and primary consumer 1 = (2619 ÷ 38750) × 100 = 6.76%
     Between the producer and primary consumer 2 = (1265 ÷ 38750) × 100 = 3.26%
     6.76 − 3.26 = **3.5%**
     (1 mark for each correct percentage efficiency of energy transfer or 3 marks for correct answer)
  f) i) Decomposers release enzymes to break down the carbon compounds/cellulose in dead producers *(1 mark)* and then they absorb the soluble products of digestion *(1 mark)*. The decomposers respire and release CO_2 into the atmosphere *(1 mark)*. Other producers then take in this CO_2 *(1 mark)*.
  f) ii) E.g. dead plants become fossil fuels over millions of years *(1 mark)*. Combustion of fossil fuels releases carbon dioxide into the atmosphere *(1 mark)*.

2 a) nitrogen fixation *(1 mark)*
  b) Ammonification is when nitrogen compounds from dead organisms and in animal waste are turned into ammonium compounds by decomposers *(1 mark)*. Nitrification is when ammonium compounds in the soil are changed into nitrogen compounds that can then be used by plants *(1 mark)*. First nitrifying bacteria change ammonium compounds into nitrites *(1 mark)*. Then other nitrifying bacteria change nitrites into nitrates *(1 mark)*. Denitrification is when nitrates in the soil are converted into nitrogen gas by denitrifying bacteria *(1 mark)*. This happens under anaerobic conditions *(1 mark)*.

  c) Nitrates leached from fertilised fields stimulate the growth of algae in ponds and rivers *(1 mark)*. Large amounts of algae block light from reaching the plants below *(1 mark)*. Eventually the plants die because they're unable to photosynthesise enough *(1 mark)*. Bacteria feed on the dead plant matter *(1 mark)*. The increased numbers of bacteria reduce the oxygen concentration in the water by carrying out aerobic respiration *(1 mark)*. Fish and other aquatic organisms die because there isn't enough dissolved oxygen *(1 mark)*.

3 a) A field of potato crops with greenfly infestation that wasn't treated with any form of pest control *(1 mark)*.
  b) Field D is the control field because the consistently high numbers of greenfly reduce the amount of energy available to the crops for growth *(1 mark)*, which means the crops are less efficient at converting energy so it will have the lowest net productivity *(1 mark)*. Field A has been treated by an integrated system because at the end of the study it has the lowest numbers of greenfly *(1 mark)*, which means the crops have lost the least energy and biomass, so net productivity will be the highest *(1 mark)*.
  Remember, integrated systems are usually better at reducing pests and increasing crop productivity than the use of pesticides or biological controls alone.
  c) i) The lacewings only reduced the number of greenfly by around half as much as the integrated system and less than the pesticides *(1 mark)*. The lacewings only increased net productivity by half as much as the integrated system and less than the pesticides *(1 mark)*. The lacewings took longer to have an effect than the integrated systems and pesticides *(1 mark)*.
  You'll need to have worked out that the lacewings were used on field B and the pesticides on field C to answer this question.
     ii) The table shows that it is a cheaper form of pest control than using pesticides at £100 per field compared to £750 per field *(1 mark)*. The integrated system will be cheaper than using pesticide on its own, but more expensive than using just lacewings *(1 mark)*. Using pesticide on its own has environmental issues — it may indirectly affect other non-pest species *(1 mark)* or it may directly affect (damage or kill) other non-pest species *(1 mark)*.

Section 4: Succession and Conservation

1. Succession

Page 80 — Application Questions

Q1 Primary succession, because there is no soil present in 1800.
   Remember, the key difference between primary and secondary succession is soil — it's present in secondary succession, but not in primary succession. If you have a good look at the graph you'll see that there's no soil moisture in 1800. That's a pretty good sign that there's no soil, either.

Q2 The dominant plant species would have been adapted to survive without much water/in a soil with low moisture content and fluctuating ground temperatures. They would have had seeds that could remain viable for long periods of time. They would have been species of small plants / they would not have been tree species.

There's a lot going on in the graph with all the different lines — and you could get something like this in the exam. Don't let the graph's complexity put you off though. Take your time and make sure you really understand what the graph is showing, and read the questions carefully so you pick out the right bits from the graph for your answers.

Q3 E.g. the average length of time dominant plant seeds remained viable for was relatively high between 1800 and 1860. This might have been because seeds that remained viable for a long time could lie dormant until conditions were favourable enough to germinate. Between about 1860 and 1880 the average length of time fell sharply, and then continued to fall more slowly until levelling off at around 1960. This may have been because the plants that were dominant between 1800 and 1860 were succeeded by other plant species which were more suited to the changed conditions, e.g. a higher soil moisture content, so they no longer needed to be viable for long periods of time.

Q4 Between 1800 and 1920 because there were no tree species present during this time, so there would have been more light / less shade cast by the trees.

Q5 The soil moisture content is 0 between 1800 and 1820 because there is no soil. The soil moisture content increased gradually from 1820 until 1940 as the soil developed, then it increased more rapidly between 1940 and 2000 because the addition of decomposed organic material helped to increase soil moisture content and the deeper soil was able to retain more water.

Page 80 — Fact Recall Questions
Q1 The process by which an ecosystem changes over time.
Q2 primary succession
Q3 The largest and most complex community of plants and animals that an ecosystem can support.
Q4 E.g. deforestation / volcanic eruption / fire
Q5 The climax community for a particular climate.

2. Conservation
Page 84 — Application Questions
Q1 a) The areas of steppe in which succession was controlled by grazing and fire had the highest percentage cover of grasses compared to the control. The area of steppe controlled by fire also had the lowest percentage cover of trees. This would suggest that fire was the most effective method of controlling succession. Mowing was the least successful method. The area of steppe in which succession was controlled by mowing had the lowest percentage cover of grasses and the highest percentage cover of trees after the control.

If you're asked to compare the effectiveness of something like different conservation methods, always make sure you know what the aim of the method is. In this case, the nature reserve want to stop the forest developing (so they want a low percentage of trees) and to keep the grassland (so they want a high percentage cover of grass).

   b) E.g. Grazing is less dangerous than fire. / Grazing could cause less harm to other species than fire.

Q2 Advantage, e.g. it can help to increase the number of saiga antelope on the reserve. / It can help prevent saiga antelope from becoming extinct.
Disadvantage, e.g. the saiga antelope could bring disease to the reserve. / The saiga antelope could harm other species living on the reserve.

Page 84 — Fact Recall Questions
Q1 The protection and management of species and habitats.
Q2 For: e.g. it could help protect species that provide resources humans need (such as drugs, clothes and food) that can be traded on a local and global scale. / Some people think we should conserve species because it's the right thing to do. / Many species and habitats bring joy to lots of people because they're attractive to look at. / Conserving species and habitats can help to prevent climate change. / Conserving species and habitats helps to prevent the disruption of food chains.
Against: e.g. some conservation methods can cause conflict with people's livelihood/other species.
Q3 The climax community produced when succession is stopped artificially.
Q4 The growing points of the trees will be cut off by the lawnmower, so the trees can't establish themselves.
Q5 A managed fire is lit. After the fire, secondary succession will occur — the plant species that grow back first (pioneer species) are the species that are being conserved. Larger plant species will take longer to grow back and will be removed again the next time the area is burnt.

3. Conservation Evidence and Data
Page 88 — Application Questions
Q1 The average percentage cover of non-native species was greatest on the control grasslands and lowest on the grazed fields. The average percentage cover of native species was greatest on the grazed fields and lowest on the harrowed and seeded fields. Overall, there were more non-native species than native species.
Q2 a) Grazing was the most successful method because it produced a larger proportion of native plants than harrowing and seeding, and the control, and a smaller proportion of non-native plants than harrowing and seeding, and the control.
   b) Grazing worked because, e.g. the sheep prefer eating non-native to native plant species. / The non-native plants may have been less likely to grow back after grazing than the non-native plants. Seeding may not have worked because, e.g. the native plant seeds that were seeded on harrowed grassland were unable to compete with non-native seeds.

For questions asking you to suggest an answer, you need to use your common sense — you won't have been taught the answer.

Q3 In the second investigation the percentage cover of native and non-native plants was slightly higher on the harrowed and seeded fields than on the control fields, whereas in the first investigation the percentage cover of native and non-native plants was lower on the harrowed and seeded fields than on the control fields. In the second investigation the percentage cover of native species was similar, and the percentage cover of non-native species lower, on grazed fields than the control fields. By contrast, in the first investigation the percentage cover of native species was higher, and non-native species lower, on the grazed fields than on the control fields.
The differences might be caused by, e.g. the first study used a much larger sample size than the first / the first study took averages which the second did not / the fields were left for different lengths of time during the two investigations.

1 a) The bird populations shows three peaks at 4-5 years, at 21 years and at 34 years *(1 mark)*. The peaks correspond with the phase during the tree coppicing cycles when the canopy closes, so this must provide the best habitat for the birds *(1 mark)*. There is a dip in population size at 2 years, 17 years and 31 years *(1 mark)*, which is just after the trees are coppiced, so the birds lose their habitat *(1 mark)*. The bird population size in the uncoppiced woods is lower but more stable over the 45 year period *(1 mark)*. The birds don't lose their habitat every 15 years because there is no coppicing, but the population size isn't as large in the mature trees as it is in trees under coppicing, suggesting that the birds are not well adapted to living in denser canopies *(1 mark)*.

b) i) E.g. any one from: the smaller peaks coincide with the higher numbers of the endangered bird species *(1 mark)*, so income may have been generated by tourists/people coming to see the endangered bird species *(1 mark)*. / The larger peaks coincide with felling the trees *(1 mark)*, so income may have been generated by the sale of wood *(1 mark)*.

b) ii) Any six from: the graph shows three coppicing cycles between 0-15 years, 15-30 years and 30-45 years *(1 mark)*. Each coppicing cycle shows one peak in biodiversity, at 5 years, 20 years and 36 years *(1 mark)* and a gradual decline in biodiversity to a low at 15 years, 30 years and 45 years *(1 mark)*. The initial rise in biodiversity may have been caused by the reduced density of the canopy cover through coppicing *(1 mark)*, which may have allowed more light to get through to the understory *(1 mark)*. This may have allowed more plant species to grow/ other species to thrive *(1 mark)*. As the density of the canopy cover increases, the light levels may fall *(1 mark)*, limiting the number of species who can survive in the new conditions and causing the forest biodiversity to fall *(1 mark)*.

2 a) The established community of plants is destroyed, leaving the soil undisturbed *(1 mark)*. Pioneer species colonise the area, making the local abiotic conditions less hostile *(1 mark)*. At each stage, organisms that are better adapted for the improved conditions move in and out-compete the species that are already there *(1 mark)*. As succession goes on, the ecosystem becomes more complex and species diversity increases, the abiotic conditions become less hostile and the amount of biomass increases *(1 mark)*. This process continues until a climax community is reached *(1 mark)*.

Examiners love it when you include lots of nice technical terms in your answer — so make sure you're really clued up about what all the ecological terms in this section mean.

b) E.g. secondary succession happens relatively quickly, so burning the heathland every 50 years might not be often enough to maintain the optimum abiotic conditions for the endangered plant species *(1 mark)*. The endangered plant species need an acidic soil to grow successfully. The soil pH may be affected by the fire, so the plant species might not be able to tolerate the changed abiotic conditions created by burning *(1 mark)*.

c) Between 1991 and mid-1992, the population size of heather and shrubs falls dramatically because they were burnt by the fire *(1 mark)*, and the population size of insects falls because the loss of heather and shrubs causes them to lose their habitat *(1 mark)*. From mid-1992 until 2000 the population size of heather, shrubs and insects starts to rise as secondary succession occurs, and shrubs and heather start to grow, providing a habitat for insects *(1 mark)*.

d) i) The first species to colonise an area during succession *(1 mark)*.

ii) In primary succession there is no soil, so the pioneer species will have features that make it adapted to cope without soil *(1 mark)*. In secondary succession there is soil present / there are different abiotic conditions, which means the pioneer species will have different adaptations *(1 mark)*.

iii) E.g. herb species X was not present before 1992, before the fire, perhaps because the abiotic conditions weren't favourable *(1 mark)*. Between 1992 and 1994 the population size of herb species X increased dramatically, so it must be better adapted than other species to the changed abiotic conditions created by the fire (e.g. alkaline soil because of the ash) *(1 mark)*. The increase in population size of herb species X slowed down and then levelled off between 1994 and 2003. It then decreased dramatically after 2003, perhaps because it was out-competed by another species or because it couldn't tolerate the changed abiotic conditions created by other plant species *(1 mark)*.

e) i) E.g. the graph only shows data over a nineteen year period since the fire and it might take longer than this for the insect population to recover / the population size of insects shows an upward trend, and this may continue after 2010 *(1 mark)*. The graph only shows data for one year before the fire, and the insect population size was decreasing — so the data in 1990 might not be representative of the normal population size of insects *(1 mark)*.

ii) E.g. animals could be allowed to graze the land and eat the growing points of the shrubs and heather, stopping them from establishing themselves *(1 mark)*. This would help to keep vegetation low and so increase the amount of light / reduce the amount of shade to the endangered plant species *(1 mark)*. Controlling the soil pH would help to keep the soil acidic for the plant *(1 mark)*.

Think about the conditions the plant needs to grow successfully in (which is given in the introduction to the question), and how these conditions can be brought about by different conservation methods.

Section 5: Inheritance, Selection and Speciation

1. Genetic Terms

Page 92 — Application Questions

Q1 A = tufted tail, B = tufted tail, C = non-tufted tail

Q2 a) yellow
   b) YY
   c) yy

You need to understand all the terms on pages 91 and 92 really well so that when you come across exam questions using any of the words, you'll understand what's being described and what you're being asked.

2. Genetic Diagrams — Simple Monohybrid Crosses
Page 95 — Application Questions
Q1 The only possible genotype of offspring is heterozygous, e.g. Tt. Worked example:

T — tall dominant allele
t — dwarf recessive allele

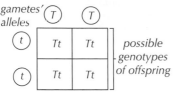

The question asked you to show your working. So even though you know that a monohybrid cross with two homozygous parents always produces all heterozygous offspring, you must draw a genetic diagram of some kind to show how you would work that out.

Q2 ½ / 0.5 / 50%. Worked example:

D — polydactyly dominant allele
d — normal recessive allele

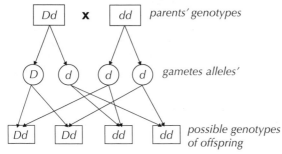

Q3 1:0:1 ratio of blue: yellow: striped organisms / 1:1 ratio of blue : striped organisms. Worked example:

C^Y *— yellow allele*
C^B *— blue allele*

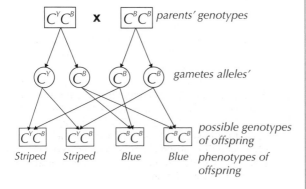

3. Genetic Diagrams — Sex-linked and Multiple Allele Crosses
Page 98 — Application Questions
Q1 $X^F X^F$ (sufferer female), $X^F Y$ (sufferer male), $X^F X^f$ (sufferer female), $X^f Y$ (normal male). Worked example:

$X^F Y$ *— male sufferer*
$X^F X^f$ *— female heterozygous*

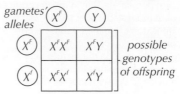

This question doesn't ask you to show your working, but it's best to always do so. Then if you write an answer down wrong for any reason, you could still pick up marks in your exam for your working.

Q2 The possible stripping patterns are Abyssinian (50%) and Mackerel (50%). Worked example:

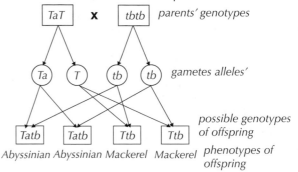

Q3 ¼ / 0.25 / 25%. Worked example:

$X^N Y$ *— normal male*
$X^N X^n$ *— female carrier*

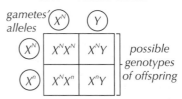

Q4 a) Melanic (M) is dominant to both of the other alleles, insularia is dominant to typical only and typical is recessive to all. / The dominance of the alleles is M > M' > m.
b) All heterozygous melanic (Mm). Worked example:

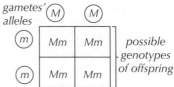

Q5 Y-linked characteristics can only be passed on down the male (XY) line. So for a child to have a Y-linked disorder, its father must also have the disorder. So if a child has hairy ears but its dad doesn't, the dad might question if he was the father.

This is fairly tricky, but drawing a quick diagram would help you out:

XY^N — *normal male*
XX — *female*

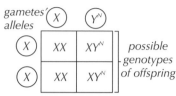

A normal male can't have a child with the disorder.

Page 98 — Fact Recall Questions

Q1 Male — XY, Female — XX.

Q2 ½ / 0.5 / 50%

Q3 If a characteristic is sex-linked it means that the allele that codes for it is located on a sex chromosome (X or Y).

Q4 Males are more likely than females to have X-linked disorders because males only have one X chromosome. Because they only have one copy of any alleles on the X chromosome, they express the characteristic of those alleles even if they're recessive, whereas women would need to inherit two copies to express the same characteristics.

4. Genetic Pedigree Diagrams

Page 99 — Application Questions

Q1 heterozygous, e.g. Hh.

The cross between individual 1 and 2 has produced one unaffected child and one affected child. As the unaffected child must have two recessive alleles, one from each parent, individual 1 must have one recessive allele and one dominant allele (Hh) to have the disorder and pass on an unaffected allele.

Q2 Heterozygous (Hh) and homozygous recessive (hh).

Individual 5 is unaffected so must be homozygous recessive (hh). Individual 3 has the disorder so must have at least one dominant allele, but they must also have one recessive allele from their unaffected parent (individual 2), so must be heterozygous (Hh). Worked example:

H — Huntington's dominant allele
h — Unaffected recessive allele

gametes'
alleles

	H	h	
h	Hh	hh	possible genotypes of offspring
h	Hh	hh	

5. The Hardy-Weinberg Principle

Page 103 — Application Questions

Q1 a) $p + q = 1$
$q = 1 - p$
$q = 1 - 0.10 = \textbf{0.90}$

You're given one allele frequency in the table and are asked to find the other, so its the simple equation.

b) $p = 0.1$, $q = 0.9$, so $2pq = 2 \times 0.1 \times 0.9 = \textbf{0.18}$

c) No, it does not apply. The frequency of the allele changes between the generations, and the Hardy-Weinberg principle is only true in cases where the allele frequency stays the same.

Q2 $q = 0.16$ and $p + q = 1$, so $p = 1 - q$
$p = 1 - 0.16 = 0.84$
homozygous dominant genotype frequency = p^2
$p^2 = 0.84^2 = \textbf{0.71}$

Q3 recessive wrinkled allele = $q^2 = 31\% \div 100 = 0.31$
$q = \sqrt{0.31} = 0.557$
$p + q = 1$, so $p = 1 - q$
$p = 1 - 0.557 = 0.443$
Heterozygous genotype = $2pq$
$2pq = 2 \times 0.443 \times 0.557 = 0.49$
$0.49 \times 100 = 49$, so **49%** of the population have a heterozygous genotype.

Page 103 — Fact Recall Questions

Q1 A group of organisms of the same species living in a particular area.

Q2 The complete range of alleles present in a population.

Q3 How often an allele occurs in a population.

Q4 The Hardy-Weinberg principle is a mathematical model that predicts that the frequencies of alleles in a population won't change from one generation to the next as long as the population is large, there's no immigration, emigration, mutations or natural selection, and mating is totally random.

Q5 $p + q = 1$ and $p^2 + 2pq + q^2 = 1$, where p = the frequency of the dominant allele, q = the frequency of the recessive allele, p^2 = the frequency of the homozygous dominant genotype, q^2 = the frequency of the homozygous recessive genotype and $2pq$ = the frequency of the heterozygous genotype.

6. Allele Frequency and Speciation

Page 107 — Application Questions

Q1 a) 3.5 cm – 1 cm = **2.5 cm**

b) Directional selection. In 1850 the average fur length was about 3.5 cm. In 1950, the average had moved to about 2.2 cm. The average has moved towards the 'extreme' shorter end, which shows directional selection.

c) Caribou with shorter fur length would have been better adapted to the warmer climate further south and so had a selective advantage. These caribou would have been more likely to survive, reproduce and pass on their alleles for shorter fur. So the average fur length has reduced and moved towards the 'extreme' shorter end.

Q2 Different populations were geographically isolated on the different islands. The different food sources caused different selective pressures, so on each island finches with different alleles for beak size and shape were more likely to survive, reproduce and pass on their alleles. Over time this caused changes in allele frequencies and gene pools, which eventually resulted in reproductive isolation and speciation.

Q3 a) The peak in allele frequency in 2000 was most likely a result of the fire in 1999. The peak may be due to an increase in the number of mammals emigrating to the south from the north as a result of the fire. The northern population had a slightly higher frequency of the allele, so an influx from this population could have caused an increase in the allele frequency in the south.

b) From 1998 to 2002 there was a big increase in the dark fur allele in the northern population. In 1999, a fire destroyed a large area in the north of the forest. This would have left a large area of barren, darkened forest and blackened soil. Mammals with darker fur would have a selective advantage and so be more likely to survive, reproduce and pass on their alleles for darker fur, causing an increase in the frequency of the dark fur allele.

c) The theory could be tested by attempting to breed individuals from the two populations together. If they can't breed to produce fertile offspring then speciation has occurred.

Page 107 — Fact Recall Questions

Q1 Differential reproductive success means that not all individuals have an equal chance of reproducing. Some individuals will have alleles that make them more likely to survive, and so reproduce and pass on their alleles.

Q2 Stabilising selection is when individuals with alleles for a characteristic towards the middle of the range are more likely to survive, reproduce and pass on their alleles. But directional selection is when individuals with alleles for a characteristic at the extreme end of the range are more likely to survive, reproduce and pass on their alleles.

Q3 Geographical isolation is when some individuals become separated from the main population due to a physical barrier, e.g. a flood or an earthquake.

Q4 When a single population gets split up, isolated and subjected to different selective pressures, the populations can experience different changes in allele frequencies. This can lead to differences accumulating in their gene pools, eventually resulting in reproductive isolation and so speciation.

Exam-style Questions — pages 109-110

1 a) i) Homozygous means an individual carries two of the same alleles (e.g. $H^N H^N$ or $H^S H^S$) *(1 mark)*.

ii) $H^N H^S$ *(1 mark)*. She has one child who is unaffected ($H^N H^N$), so both parents must have at least one H^N allele. She also has two children who have the sickle-cell trait ($H^S H^N$), so these children must have inherited a H^S allele off one parent. Individual 2 is $H^N H^N$ as he's unaffected, so individual 1 must be $H^N H^S$ *(1 mark)*.

iii) ¼ / 0.25 / 25%. Example working:

gametes/alleles	H^S	H^N	
H^S	$H^S H^S$	$H^S H^N$	possible
H^S	$H^S H^S$	$H^S H^N$	genotypes of offspring

Chance of having a girl with sickle-cell trait = 0.5 ÷ 2 = **0.25**

(2 marks for correct answer, otherwise allow 1 mark for correctly showing that there's a ½ / 0.5 / 50% probability of having at least one child with the $H^N H^S$ phenotype)

Don't forget to divide the chance of the child having sickle-cell trait (0.5) by 2, because there's a 0.5 chance it'll be a girl.

b) As the prevalence of malaria increases the sickle allele frequency increases. / There is positive correlation between the prevalence of malaria and sickle allele frequency. *(1 mark)*. Individuals with sickle-cell trait are more tolerant to malaria. So in regions where malaria is prevalent, this will make these individuals more likely to survive, reproduce and pass on their alleles to the next generation *(1 mark)*. Over time this selection will lead to an increase in the sickle allele frequency in these regions *(1 mark)*.

2 a) After many generations the populations could no longer breed together *(1 mark)*.

b) Different populations were isolated, and the flies were fed different foods meaning they experienced different conditions, causing different selection pressures *(1 mark)*. Some flies were more likely to survive, reproduce and pass on their alleles *(1 mark)*. This caused changes in allele frequencies and gene pools between the populations, which eventually resulted in speciation/individuals changing so much they became reproductively isolated *(1 mark)*.

c) i) No, because looking at a single generation each time, the allele frequencies do not add up to one (e.g. 0.68 + 0.14 = 0.82), so one or more alleles are missing *(1 mark)*.

ii) Dominant allele = p = 0.82
$p + q = 1$, so $q = 1 - p = 1 - 0.82 = 0.18$
Heterozygous genotype = $2pq = 2 \times 0.82 \times 0.18$
= 0.295 × 100 = **29.5%**
(2 marks for correct answer, otherwise allow 1 mark for either p = 0.82 and q = 0.18, or for 2pq = 0.295).

3 a) Sex-linked recessive characteristics are those where the allele that codes for the characteristic is located on a sex-chromosome *(1 mark)* and the characteristic only appears in the phenotype if two copies of the allele are present in the genotype *(1 mark)*.

b) 0% / no chance / 0. Example working:
H - normal allele
h - recessive haemophilia allele

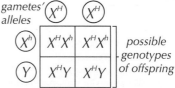

gametes/alleles	X^H	X^H	
X^h	$X^H X^h$	$X^H X^h$	possible genotypes
Y	$X^H Y$	$X^H Y$	of offspring

(2 marks for correct answer, otherwise allow 1 mark for showing the correct gametes)

There's no $X^h X^h$ or $X^h Y$, so there's no chance that their child would have haemophilia.

Unit 5

Section 1: Responding to the Environment

1. Survival and Response
Page 111 — Fact Recall Questions
Q1 To increase their chances of survival.
Q2 Directional movement in response to a stimulus.
Q3 Non-directional (random) movement in response to a stimulus.

2. Nervous and Hormonal Communication
Page 115 — Application Questions
Q1 Scenario 1 — B/hormonal response, because it involves a hormone (DHT) released by a gland and it has a slow, widespread effect.
Scenario 2 — C/simple reflex, because it is a rapid, involuntary response that protects the foot from further damage.
Scenario 3 — A/nervous response, because it is a voluntary response.
Q2 a) Any one from, e.g. the response would be slower / the response would be voluntary.
b) Stimulus — light tap/touch, effector — quadriceps muscle.
c) i) The knee-jerk reflex doesn't involve a relay neurone in the spinal cord. / There are usually three neurones involved in a simple reflex.
ii) E.g. the quadriceps muscle may not contract/there may be no response. If the spinal cord is damaged then the sensory neurone may not be able to transmit nervous impulses to the motor neurone / the motor neurone may not be able to transmit nervous impulses to the leg muscle.
d) To protect the body/leg from being damaged.
The answer to this question might not be obvious, but you've learnt that simple reflexes prevent damage to the body, so this would be a good suggestion. (In fact, the reflex prevents knee muscles from being over-stretched... but you don't need to know this.)

Page 115 — Fact Recall Questions
Q1 To detect stimuli.
Q2 Muscle cells, cells found in glands.
Q3 Receptor cells detect a stimulus. Sensory neurones transmit electrical impulses from the receptors to the CNS. The CNS processes the information, decides what to do with it and sends impulses along motor neurones to effectors, which respond.
This question asks about a voluntary response, so make sure that your answer includes the CNS processing the information and deciding what to do with it.
Q4 The response is localised because neurotransmitters are secreted directly onto cells. The response is short-lived because neurotransmitters are quickly removed once they have done their job.
Q5 Because they're so rapid.
Q6 glands
Q7 A change in concentration of a specific substance/another hormone, electrical impulses.
Q8 Hormones aren't released directly onto their target cells, they must travel in the blood to get there. This is slower than the electrical impulses in nervous communication.

Q9 Hormones are transported all over the body, so the response may be widespread if the target cells are widespread. Hormones are not broken down quickly, so the response may be long-lasting.

3. Chemical Mediators
Page 116 — Fact Recall Questions
Q1 Because their target cells are right next to where the chemical mediators are produced.
Q2 Chemical mediators only have to travel a short distance to their target cells, so produce a quicker response than hormones which are transported in the blood.
Q3 The body being injured or infected.
Q4 E.g. prostaglandins

4. Receptors
Page 118 — Application Questions
Q1 a) threshold level
b) B, because its generator potential reaches -60mV/the threshold level.
c) Approximately -87.5 mV (accept any value between -87 mV and -88 mV)
Make sure you always read the axes carefully — especially on graphs to do with potential differences across cell membranes, because they nearly always involve negative numbers.
Q2 E.g. the vibration stimulus would normally deform the stretch-mediated sodium channels in Pacinian corpuscles. However, the drug would stop the sodium channels from opening, meaning sodium ions wouldn't diffuse into the cell. An action potential wouldn't be activated, meaning the person would not detect the vibration.

Page 120 — Fact Recall Questions
Q1 When a stimulus is detected, the cell membrane is excited and becomes more permeable, allowing more ions to move in and out of the cell. This alters the potential difference across the cell membrane and therefore produces a generator potential.
Q2 mechanical
Q3 A Pacinian corpuscle contains the end of a sensory neurone. The sensory nerve ending is wrapped in layers of connective tissue called lamellae.
Q4 When a Pacinian corpuscle is stimulated the lamellae are deformed and press on the sensory nerve ending. This causes deformation of stretch-mediated sodium channels in the sensory neurone's cell membrane. The sodium ion channels open and sodium ions diffuse into the cell, creating a generator potential. If the generator potential reaches the threshold, it triggers an action potential.
Q5 Cones are close together and one cone joins one neurone. This means that when light from two points hits two cones, an action potential from each cone goes to the brain, so the light can be distinguished as coming from two separate points. This doesn't happen in rods because many rods join the same neurone, which means light from two objects close together can't be told apart.
Q6 Any three from: e.g. rods are found mainly in the peripheral parts of the retina and cones are found packed together in the fovea. / Rods only give information in black and white but cones give information in colour. / Rods are very sensitive to light but cones are less sensitive. / Many rods join one neurone, but only one cone joins one neurone.

5. The Nervous Impulse

Page 125 — Application Questions

Q1 A — The neurone is stimulated.
B — Depolarisation / Lots of sodium ion channels are open and lots of sodium ions are diffusing into the neurone.
C — The sodium ion channels are closed and the potassium ion channels are open.

Q2 −40 mV

Q3 −60 mV
Remember to always include units in your answer when they're given on the graph.

Q4 a) At a potential difference of +40 mV the sodium ion channels close and the potassium ion channels open. The membrane is more permeable to potassium so potassium ions diffuse out of the neurone down the potassium ion concentration gradient. This starts to get the membrane back to its resting potential. At the bottom of the curve the potassium ion channels are slow to close so there's a slight 'overshoot' where too many potassium ions diffuse out of the neurone. The potential difference (−70 mV) is more negative than the resting potential (−60 mV). The sodium-potassium pump then returns the membrane to its resting potential (−60 mV).
b) refractory period

Q5 The action potential would have the same potential difference values as the graph shown because once the threshold is reached, an action potential will always fire with the same change in voltage, no matter how big the stimulus is. However, there may be another action potential shown on the graph because a bigger stimulus will cause action potentials to fire more frequently.

Page 125 — Fact Recall Questions

Q1 Sodium-potassium pumps and potassium ion channels.
Sodium ion channels are involved when a stimulus excites the neurone cells membrane but they're not involved in maintaining the resting membrane potential.

Q2 Sodium ions diffuse into the neurone down the sodium ion electrochemical gradient. This makes the inside of the neurone less negative and so decreases the potential difference across the membrane.

Q3 More sodium ions diffuse into the neurone because more sodium ion channels open.

Q4 a) The ion channels are recovering and can't be made to open.
b) It makes action potentials discrete/separate impulses. It makes action potentials unidirectional.

Q5 During an action potential, some of the sodium ions that enter the neurone diffuse sideways. This causes sodium ion channels in the next region of the neurone to open and sodium ions diffuse into that part. This causes a wave of depolarisation.

Q6 A myelinated neurone has a myelin sheath. The myelin sheath is made of a type of cell called a Schwann cell. Between the Schwann cells are tiny patches of bare membrane called the nodes of Ranvier. Sodium ion channels are concentrated at the nodes of Ranvier.

Q7 In a myelinated neurone depolarisation/action potentials only happen at the nodes of Ranvier. However in a non-myelinated neurone, depolarisation/action potentials occur as a wave along the whole length of the axon membrane. Conduction along a myelinated neurone is faster than along a non-myelinated neurone.

Q8 Axon diameter and temperature.

Exam-style Questions — pages 126-127

1 a) i) Schwann cell *(1 mark)*
ii) B — node of Ranvier *(1 mark)*
C — dendrites *(1 mark)*
b) i) Myelin is an electrical insulator *(1 mark)*. It allows nervous impulses to travel very fast by saltatory conduction *(1 mark)*.
ii) Conduction of nervous impulses in non-myelinated neurones is slower than in myelinated neurones *(1 mark)*. If the myelin is damaged then the nerve impulse may happen much more slowly or not at all, resulting in muscle weakness or paralysis *(1 mark)*.
c) i) Action potentials have a refractory period *(1 mark)*. During this period the ion channels are recovering and can't be made to open *(1 mark)*. This means that no more sodium ions can diffuse into the neurone to trigger another action potential *(1 mark)*.
ii) There are 5 action potentials in 20 ms.
500 ms ÷ 20 ms = 25. So 5 × 25 = **125 action potentials**.
(2 marks for correct answer, otherwise 1 mark for correct working).
iii) Axon Y has the biggest diameter as it conducts action potentials faster than axon X *(1 mark)*. Action potentials are conducted quicker along axons with bigger diameters because there's less resistance to the flow of ions than in the cytoplasm of a smaller axon *(1 mark)*. With less resistance, depolarisation reaches other parts of the neurone cell membrane quicker *(1 mark)*.
Still award marks for a correct explanation, even if an incorrect calculation in part b(ii) means that axon X is chosen.

2 a) chemical mediators *(1 mark)*
b) Histamine is released from immune cells right next to the target cells on the capillaries surrounding the site of the bee sting *(1 mark)*. Histamine only has to travel a short distance to the target cells so the response is very fast *(1 mark)*.
c) Histamine wouldn't be able to bind to the receptors on the target cells *(1 mark)* so the area wouldn't become inflamed *(1 mark)*.

3 a) Time 1 shows repolarisation *(1 mark)* because the sodium ion channels are closed and the potassium ion channels are open *(1 mark)*. The membrane is more permeable to potassium so potassium ions diffuse out of the neurone down their concentration gradient *(1 mark)*. Time 2 shows hyperpolarisation/the refractory period *(1 mark)* because both the sodium and potassium ion channels are closed *(1 mark)*. There is no movement of sodium or potassium through their ion channels (by facilitated diffusion) *(1 mark)*.
If a question tells you to 'use evidence' from a source (like a diagram, graph, table, etc.) this means you need to include figures or descriptions using the source. So in this case, you need to say which ion channels are open and closed in the diagram.
b) i) Sodium-potassium pumps use active transport *(1 mark)* to move three sodium ions out of the cell *(1 mark)* for every two potassium ions moved in *(1 mark)*.
ii) The potassium ion channel is slow to close *(1 mark)* so too many potassium ions diffuse out of the neurone *(1 mark)*. The potential difference is more negative than the neurone cell membrane's resting potential, so the pump returns the membrane to its resting potential *(1 mark)*.

c) When a stimulus excites the neurone, sodium ions won't be able to diffuse into the neurone through sodium ion channels *(1 mark)*. This means that the threshold level won't be reached *(1 mark)* so there will be no action potentials/no nervous impulses *(1 mark)*.

6. Synaptic Transmission
Page 132 — Application Questions
Q1 The main symptom will be muscle weakness. Calcium ions are unable to enter the synaptic knob. This means the synaptic vesicles won't fuse with the presynaptic membrane so ACh will not be released. Without the release of ACh there will be no action potential triggered in the muscle cell and therefore no response in the muscle.
If you understand what happens when Ca^{2+} ions do enter the synaptic knob then it should be pretty logical that when they can't enter, the opposite happens.

Q2 a) They will reduce the sensation of pain. They function as inhibitory neurotransmitters so when they bind to receptors on the postsynaptic membrane it will be hyperpolarised. This means no action potential will be fired and therefore pain signals will not be transmitted.
b) It will reduce the sensation of pain / it will have the same effect as endorphins. This is because it is very similar in structure to an endorphin molecule so it is likely to cause the same effect.

Q3 Carbachol mimics the action of ACh so the presence of carbachol will activate even more cholinergic receptors. This will make more action potentials fire in the postsynaptic neurone, so more saliva will be produced.

Page 132 — Fact Recall Questions
Q1 A — synaptic knob, B — vesicle, C — Acetylcholine/ACh, D — presynaptic membrane, E — ACh receptor, F — postsynaptic membrane, G — synaptic cleft.
Q2 neurone, muscle, gland
Q3 Receptors are only on postsynaptic membranes. This means the neurotransmitter can't activate an action potential back along the presynaptic neurone.
Q4 a) The action potential stimulates voltage-gated calcium ion channels in the presynaptic neurone to open, so calcium ions diffuse into the synaptic knob.
b) The influx of calcium ions into the synaptic knob causes the synaptic vesicles to fuse with the presynaptic membrane. The vesicles release ACh into the synaptic cleft. ACh diffuses across the synaptic cleft and binds to specific cholinergic receptors on the postsynaptic membrane. This causes sodium ion channels in the postsynaptic neurone to open. If the threshold is reached, the influx of sodium ions into the postsynaptic membrane causes an action potential on the postsynaptic membrane.
Q5 So the response doesn't keep happening.
Q6 A cholinergic synapse between a motor neurone and a muscle cell.
Q7 E.g. The postsynaptic membrane at a neuromuscular junction has lots of folds that form clefts which store AChE. / The postsynaptic membrane at a neuromuscular junction has more receptors than other synapses. / When a motor neurone fires an action potential at a neuromuscular junction, it always triggers a response in a muscle cell.
Q8 An inhibitory neurotransmitter hyperpolarises the postsynaptic membrane, preventing it from firing an action potential.

Q9 a) Where two or more presynaptic neurones release their neurotransmitters at the same time onto the same postsynaptic neurone, the small amount of neurotransmitter released from each of these neurones can be enough altogether to reach the threshold in the postsynaptic neurone. This makes an action potential more likely.
b) Where two or more nerve impulses arrive in quick succession from the same presynaptic neurone, more neurotransmitter is released into the synaptic cleft. This makes an action potential more likely.

7. Effectors — Muscles
Page 135 — Application Questions
Q1 a) B
b) C
c) A and C
d) B
Q2 Option 1. The A-band has stayed the same length, the I-band is shorter and the H-zone is shorter.
Remember, the A-band is the length of the myosin filament and this doesn't get shorter during contraction. During contraction more of the actin filament slides over the myosin filament so the sections with only actin (the I-bands) get shorter and the sections with only myosin (the H-zones) get shorter too.

Page 137 — Application Questions
Q1 a) i) X. The Ca^{2+} concentration is low, suggesting that the muscle is at rest. Muscle fibres are longest when they are relaxed.
ii) Y. There is an influx of Ca^{2+} ions into the sarcoplasm following an action potential, and the Ca^{2+} ions bind to troponin.
iii) Y. The Ca^{2+} ion concentration is high and Ca^{2+} ions activate ATPase.
b) The Ca^{2+} ions are moved by active transport from the sarcoplasm back into sarcoplasmic reticulum, where they're stored.
c) An action potential from a motor neurone stimulates a muscle cell and depolarises the sarcolemma. Depolarisation spreads down the T-tubules to the sarcoplasmic reticulum, causing the sarcoplasmic reticulum to release stored Ca^{2+} ions into the sarcoplasm.
Q2 The influx of calcium ions triggers muscle contraction, so more calcium ions in the sarcoplasm would increase the strength of contraction of cardiac/heart muscle, which would help to pump more blood around the body of patients with heart failure.

Page 139 — Application Question
Q1 a) For the first 26 miles, ATP is likely to be generated via aerobic respiration because the body is being supplied with oxygen. As she sprints the last 385 yards ATP is likely to be generated via anaerobic respiration because the body won't be taking in enough oxygen.
b) Slow twitch. E.g. because they can contract slowly and can work for a long time without getting tired, which makes them good for endurance activities like long-distance running.

Page 139 — Fact Recall Questions
Q1 The T-tubules are parts of the sarcolemma that fold inwards across the muscle fibre and stick to the sarcoplasm. They help to spread electrical impulses throughout the sarcoplasm so they reach all parts of the muscle fibre.

Q2 An A-band contains myosin filaments and some overlapping actin filaments. Under an electron microscope it appears as a dark band.

Q3 Myosin and actin filaments slide over one another to make the sarcomeres contract (the myofilaments themselves don't contract).

Q4 Troponin and tropomyosin.

Q5 Calcium ions in the sarcoplasm bind to troponin in the myofibrils, causing troponin to change shape. This pulls the attached tropomyosin out of the actin-myosin binding site on the actin filament. This exposes the binding site, which allows the myosin head to bind and form an actin-myosin cross bridge.

Q6 ATP is broken down by ATPase to provide the energy needed to move the myosin head from side to side, which pulls the actin filament along in a rowing action. ATP also provides the energy needed to break the myosin-actin cross bridge, so the myosin head detaches from the actin filament after it's moved.

Q7 a) ATP is made by phosphorylating ADP with a phosphate group taken from PCr.
   b) Advantage: e.g. the ATP-PCr system generates ATP very quickly / it can be used during short bursts of vigorous exercise / it's anaerobic/doesn't need oxygen / it's alactic/ doesn't form any lactate.
   Disadvantage: e.g. PCr runs out after only a few seconds.
   c) Aerobic respiration and anaerobic respiration.

Q8 E.g. they have lots of mitochondria and blood vessels to supply the muscles with oxygen, as they use aerobic respiration. They are rich in myoglobin, a red-coloured protein that stores oxygen.

8. Control of Heart Rate
Page 141 — Application Question
Q1 The chemoreceptors in a person with anaemia will detect low oxygen levels in the blood. The chemoreceptors will send impulses along sensory neurones to the medulla, which will send impulses along sympathetic neurones. These neurones will secrete noradrenaline, which will bind to receptors on the sinoatrial node/SAN and cause the heart rate to increase.

Page 141 — Fact Recall Questions
Q1 a) To control unconscious activities of the body.
   b) The sympathetic nervous system and the parasympathetic nervous system.

Q2 medulla (oblongata)

Q3 a) baroreceptor/pressure receptor
   b) vena cava and aorta

8. Responses in Plants
Page 144 — Application Questions
Q1 9.9 – 1.2 = 8.7 cm growth in 30 days
8.7 cm × 10 = 87 mm
30 days × 24 = 720 hours
87 ÷ 720 = **0.12 mm/hour**

Q2 IAA is an auxin which stimulates the growth of shoots, so plant 2 must have had the highest concentration to produce the greatest growth rate (13.1 cm in 30 days).
To answer this question you'll need to have worked out how much each plant grew. Plant 1 grew by 8.7 cm, plant 2 by 13.1 cm, plant 3 by 4.7 cm and plant 4 by 11.5 cm — so plant 2 grew the most.

Q3 Strengths, e.g. a control was used, with glucose but no IAA in the paste, to rule out any factor other than IAA having an effect on shoot growth. The plants were left for 30 days to establish growth and measured at constant regular intervals. Each stump was completely coated with IAA so the shoots would have grown straight upwards, which gives an easy way to measure height (more accurate than measuring the height of a bent shoot).
Weaknesses, e.g. only four shoots were used so the sample size was small, so the results aren't very reliable. The experiment was not repeated to increase its reliability.

Page 145 — Fact Recall Questions
Q1 phototropism
Q2 They grow in the opposite direction to the force of gravity.
Q3 The growing regions of the plant / shoots and leaves.
Q4 They stimulate growth by cell elongation.
Q5 IAA is an auxin that's produced in the tips of shoots in flowering plants.
Q6 By diffusion and active transport over short distances, and via the phloem over long distances.
Q7 a) IAA moves to the more shaded parts of the shoot. This means the cells on the shaded part of the shoot grow faster than the cells most exposed to light. This pattern of growth causes the shoot to bend towards the light.
   b) IAA moves to the underside of roots. This means the cells on the underside of the root don't grow as quickly as the cells on the upper-side. This pattern of growth causes the root to grow downwards in the same direction as gravity.

Exam-style Questions — pages 147-148
1 a) The GLUT4 protein content of MHC I/slow twitch muscle fibres increased from a mean value of around 47% of the standard before training, to a mean value of around 57% of the standard after training *(1 mark)*. The GLUT4 protein content of MHC IIA/fast twitch muscle fibres increased from a mean value of around 39% of the standard before training, to a mean value of around 45% of the standard after training *(1 mark)*.
   b) i) Myosin filaments have globular heads that are hinged *(1 mark)*. Each myosin head has a binding site for actin *(1 mark)* and a binding site for ATP *(1 mark)*.
      ii) The myosin head binds to the actin filament and forms an actin-myosin cross bridge *(1 mark)*. Energy released from ATP moves the myosin head to the side, which pulls the actin filament along in a rowing action/power stroke *(1 mark)*. ATP also provides the energy to break the actin-myosin cross bridge *(1 mark)* so the myosin head detaches from the actin filament after it's moved *(1 mark)*. The myosin head then returns to it's starting position and reattaches to a different binding site further along the actin filament *(1 mark)*. As the cycle is repeated, the myosin head pulls the actin filament along, causing the muscle to contract *(1 mark)*.
   c) Low-intensity exercise uses aerobic respiration, which is how energy is released in MHC I/slow twitch muscle fibres *(1 mark)*.
   d) Function — e.g. to contract very quickly / to contract powerfully *(1 mark)*.
   Adaptations — e.g. energy is released quickly through anaerobic respiration using glycogen in fast twitch muscle fibres *(1 mark)*. They have stores of PCr so that energy can be generated very quickly when needed *(1 mark)*.

2 a) The action potential arrives in the synaptic knob of the motor neurone and stimulates voltage-gated calcium ion channels to open *(1 mark)*. Calcium ions diffuse into the synaptic knob *(1 mark)* and cause the synaptic vesicles to fuse with the presynaptic membrane *(1 mark)*. The vesicles release acetylcholine (ACh) into the synaptic cleft *(1 mark)*. ACh diffuses across the synaptic cleft *(1 mark)* and binds to specific (nicotinic) cholinergic receptors on the motor end plate/postsynaptic membrane *(1 mark)*. This causes sodium ion channels in the muscle cell to open *(1 mark)*. The influx of sodium ions into the muscle cell membrane causes an action potential if the threshold is reached *(1 mark)*. **Up to a maximum of 6 marks.**

   b) i) temporal summation *(1 mark)*
      ii) More neurotransmitter/ACh will be released into the synaptic cleft *(1 mark)*. This means more neurotransmitter/ACh will bind to receptors on the postsynaptic membrane/muscle cell *(1 mark)*. This causes more sodium ion channels to open *(1 mark)* and a greater influx of sodium ions *(1 mark)*, which makes the muscle cell more likely to reach threshold and fire an action potential *(1 mark)*.

   c) Tubocurarine prevents ACh from binding to the (nicotinic) cholinergic receptors *(1 mark)*. This means sodium ion channels on the muscle cell do not open *(1 mark)* so there's no influx of sodium ions into the muscle cell *(1 mark)*. No action potentials can be fired so the muscles cannot be stimulated to contract/move *(1 mark)*.

   This question's worth 4 marks, which tells you that a bit of detail is needed in your answer.

3 a) phototropism *(1 mark)*
   b) The seedling should have been from a Goosegrass plant and potted in soil from the same source *(1 mark)*. There should have been no lamp/light from any direction present *(1 mark)*.
   c) Seeding A will be bent to the right *(1 mark)* because it will have grown towards the light *(1 mark)*. Seedling B will have grown straight up *(1 mark)* because the rotation of the seedling means that the light is not continuously coming from one direction *(1 mark)*. Seedling C will be bent towards the left but will have a kink in, so that it is not a smooth bend *(1 mark)* because it will have grown to the right for five days, then to the left for five days and to the right again for the last five days, as the light has been coming from a different direction *(1 mark)*.
   d) IAA/auxins *(1 mark)* move to the most shaded parts of the plant *(1 mark)*. This means the shaded parts of the shoot grow faster/elongate more than the parts exposed to light *(1 mark)*. This uneven growth leads to the shoot bending towards the light *(1 mark)*.

Section 2: Homeostasis

1. Homeostasis Basics
Page 152 — Application Questions
Q1 a) At point A low concentrations of calcium in the blood are detected. This stimulates the secretion of PTH, which travels in the blood to effectors. At point B effectors are responding by increasing the concentration of calcium in the blood.
   b) At point C high concentrations of calcium in the blood are detected. This stimulates the secretion of calcitonin which travels in the blood to effectors. At point D effectors are responding by decreasing the concentration of calcium in the blood.

Q2 Having more than one negative feedback mechanism means there is more control over changes in the blood calcium concentration. It means that the blood calcium concentration can be actively increased or decreased to return it to normal rather than just changing it in one direction. Also the response is faster than only having one negative feedback mechanism.

Q3 The concentration of calcium in the blood may fall very low. This is because less PTH will be released to bring the levels back up to normal.

Page 152 — Fact Recall Questions
Q1 The maintenance of a constant internal environment.
Q2 So that metabolic reactions can occur at an optimum rate. Low temperatures make metabolic reactions slower, but if the temperature gets too high the reaction essentially stops.
Q3 If blood glucose concentration is too high the water potential of blood is reduced to a point where water molecules diffuse out of cells into the blood by osmosis. This can cause the cells to shrivel up and die. If blood glucose concentration is too low, cells are unable to carry out normal activities because there isn't enough glucose for respiration to provide energy.
Q4 A positive feedback mechanism amplifies a change from the normal level, whereas a negative feedback mechanism restores the level to normal.

2. Control of Body Temperature
Pages 153-154 — Application Questions
Q1 a) The external temperature was low/it was cold because the snake is an ectotherm and appears dark/is not radiating any heat/is cold.
   b) The mouse because it's warmer than the snake, meaning it has more energy available (from metabolic reactions) for activity.

Q2 a) The internal temperature of the chuckwalla increases as the external temperature increases. This suggests that the chuckwalla is an ectotherm as its internal temperature depends on the external temperature. The internal temperature of the hoatzin stays roughly the same as the external temperature increases. This suggests that the hoatzin is an endotherm as it can control its internal body temperature by homeostasis.
   b) The chuckwalla because it's internal temperature varied the most, meaning its metabolic reactions would have been most disrupted.

   Remember, metabolic reactions are controlled by enzymes and enzyme activity is greatest at an optimum temperature. Any variation from the optimum temperature will reduce enzyme activity and therefore slow down metabolic reactions.

Page 156 — Application Questions
Q1 The hot water in the bath heats up the temperature of the skin. Thermoreceptors in the skin detect body temperature is too high and send impulses to the hypothalamus. The hypothalamus then sends impulses to (muscle cells in) the arterioles near the surface of the skin causing them to dilate. More blood then flows through the capillaries in the surface layers of the dermis so more heat is lost by radiation and the body temperature is lowered. The increased blood flow in the capillaries might make the skin appear pink.

Q2 A cold external environment. When internal body temperature falls the body's responses include shivering and increased release of adrenaline and thyroxine. These mechanisms increase the rate of metabolism, which means more glucose is used. Blood glucose concentration will fall, so feelings of hunger will occur more quickly than they would do in a hot environment.

Q3 In hot weather the internal body temperature rises. Normally one of the ways the body responds to this is by vasodilation to increase heat loss. However, cocaine causes the opposite effect — vasoconstriction. This will reduce heat loss so the internal temperature will remain high. Also, an increase in muscular activity will increase respiration, so more heat will be produced. This will increase the internal body temperature further and make the person at risk of hyperthermia.

Page 156 — Fact Recall Questions
Q1 a) By changing behaviour.
   b) Internally by homeostasis as well as by changing behaviour.
Q2 Ectotherms have a variable metabolic rate and endotherms have a constantly high metabolic rate.
Q3 When the body's too hot sweat glands secrete more sweat. The water in sweat evaporates from the surface of the skin and takes heat from the body so the skin is cooled. When the body's too cold sweat glands secrete much less sweat, reducing the amount of heat lost.
   In this question you need to write about how sweat glands help the body lose heat and how they help it to conserve heat.
Q4 Muscles in the body contract in spasms when it's cold. This makes the body shiver and more heat is produced from increased respiration. The hormones adrenaline and thyroxine are released, which increases metabolism, so more heat is produced.
Q5 They constrict.
Q6 The hypothalamus.
Q7 Thermoreceptors in the skin detect skin temperature and send impulses via sensory neurones to the brain/hypothalamus.
Q8 When thermoreceptors detect body temperature is too low, they send impulses to the hypothalamus, which sends impulses to effectors. Effectors respond to decrease heat loss from the body and increase heat production so body temperature returns to normal.

3. Control of Blood Glucose Concentration
Page 158 — Application Questions
Q1 Carbohydrates are broken down into glucose, so their blood glucose concentration will increase. When the pancreas detects the blood glucose concentration is too high, the β cells will secrete insulin and the α cells will stop secreting glucagon. Insulin will then bind to receptors on liver and muscle cells (the effectors). These cells will respond by taking up more glucose, activating glycogenesis and by respiring more glucose. Blood glucose concentration will then return to normal.
Q2 Glycogenolysis and gluconeogenesis both increase blood glucose concentration. If these processes don't work properly then when blood glucose concentration falls (i.e. if the person doesn't eat regularly) the body will be unable to raise the blood glucose concentration back to normal, so the person will suffer from hypoglycaemia.

Page 160 — Application Questions
Q1 a) Day 1 because blood glucose concentration increased more after lunch on day 1 (by 4.5 mmol/l) than it did after lunch on day 2 (by 3.8 mmol/l).
   b) E.g. the same dose of insulin was injected on both days. / Insulin was injected at the same time on both days.

Q2 Before lunch on day 2, because adrenaline is released when there is a low blood glucose concentration.
   There are many factors other than blood glucose concentration that affect the concentration of adrenaline in the blood, e.g. stress levels, exercise. However, in this question you've been asked to use data from the table so your answer should be about blood glucose concentration.

Page 160 — Fact Recall Questions
Q1 Insulin is secreted from the β cells and glucagon from the α cells of the islets of Langerhans in the pancreas.
Q2 It increases the permeability of liver and muscle cell membranes to glucose, activates enzymes that convert glucose into glycogen/activates glycogenesis and increases the rate of respiration of glucose in those cells.
Q3 glycogenesis
Q4 Gluconeogenesis — glycerol or amino acids are converted to glucose. Glycogenolysis — glycogen is converted to glucose.
Q5 The pancreas detects blood glucose is too low. α cells secrete glucagon and β cells stop secreting insulin. Glucagon binds to receptors on liver cells. The liver cells respond to increase the blood glucose concentration (e.g. glycogenolysis is activated), so blood glucose concentration returns to normal.
Q6 Adrenaline binds to its specific receptors on the cell surface membrane (of liver cells), which causes an enzyme called adenylate cyclase to be activated inside the cell. Activated adenylate cyclase converts ATP into a second messenger called cAMP. cAMP activates a cascade (chain of reactions) that breaks down glycogen into glucose.
Q7 By controlling simple carbohydrate intake and losing weight, or taking glucose-lowering tablets if these don't work.

4. Control of the Menstrual Cycle
Page 161 — Fact Recall Questions
Q1 FSH stimulates the follicle to develop. LH stimulates ovulation and stimulates the corpus luteum to develop.
Q2 a) oestrogen
   b) progesterone
Q3 a) FSH and LH
   b) oestrogen and progesterone

Pages 163-164 — Application Questions
Q1 a) Between day 10 and day 13 oestrogen concentration rises. Oestrogen inhibits FSH release from the anterior pituitary gland, so the levels of FSH are kept low, preventing the development of any more follicles.
   b) A high concentration of oestrogen stimulates the anterior pituitary gland to release LH. LH stimulates the ovaries to release more oestrogen. Oestrogen further stimulates the anterior pituitary gland to release more LH, and so on, causing LH concentration to surge.
   c) i) Day 0, because there is an LH surge which stimulates ovulation.
      ii) Day 15, because the concentration of progesterone starts to fall.
Q2 After menopause, the ovaries will no longer produce oestrogen. This means that the blood concentration of oestrogen will fall, so the release of FSH will no longer be inhibited and so the blood concentration of FSH will be high. Also the ovaries will no longer produce progesterone, which means that it won't inhibit FSH release from the anterior pituitary, so the blood concentration of FSH will be very high.
   Remember that ovaries produce both oestrogen and progesterone, so you need to consider the effects of both hormones in your answer.

Q3 Giving the sows progesterone will 'pause' their menstrual cycles because the release of FSH and LH is inhibited. This means the follicles won't be able to develop and the sows can't ovulate. When the progesterone is stopped, FSH and LH will be released, which will stimulate ovulation. As all the sows stop having the progesterone simultaneously, they should all ovulate (and be ready for breeding) at the same time.

Q4 LH is detected. When LH concentrations surge/are very high ovulation occurs, meaning the follicle ruptures and the egg is released, ready to be fertilised.

Exam-style Questions — pages 165-166

1   a) As the temperature increases the activity level of Organism A increases, and as the temperature decreases the activity level of Organism A decreases / there is a positive correlation between the activity level of Organism A and temperature *(1 mark)*. The activity level of Organism B changes randomly as the temperature changes / there is no correlation between the activity level of Organism B and temperature *(1 mark)*.

   b) i) Organism A because an ectotherm is more active in warmer external temperatures than it is in colder temperatures *(1 mark)*.

       ii) Squirrels are endotherms so they can control their body temperature internally by homeostasis *(1 mark)*. This means their internal temperature is much less affected by external temperature compared to tortoises, so they can survive in a wider range of external temperatures *(1 mark)*.

   c) i) Point X was relatively cold compared to point Y, so thermoreceptors in the squirrels's skin will have detected a fall in temperature *(1 mark)*. The thermoreceptors will have sent impulses to the hypothalamus *(1 mark)* which will have sent impulses to erector pili muscles / effectors to make the hairs stand up *(1 mark)* to trap more air and so prevent heat loss *(1 mark)*.

       ii) More sweat may be secreted from the squirrel's sweat glands *(1 mark)*. When the sweat evaporates it will take heat from the body so the skin is cooled *(1 mark)*. The squirrel's erector pili muscles may relax so its hairs lie flat *(1 mark)*. This means less air is trapped, so the skin is less insulated and heat can be lost more easily *(1 mark)*. Vasodilation may occur near the surface of the squirrel's skin *(1 mark)*. This means more heat is lost form the skin by radiation so the temperature of the skin is lowered *(1 mark)*.

2   a) Low levels of FSH would decrease a woman's fertility *(1 mark)*, because a high FSH concentration is needed to stimulate follicle development *(1 mark)*.

   b) i) E.g. the level of oestrogen is maintained at a level that won't stimulate the release of LH *(1 mark)*, which means ovulation won't occur *(1 mark)*. / The level of progesterone is kept high, which inhibits the release of FSH and LH *(1 mark)* so no follicles will develop *(1 mark)*.

       ii) Within the 7 days the uterus lining will break down and menstruation will occur *(1 mark)*. This is because a high progesterone concentration is needed to maintain the uterus lining and progesterone concentration will fall when the pill isn't taken *(1 mark)*.

   c)   positive feedback *(1 mark)*

3   a) i) The Type II diabetic doesn't produce as much insulin as the non-diabetic. / The body's cells don't respond properly to the insulin that's produced *(1 mark)*. Insulin lowers blood glucose concentration when it's too high, so if there's not enough insulin / the body can't respond to insulin properly, this process will be much slower *(1 mark)*.

       ii) More quickly, because more glucose is respired during exercise to provide energy *(1 mark)*.

   b) A Type I diabetic wouldn't produce any insulin *(1 mark)*. This means that blood glucose concentration would remain high for much longer than for this Type II diabetic *(1 mark)*.

   c) i) 22.5 minutes *(1 mark)*. This is because this is the time when the blood glucose concentration is at its upper limit / 110 mg/100 cm³ *(1 mark)*.

   You're told the normal range for blood glucose concentration in the introduction to the question — make sure you always read questions thoroughly in the exam.

       ii) Insulin is a hormone, so it takes time to travel in the blood to receptor cells *(1 mark)*.

   d) When blood glucose concentration falls below 82 mg/100 cm³ the pancreas is stimulated to secrete glucagon *(1 mark)* and stop secreting insulin *(1 mark)*. Glucagon binds to specific receptors on liver cells *(1 mark)*. The liver cells respond to increase blood glucose concentration — glycogenolysis is activated *(1 mark)*, gluconeogenesis is activated *(1 mark)* and the cells respire less glucose *(1 mark)*.

Section 3: Genetics
1. DNA and RNA
Page 169 — Fact Recall Questions
Q1 ribose sugar

Q2 a) adenine, thymine, guanine and cytosine
       b) adenine, uracil, guanine and cytosine
       c) adenine, uracil, guanine and cytosine
   Remember, mRNA and tRNA both have the same bases.

Q3 DNA and mRNA are both polynucleotide chains with a sugar-phosphate backbone. But while DNA is a double-stranded molecule twisted into a double helix shape, mRNA molecules are single-stranded. Also, the sugar in DNA is deoxyribose whereas in mRNA it's ribose. The base T (thymine) in DNA is replaced by U (uracil) in mRNA.

Q4 tRNA is a single polynucleotide strand that's folded into a clover shape. It's held together by hydrogen bonds between the base pairs. Every tRNA molecule has a specific sequence of three bases on one end called an anticodon. They also have an amino acid binding site at the other end.

2. Protein Synthesis
Pages 171-172 — Application Questions
Q1 It will inhibit protein synthesis. By inhibiting RNA polymerase, α–amanitin will prevent the transcription of mRNA from DNA, preventing protein synthesis from taking place.

Q2 a) UCAAGCCUGCUCGGCUACGAGCAUUU
       b) UCAAGCUCGGCUACGAGC
       c) 6
   Remember, one amino acid is coded for by three bases in an exon.

Page 173 — Application Questions

Q1 E.g. it may affect the function of the ribosomes, preventing them from translating mRNA into amino acids. This could prevent/impair protein synthesis.

You don't need to have learnt about Diamond-Blackfan anaemia to answer this question — so long as you know the process of translation, you can work out the answer.

Q2 It could be shorter and so could be a different protein. Translation of the mRNA sequence only continues until a stop signal is reached. Any codons after the stop signal would not be translated into amino acids.

Page 173 — Fact Recall Questions

Q1 Transcription — takes place in the nucleus. Translation — takes place at the ribosomes in the cytoplasm.

Q2 a) an enzyme
   b) transcription
   c) RNA polymerase attaches to the DNA double helix, and it lines up free RNA nucleotides alongside the template strand. It then moves along the DNA strand, assembling a complementary mRNA sequence from free RNA nucleotides.

Q3 Because of specific base pairing.

Q4 Eukaryotic DNA contains introns/regions that don't code for amino acids. These get transcribed into pre-mRNA along with the exons/coding regions. Splicing removes the introns from pre-mRNA and joins together the exons to create mRNA ready for translation into a protein.

Q5 tRNA molecules carry amino acids to the ribosome during translation.

Q6 A tRNA molecule with an anticodon that's complementary to the first codon on the mRNA attaches itself to the mRNA by specific base pairing. A second tRNA molecule attaches itself to the next codon on the mRNA in the same way, and so on.

Q7 peptide bond

3. The Genetic Code and Nucleic Acids

Page 176 — Application Questions

Q1 UACUUUCAAAUAGCGCAU

Q2 TACAAAGTTGTTCGCATGTAT

Remember, DNA is a complementary sequence to mRNA and in DNA, T replaces U as a base.

Q3 UACGUAUAUGUAAAAGUU

tRNA codons also have a complementary sequence to mRNA codons, but tRNA still has U as a base.

Q4 Phe - Gln - Ile - His - Ala - Tyr

To answer this question, work out what the complementary mRNA codons would be first then match up the appropriate amino acids using the table.

Q5 The DNA sequence is missing the base triplets: CGC, TAT and GTT. The amino acid sequence is missing: Tyr and His.

Page 177 — Application Questions

Q1 Uracil is present as a base in mRNA but not DNA, so the scientists would have been able to use uracil as a marker for RNA synthesis.

Q2 As the concentration of puromycin increased, the % inhibition of the development of respiration, leucine uptake and uracil uptake also increased. The development of respiration and leucine uptake were strongly inhibited, with uracil uptake being inhibited to a slightly lesser degree.

Q3 protein synthesis

Page 177 — Fact Recall Questions

Q1 Each triplet is read in sequence, separate from the triplet before it and after it — base triplets don't share their bases.

Q2 A base triplet that tells the cell when to start production of a particular protein.

Q3 universal

4. Regulation of Transcription and Translation

Page 179 — Application Questions

Q1 Less of the transcription factor coded for by the MECP2 gene is produced, so it is unable to repress the transcription of other genes. These genes remain active which affects the normal functioning of nerve cells, leading to Rett syndrome.

You don't need to know anything about Rett syndrome to answer this question because it's testing your knowledge of transcription. But you still need to make sure that you apply your knowledge to the disease in the question.

Q2 siRNA could be produced that is complimentary to the genes causing AMD. The siRNA and associated proteins would bind to the target mRNA and the proteins would cut up the mRNA into sections so it would no longer be translated.

Page 181 — Application Questions

Q1 Any three from, e.g. temperature / the presence of other amino acids / the length of time the bacteria are left for / volume of culture / number of bacteria / amount of tryptophan added.

Q2 a) In normal bacteria in the presence of tryptophan, the amount of target mRNA is reduced by about 70-fold. This is because when tryptophan is present it binds to the repressor, allowing it to bind to the target gene and reduce transcription. A reduction in transcription means much less mRNA is produced, and therefore much less tryptophan is produced.
   b) Bacteria do not need to produce more tryptophan if it's already present, so transcription stops to prevent the bacteria from wasting energy on producing something they don't need.

Q3 The mutant bacteria produce a similar amount of tryptophan in both the presence and absence of tryptophan. This could be because, e.g. the mutation affected the DNA base sequence of the tryptophan repressor, so it can no longer bind to DNA even in the presence of tryptophan. This means it can't prevent transcription and so tryptophan is always produced.

Page 181 — Fact Recall Questions

Q1 Protein molecules that control the transcription of genes.

Q2 a) A transcription factor that increases the rate of transcription.
   b) A transcription factor that decreases the rate of transcription.

Q3 Because not all cell types have oestrogen receptors.

Q4 the type of cell, the target gene

Q5 A small, double-stranded RNA molecule that can interfere with the expression of specific genes. / Small interfering RNA.

1 a) RNA polymerase attaches to the DNA double helix at the beginning of a gene *(1 mark)*. The hydrogen bonds between two DNA strands in the gene break, separating the strands and the DNA molecule uncoils to allow one of the strands to be used as a template *(1 mark)*. The RNA polymerase lines up free RNA nucleotides alongside the template strand *(1 mark)*. Once the RNA nucleotides have paired up with their specific bases on the DNA strand they're joined together, forming a complementary mRNA molecule *(1 mark)*. The RNA polymerase moves along the DNA, separating the strands and assembling the mRNA strand *(1 mark)* until it reaches a stop signal and stops making the mRNA *(1 mark)*.

b) i) AGCGGUUGUUGUGAGC *(1 mark)*

ii) Genes in eukaryotic DNA contain introns (sections that don't code for amino acids) *(1 mark)*. After transcription the introns are removed from pre-mRNA strands by splicing, leaving only the exons (parts of the gene that code for amino acids) which form mRNA *(1 mark)*. So eukaryotic mRNA would be shorter than prokaryotic mRNA *(1 mark)*.

c) i) deletion *(1 mark)*

ii) mRNA codons: ACG GUU GUU GUG AGC
amino acids: Threonine, Valine, Valine, Valine, Serine
(1 mark for correct mRNA codons, 1 mark for correct amino acids,)

It's always a good idea to show your working for questions like this, even if it doesn't say to in the question, as you might pick up a mark even if you get the amino acids wrong.

d) It is an activator. The results show that both the normal and the mutant bacteria produce the transcription factor (7.9 and 7.7 arbitrary units) *(1 mark)*. But the mutant bacteria produce much less antibiotic mRNA (0.9 arbitrary units compared to 8.2) and much less of the antibiotic itself (the blue-colour of the antibiotic can't be seen around the mutant bacteria) *(1 mark)*. This means that the mutation must affect the transcription of mRNA *(1 mark)*. This suggests the mutant bacteria have a faulty transcription factor protein which can't bind to the start of the target gene and so can't activate transcription *(1 mark)*.

The introduction to question 1 says that the bacteria produce a blue-coloured antibiotic. Figure 1 shows that mutant bacteria don't produce the blue colour, which suggests they don't produce the antibiotic.

2 a) i) The sequence of base triplets (codons) in mRNA which code for specific amino acids *(1 mark)*.

ii) It is universal because the same specific base triplets code for the same amino acids in all living things *(1 mark)*. It is non-overlapping because each base triplet/codon is read in sequence, separate from the triplet before it and after it, so triplets don't share their bases *(1 mark)*. It is degenerate because there are more possible combinations of triplets than there are amino acids *(1 mark)*.

b) i) DNA sequence: CCT GTG CGT GGA GTG
tRNA anticodons: CCU GUG CGU GGA GUG
(1 mark for correct tRNA anticodons. Allow 1 mark if tRNA anticodons are correct but T hasn't been replaced with U.)

Remember, tRNA is complementary to a strand of mRNA — so it's just like DNA but with U replacing T.

ii) tRNA is folded into a clover shape and held together by hydrogen bonds whereas mRNA is not *(1 mark)*. Three adjacent bases in mRNA form a codon whereas tRNA has three specific bases called an anticodon *(1 mark)*. tRNA has an amino acid binding site whereas mRNA does not *(1 mark)*.

c) i) ribosome *(1 mark)*

ii) tRNA molecules carry amino acids to the ribosome *(1 mark)*. A tRNA molecule with an anticodon that's complementary to the first codon on the mRNA attaches itself to the mRNA by specific base pairing *(1 mark)*. A second tRNA molecule attaches itself to the next codon on the mRNA in the same way and the two amino acids are joined by a peptide bond *(1 mark)*. The first tRNA molecule moves away, leaving its amino acid behind *(1 mark)*. A third tRNA molecule binds to the next codon on the mRNA, it's amino acid binds to the first two and the second tRNA molecule moves away *(1 mark)*.

Always look at the number of available marks — the more marks there are, the more detailed your answer should be.

d) siRNA bases are complementary to specific sections of a target gene *(1 mark)*. siRNA and associated proteins bind to the target mRNA *(1 mark)*. The proteins then cut up the mRNA into sections *(1 mark)*. This prevents the expression of the gene so no protein/enzyme is produced *(1 mark)*.

5. Mutations
Page 186 — Application Questions

Q1 Mutation A: Leu-His-Asp-Thr
Mutation B: Leu-His-His-Thr
Mutation C: Leu-Met-Ile
Mutation D: Leu-Tyr-Asp-Thr
For questions like this, it's a good idea to split up the DNA base sequence into groups of three letters (CTT/CAT/GAT etc). Then you'll be able to see what's going on more easily.

Q2 Mutation A: no effect. CTC still codes for Leu so the amino acid sequence/primary structure of the protein won't change.
Mutations B, C and D: may change the tertiary structure of the protein since the amino acid sequence/primary structure has been altered. This may affect the protein's function.

Page 186 — Fact Recall Questions

Q1 A change to the base sequence of DNA.

Q2 No. The genetic code is degenerate/some amino acids are coded for by more than one triplet. This means that not all (substitution) mutations will result in a change to the amino acid sequence of a protein.

Q3 E.g. during DNA replication.

Q4 Something that causes an increase in the rate of mutations.

Q5 E.g. ultraviolet radiation / ionising radiation / base analogs / alkylating agents / some chemicals / some viruses.

Q6 Hereditary mutations are inherited from your parents. They're carried in the gametes, so if a gamete is fertilised the fetus will have the mutation. Acquired mutations develop during your lifetime and occur in individual cells after fertilisation.

6. Mutations and Cancer
Page 187 — Application Questions

Q1 It slows cell division by producing a protein that stops cells dividing or causes them to self-destruct.

Q2 A mutation in p53 could inactivate the gene. The protein it codes for won't be produced. This will cause cells to start dividing uncontrollably, eventually leading to cancer. *Don't worry if you've never heard of the p53 gene — you can still answer the question. You just need to apply your knowledge of tumour suppressor genes to the p53 example. You're likely to get a lot of questions like this in the exam.*

7. Diagnosing and Treating Cancer and Genetic Disorders

Page 191 — Application Questions

Q1 a) If a mutation only occurs in one of the RB1 alleles, the other one will still be able to produce a normal pRB tumour suppressor protein. This means that cell division can still be controlled. If a mutation occurs in both RB1 alleles, a normal pRB protein won't be produced and cells will start dividing uncontrollably. This could eventually lead to cancer.

b) E.g. it means that children who have inherited an RB1 mutation can be regularly screened, so that if further tumours do develop they can be diagnosed and treated earlier.

Q2 a) If CD117 is present, then it may be possible to treat the cancer with Imatinib. If it is not present, then Imantinib will be ineffective and another course of treatment will be necessary.

b) E.g. mutated tumour suppressor genes are inactivated. The protein they produce doesn't function. A drug which targets a mutated tumour suppressor gene would have to restore the function of the tumour suppressor protein, which could be difficult.

This is one of those 'suggest' questions where you're not expected to know the exact answer, but you should be able to come up with a suggestion using what you already know. A sensible answer, like the one above, will get you the marks in the exam.

Q3 E.g. any one from: if the person has inherited a HTT mutation they will definitely develop Huntington's disease, so knowing whether they have the mutation would prepare them for this. / They could be tested before having children, so they would know whether or not it was possible to pass on the HTT mutation. This may help them to decide whether or not to have children.

Q4 a) E.g. any one from: by avoiding foods containing phenylalanine. / By gene therapy to replace the faulty PKU gene, so that a functional enzyme is produced.

b) E.g. it means that treatment for PKU can begin very early in a patient's life — before phenylalanine has a chance to build up to level that will cause seizures/problems with brain development.

8. Stem Cells

Page 194 — Application Questions

Q1 The test culture of plant species A shows a greater relative mass increase than its control. Test cultures of all the other plant species show a smaller relative mass increase than their controls. Plant species B and E did not increase in mass at all when treated with gibberellin.

Q2 Gibberellin appears to completely inhibit the growth of species B and E in tissue culture and reduce the growth of species C and D. It promotes the growth of species A. This may be because, e.g. some plants are more sensitive to gibberellin than others / gibberellin interacts with other growth factors present in some plant species.

Page 194 — Fact Recall Questions

Q1 E.g. any two from: they are unspecialised cells. / They can divide to form new cells, which then become specialised. / They can divide to produce more stem cells/self-renew.

Q2 In embryos and in some adult tissues.

Q3 Totipotent stem cells can mature/develop into any type of body cell in an organism. Multipotent stem cells can only develop into a few types of cells.

Q4 Stem cells become specialised by only expressing certain genes and switching off others. Genes that are expressed get transcribed into mRNA, which is then translated into proteins. These proteins modify the cell. Changes to the cell produced by the proteins cause the cell to become specialised.

Q5 Stem cells in mature plants are totipotent/can develop into any type of cell. Stem cells in adult mammals are multipotent/can only develop into a few types of cell.

Q6 A single totipotent stem cell is taken from a meristem and placed in some sterile growth medium containing nutrients and growth factors. The stem cell will grow and divide into a mass of unspecialised cells. If the conditions are suitable the cells will mature into specialised cells. These cells can form an entire plant.

9. Stem Cells in Medicine

Page 197 — Application Questions

Q1 The bone marrow comes from a healthy donor who does not carry the mutation for sickle cell anaemia. As a result, the multipotent cells in the donor marrow will divide and differentiate to produce new, healthy red blood cells. These red blood cells won't sickle and so will function normally, curing the patient.

Q2 a) Because the stem cells can be used to form new, specialised corneal cells to replace the damaged ones.

b) E.g. any two from: there's a reduced risk of rejection as the donated cells are from the same patient. / There's no need to use embryonic stem cells, so avoids the ethical issues surrounding their use. / There's no need to wait for a donor cornea to become available.

Q3 Answer should include a discussion of the pros and cons of using embryonic stem cells in this particular investigation. E.g. pros: the embryonic stem cells are taken from donated embryos, which would otherwise be discarded. The treatment could improve the quality of the patients lives/reduce the amount of medical care they require by giving them movement.
E.g. cons: the embryonic stem cells come from embryos which could have become a fetus if placed in the womb. There are other treatments also being developed, which means the patients could potentially be treated without needing embryonic stem cells to be used.
If you're asked to discuss an issue such as this one, make sure you give both sides of the argument.

Exam-style Questions — pages 199-200

1 a) i) The APC gene must be the tumour suppressor gene. It slows cell division by preventing ß-catenin from carrying out its function *(1 mark)*. ß-catenin activates genes needed for cell division, so the ß-catenin gene must be the proto-oncogene *(1 mark)*.

ii) E.g. a mutation in the ß-catenin gene could cause it to become overactive and stimulate the cell to divide uncontrollably, causing cancer *(1 mark)*. A mutation in the APC gene could prevent the protein from carrying out its function of destroying ß-catenin, so the cell would be stimulated to divide uncontrollably *(1 mark)*.

b) A deletion of one or more bases will affect the number of bases present, causing a shift in all the base triplets that follow *(1 mark)* and this could cause a change in the amino acid sequence/primary structure of the protein *(1 mark)*. This could change the tertiary structure of the protein and prevent it from functioning *(1 mark)*.

c) E.g. any one from: it could allow you to have regular screening/tests to help doctors diagnose colon cancer in its early stages. / It may affect the treatment you are given if and when you develop colon cancer. *(1 mark for any sensible answer.)*

2 a) Something that increases the rate of mutations in DNA *(1 mark)*.

b) E.g. any one from: it could cause a shift in the way the base triplets are read *(1 mark)*, which could change the sequence of coded amino acids *(1 mark)*. / It could stop the amino acid sequence being transcribed after this point *(1 mark)*, resulting in a shorter amino acid sequence *(1 mark)*. / It could stop the gene being transcribed at all *(1 mark)*, which could prevent the protein being produced *(1 mark)*.

c) E.g. if they insert into a mutated proto-oncogene (an oncogene) *(1 mark)*, they may alter the amino acid sequence of the protein it produces and prevent it from functioning normally *(1 mark)*. The protein would no longer be able to stimulate the cell to divide uncontrollably *(1 mark)*.

3 a) i) As the plant cells become more specialised, the relative concentration of alkaloid in the cells increases *(1 mark)*.

ii) $1.85 - 0.45 = 1.4$ (accept 1.35 to 1.45)
$\frac{1.4}{0.45} \times 100 = \textbf{311\%}$ (accept 300 to 322%)

(1 mark for correct working, 2 marks for correct answer)

b) i) E.g. the auxins are needed to quickly produce a large number of cells early on in the tissue culture *(1 mark)*, but alkaloid production is much higher in specialised cells, so auxins are later removed because they reduce cell specialisation *(1 mark)*.

ii) E.g. cells become specialised by expressing certain genes and switching off others *(1 mark)*. Genes that are expressed get transcribed into mRNA and then translated into proteins *(1 mark)*. The proteins then modify the cell, causing it to become specialised *(1 mark)*. If auxins alter the genes that get expressed, the cell will transcribe and translate different proteins *(1 mark)*. These proteins could then modify the cell in a different way, changing the type of cell it specialises into *(1 mark)*.

c) That alkaloid production increases with cell density up to an optimum *(1 mark)* but decreases if cell density becomes too high *(1 mark)*.

Section 4: Gene Technology

1. Making DNA Fragments
Page 204 — Application Questions
Q1 reverse transcriptase
Q2 a) top strand = CGTA, bottom strand = GGTA
b) $2 \times 2 \times 2 \times 2 \times 2 \times 2 \times 2 = \textbf{128}$
Remember, you start with two single strands of DNA. The amount of DNA then doubles with each PCR cycle.

Q3 There is a *Bam*HI site on the left hand side of the fragment and an *Eco*RI site towards the right hand side. The DNA sample could be incubated with *Bam*HI and *Eco*RI, which would cut the DNA via a hydrolysis reaction at these sites. This is because the shape of each recognition sequence is complementary to each enzyme's active site.

Page 204 — Fact Recall Questions
Q1 a) complementary DNA / a DNA copy of an mRNA molecule
b) mRNA is isolated from cells, then mixed with free DNA nucleotides and reverse transcriptase. The reverse transcriptase uses the mRNA as a template to synthesise new strands of cDNA.
c) mRNA is often easier to obtain than a DNA fragment containing the target gene. / There are generally more mRNA versions of a gene than DNA versions of a gene in a cell.

Q2 polymerase chain reaction
Q3 A sequence of DNA that consists of antiparallel base pairs/ base pairs that read the same in opposite directions.
Q4 Small tails of unpaired bases at the end of a DNA fragment. They can be used to bind/anneal the DNA fragment to another piece of DNA that has sticky ends with complementary sequences.

2. Gene Cloning
Pages 207-208 — Application Questions
Q1 a) He's studying a protein, so possibly was using *in vivo* cloning to produce the protein. *In vitro* cloning only produces DNA.
Other possible answers: He might have wanted to produce mRNA and *in vitro* cloning only produces DNA. / He might have wanted to produce modified mRNA/ DNA/protein and *in vitro* cloning only produces DNA. / The gene maybe too long for *in vitro* cloning.
Although there are other possible answers here the top one is most likely given the information you're given in the question.

b) Vector DNA was cut with the same restriction endonucleases as the DNA fragment, so complementary sticky ends were produced. The DNA fragment and cut vector were mixed with ligase and the pieces were joined together to form the recombinant DNA. A marker gene must also be present in the recombinant DNA, so may have been inserted at the same time as the DNA fragment or existed in the vector DNA already.
In the exam, put down as much information as you can. Here there are a few details on how the DNA fragment was made and how the marker gene got in there, as they all form part of the recombinant DNA.

c) It's likely he put a marker gene for resistance to penicillin in as part of the recombinant DNA. He grew the plates on agar containing penicillin so he could identify which colonies contained transformed cells (cells with the target gene in).

Q2 a) The plasmids are vectors — they're used to transfer the target gene into the host cells/*E.coli*.
b) The ampicillin resistance gene is a marker gene. It means that only *E. coli* containing the plasmid will grow on the agar (which contains ampicillin).

c) *E.coli* that have taken up plasmids containing the target gene will be white/colourless because the target gene has disrupted the LacZα gene in the bacterial plasmids. This means the LacZα gene won't have produced the correct protein, so the *E.coli* won't have been able to produce β-galactosidase and therefore won't have been able to break down X-gal into a blue pigment.
E.coli containing plasmids without the target gene will be blue because they will contain both the LacZα and LacZΩ genes — this will enable them to produce functional β-galactosidase and therefore breakdown X-gal into a blue pigment.

Page 208 — Fact Recall Questions
Q1 The polymerase chain reaction (PCR).
Q2 In *in vivo* cloning, gene copies are made inside a living organism. In *in vitro* cloning, gene copies are made outside of a living organism (using PCR).
Q3 A vector is something that's used to transfer DNA into a cell.
Q4 E.g. a plasmid / bacteriophage
Q5 restriction endonuclease enzymes
Q6 Ligases are used to join the sticky ends of the DNA fragment containing the target gene to the sticky ends of the vector DNA.
Q7 A cell into which the target gene/recombinant DNA is transferred into.
Q8 That it has taken up the vector containing the target gene.
Q9 Not all cells will take up the vector — the ones that do need to be identified so they can be allowed to grow and produce lots of copies of the cloned gene.
Q10 Identifying transformed cells.
Q11 E.g. it's quite a slow process. / The DNA fragment has to be isolated from other cell components.

3. Genetic Engineering
Page 211 — Application Questions
Q1 A DNA fragment containing the resistance gene could be made using reverse transcriptase, PCR or cut out using restriction endonucleases. The DNA fragment could be inserted into a plasmid vector which could then be added to a bacterium. The bacterium could then be used as a vector to get the gene into the soybean pant cells.
Q2 Fields of the soybean crop could be sprayed with the herbicide, killing the weeds but not the crop. This could increase the yield from the field.
Q3 E.g. if the transformed soybean crop interbreed with wild plants it could possibility result in 'superweeds' — weeds that are resistant to a herbicide. / Farmers might plant only this soybean crop, which could make the whole crop vulnerable to disease because the plants are genetically identical/reduce biodiversity in the area. / This one large agricultural company could end up controlling soybean production, forcing smaller companies out of business.
These are all good answers, but as the question specifically talks about herbicide resistance, the superweed concern is probably the best answer to give as it's the most specific to the context you're given.

4. Genetic Fingerprinting
Page 215 — Application Questions
Q1 Some parts of an organism's genome consist of repetitive, non-coding base sequences. These repeated sequences occur in lots of places in the genome and the number of times these sequences are repeated differs from organism to organism. Genetic fingerprinting looks at the number of times some of these sequences are repeated at different loci in an individual's genome.

Q2 a) To make many copies of the areas of DNA that contain the repeated sequences. / To add fluorescent tags to the DNA so it can be seen under UV light.
b) To separate the fragments of DNA by length, producing a genetic fingerprint.
These techniques can be used for lots of different reasons in gene technology. So make sure you clearly understand what each one does, then you should be able to work out why it's been used in any situation you're given.
Q3 No, the woman does not appear to be the diplomat's daughter. Only one band is found in the same position for both the woman and the diplomat. You would expect more than this if he was her father.

5. Locating and Sequencing Genes
Page 220 — Application Questions
Q1 a) Three, because in the total digest column there are four fragments produced.
Even if you aren't asked for the total number of recognition sequences in a DNA fragment, it can be a really good place to start when working out a restriction map — here you can already sketch a very rough map with three 'cut lines'.
b)

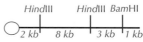

This is a tough one, so let's go through it together. Let's look at the simplest column first — the BamHI column gives two fragments, so there's only one BamHI recognition site. This could be either of the following:

The radioactive column shows a 13 kb piece but no 1 kb piece, so it must be the second map (13 kb on the left).
Next you've got the HindIII column. There are three fragments, so two sites recognition sites and lots of possible combinations. Looking at the radioactive column again, there's a 2 kb fragment, so the 2 kb piece must be radioactively tagged. So the map could be either of:

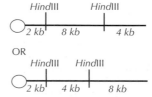

Combine both of these with BamHI and you get either:

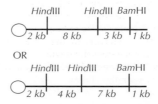

Looking in the total digest column you can see there's a 3 kb piece but no 7 kb piece, so it must be the first map — hurrah.

Q2 a) A sample of DNA from each species was digested into fragments using restriction enzymes and separated using electrophoresis. The separated DNA fragments were then transferred to a nylon membrane and incubated with the fluorescently labelled DNA probe which is complementary to part of the antibiotic gene sequence. The membrane was then exposed to UV light.

b) It appears that B might produce a similar antibiotic. *Don't worry that the florescent bands are at different heights in the Known species lane and the Species B lane — the restriction enzymes will have just cut at different places to give DNA fragments of slightly different lengths. The important part is that it has a fluorescent band and so some similar DNA.*

Page 220 — Fact Recall Questions

Q1 DNA (gene) probes are short strands of DNA that have a specific base sequence that's complementary to the base sequence of part of a target gene.

Q2 A DNA sample is digested into fragments by restriction enzymes and is then separated by electrophoresis. The fragments are transferred to a nylon membrane and incubated with the fluorescently labelled DNA probe. If the gene is present, the DNA probe will hybridise/bind to it. The membrane is then exposed to UV light. If the gene is present, then there will be a fluorescent band.

Q3 A diagram of a piece of DNA showing where the recognition sites of the enzymes used to cut the DNA are found.

Q4 restriction endonucleases/restriction enzymes

Q5 a) Where all the restriction endonucleases used to create the map are present in the digest and the DNA is cut at all of the recognition sequences present.

b) Where the restriction enzymes haven't been left long enough to cut all of their recognition sequences.

Q6 The process used to determine the order of bases in a section of DNA.

Q7 A single-stranded DNA template, DNA polymerase, lots of DNA primer, free nucleotides and a different fluorescently-labelled modified nucleotide are added to each of four separate tubes. The tubes undergo PCR. The DNA fragments in each tube are separated by electrophoresis and visualised under UV light. The complementary base sequence can be read from the gel — the smallest nucleotide is at the bottom of the gel and you build up the DNA sequence reading upwards one base at a time.

6. DNA Probes in Medical Diagnosis

Page 223 — Application Questions

Q1 A DNA microarray should be used — microscopic spots of DNA probes for different genetic mutations (different genetic disorders) are attached to a glass slide in rows. A labelled sample of the child's DNA is washed over the array. The array is washed and visualised under UV light. Any labelled DNA attached to a probe will fluoresce, identifying any mutations in the child's DNA and so what genetic disorder they have.

Q2 They may undergo genetic counselling to help provide them with information on the treatment available for their child. They might also have counselling to help them understand the chances of them having another child with the recessive disorder. Genetic counselling will provide them with unbiased advice on the possibility of having IVF and screening their embryos for the alleles.

7. Gene Therapy

Page 226 — Application Questions

Q1 The virus is acting as a vector — it is being used to carry the new FIX gene into the body cells of the sufferers of haemophilia.

Q2 $2 + 2 + 3 + 4 + 8 + 12 \div 6 = 5.16 = \mathbf{5.2\%}$

Q3 E.g. Yes. The maximum level after gene therapy was more than 1% for all the patients and so could improve their health.

Q4 E.g. Advantages: this therapy could provide sufferers with a greater quality of life, as they may not have to receive injections for the protein multiple times a week in the future. / This therapy could save health authorities money, as the injections usually required by sufferers are expensive. Disadvantages: the effects of the treatment may be short-lived. / Multiple treatments still may be required. / The patients may have suffered from side effects, e.g. the body could identify vectors as foreign bodies and start an immune response against them. / The allele could be inserted into the wrong place in the DNA, possibly causing more problems, e.g. cancer. / The allele could be over expressed and produce too much of the protein, causing other problems.

Exam-style Questions — pages 228-229

1 a) E.g. Yes. This plant would benefit farmers living in drought-affected areas enabling them to increase their production of wheat/produce higher yields *(1 mark)*, which could help reduce the risk of famine and malnutrition *(1 mark)*. /
No. This plant could encourage farmers to carry out monoculture which decreases biodiversity *(1 mark)*. Also, transformed crops may breed with wild-type plants, leading to the spread of the genetically engineered DNA *(1 mark)*.
With questions like this, there's no right or wrong answer. The important thing is to be able to back your answer up with appropriate reasons.

b) i) To help sequence genes *(1 mark)*.
ii) DNA is radioactively labelled *(1 mark)*. The DNA is digested using restriction endonucleases/restriction enzymes *(1 mark)* and the digested fragments are separated by electrophoresis *(1 mark)*. The lengths of the are used to determine the relative locations of the cut sites *(1 mark)*. This information is used to produce the restriction map *(1 mark)*.

c) i) Colonies were added to the plate containing penicillin to identify the transformed cells (those that have taken up the recombinant DNA containing the target gene) *(1 mark)*. A marker gene for penicillin resistance was added to the recombinant DNA so that only transformed cells will grow on plates containing penicillin, allowing them to be identified *(1 mark)*. Colonies of bacteria were also added to a standard agar plate as a control to show that the penicillin stopped colonies without the penicillin-resistance gene growing *(1 mark)*.
ii) Bacteria A is a negative control *(1 mark)*, to make sure nothing in the host cells on their own makes them resistant to penicillin/ to make sure the penicillin is working *(1 mark)*.
iii) Any one of 1, 3, 5 or 7. These grew on the penicillin plate, and so must be transformed cells/contain the recombinant DNA with the gene of interest and the marker gene for penicillin-resistance *(1 mark)*.

2 a) PCR is used to make many copies of the areas of the DNA that contain the repeated sequences in each DNA sample *(1 mark)*. A fluorescent tag is added to all the DNA (to allow it to be seen under UV light) *(1 mark)*. The PCR mix from each sample is separated using gel electrophoresis *(1 mark)*. Shorter DNA fragments move faster and travel further through the gel, so the DNA fragments separate according to length with longer pieces nearer the top *(1 mark)*. The gel is placed under UV light to see the bands produced for each sample — these are the genetic fingerprints *(1 mark)*.

b) Genetic fingerprint technology involves comparing the number of times repetitive, non-coding base sequences *(1 mark)* are repeated at a number of different, specific places (loci) in a genome *(1 mark)*. The probability of two individuals having the same genetic fingerprint is very low because the chance of two individuals having the same number of sequence repeats at each locus tested is very low *(1 mark)*.

c) Yes. The genetic fingerprint of the stolen horse and genetic fingerprint of horse 3 have exactly the same band pattern, so the DNA that produced both genetic fingerprints must have come from the same horse *(1 mark)*.

d) Horse 4 and the stolen horse have 6 matching bands *(1 mark)*, which suggests they must be closely related in some way *(1 mark)*. The stolen horse had previously been sent to the farm for breeding purposes, so it seems likely that horse 4 is a child of the stolen horse *(1 mark)*. *Offspring get 50% of their DNA from each parent, so roughly 50% of bands will match between a parent and child in a genetic fingerprint.*

e) E.g. determining genetic relationships / determining genetic variability within a population / medical diagnosis / animal and plant breeding *(1 mark)*.

3 a) E.g. they could use reverse transcriptase *(1 mark)* to make a cDNA copy of the mRNA that codes for the protein *(1 mark)*. / They could use restriction endonuclease enzymes *(1 mark)* to cut the DNA at specific palindromic recognition sequences *(1 mark)*.

b) They are important in *in vivo* cloning as complementary sticky ends *(1 mark)* are required to anneal (bind) the target DNA fragment and vector DNA together *(1 mark)*.

c) Any six from: the vector DNA is cut using the same restriction enzyme to produce complementary sticky ends *(1 mark)*. The DNA fragment containing the target gene and vector DNA are mixed together with DNA ligase *(1 mark)*, which joins the sticky ends together creating recombinant DNA *(1 mark)*. Marker genes are inserted into the vector at the same time as the DNA fragment *(1 mark)*. The vector with the recombinant DNA and the fluorescent marker gene is then used to transfer the gene into host cells *(1 mark)*. The host cells are grown on agar plates to produce colonies of cloned cells *(1 mark)*. If the agar plate is placed under UV light, only colonies of transformed cells will fluoresce because only these cells will contain the marker gene *(1 mark)*. Identified transformed cells are allowed to grow more producing lots of copies of the cloned gene *(1 mark)*.

d) E.g. The scientists are interested in the protein the gene codes for *(1 mark)*. Cloning *in vivo* can be used to produce the protein as well as copies of the gene itself and mRNA, whereas cloning *in vitro* only produces copies of the gene DNA *(1 mark)*.

Glossary

A

Abiotic condition
A non-living feature of an ecosystem.

Abundance
The number of individuals of one species in a particular area.

Accurate result
A result that is really close to the true answer.

Acetylcholine (ACh)
A type of neurotransmitter that binds to cholinergic receptors.

Acquired mutation
A mutation you develop during your lifetime.

Actin
The thin myofilament protein in muscle fibres.

Actin-myosin cross bridge
The bond formed when a myosin head binds to an actin filament.

Activator
A transcription factor that increases the rate of transcription.

Adaptation
A feature that increases an individual's chance of survival and reproduction.

ADP (adenosine diphosphate)
A molecule made up of adenine, a ribose sugar and two phosphate groups. ATP is synthesised from ADP and a phosphate group.

Adrenaline
A hormone secreted from the adrenal glands that has many effects, including increasing the blood glucose concentration.

Age-population pyramid
A diagram showing the age structure and gender of a population.

Allele
One or more alternative versions of the same gene.

Allele frequency
How often an allele occurs in a population.

Ammonification
The process in which nitrogen compounds from dead organisms or waste material are turned into ammonium compounds by decomposers.

Anomalous data
Measurements that fall outside the range of values you'd expect or any pattern you already have.

ATP (adenosine triphosphate)
A molecule made up of adenine, a ribose sugar and three phosphate groups. It is the immediate source of energy in a cell.

ATPase
An enzyme which catalyses the hydrolysis of ATP into ADP and a phosphate group.

ATP-phosphocreatine (PCr) system
A system that generates ATP very quickly by phosphorylating ADP using a phosphate group from phosphocreatine.

ATP synthase
An enzyme which catalyses the synthesis of ATP from ADP and a phosphate group.

Autonomic nervous system
A division of the peripheral nervous system that controls unconscious activities, e.g. heart rate.

B

Bias
When someone intentionally, or unintentionally, favours a particular result.

Biological agent
An organism used to kill crop pests.

Biotic condition
A living feature of an ecosystem.

Birth rate
The number of live births each year for every 1000 people in the population.

C

Cancer
A tumour that invades and destroys surrounding tissues.

Carbon cycle
The movement of carbon through living organisms and the non-living environment.

Causal relationship
Where a change in one variable causes a change in the other.

cDNA (complementary DNA)
A DNA copy of mRNA made using reverse transcriptase.

Chain termination method
A technique used to sequence DNA.

Chemical mediator
A chemical messenger that acts locally (i.e. on nearby cells).

Chlorophyll
A photosynthetic pigment found in chloroplasts. There are different types of this pigment, e.g. chlorophyll a.

Cholinergic synapse
A synapse that uses the neurotransmitter acetylcholine.

Climax community
The largest and most complex community of plants and animals an ecosystem can support.

Codominant allele
An allele whose characteristic appears together with another allele in the phenotype because neither allele is recessive.

Codon
A base triplet (three nucleotides) in DNA or mRNA that codes for an amino acid.

Coenzyme
A molecule that aids the function of an enzyme. They work by transferring a chemical group from one molecule to another.

Coenzyme A (CoA)
A type of coenzyme involved in respiration. It transfers acetate from one molecule to another.

Community
All the populations of different species in a habitat.

Confounding variable
See control variable.

Conservation
The protection and management of species and habitats (ecosystems).

Control experiment
An extra experiment set up to eliminate the effect of some variables that can't be controlled.

Control group
A group in a study that is treated in exactly the same way as the experimental group, apart from the factor you're investigating.

Control variable
A variable you keep constant throughout an experiment.

Corpus luteum
A structure that develops from the remains of a follicle.

Correlation
A relationship between two variables.

Death rate
The number of people that die each year for every 1000 people in the population.

Demographic Transition Model (DTM)
A graph that shows changes in birth rate, death rate and total population size for a human population over a long period of time.

Denitrification
The process in which nitrates in the soil are converted into nitrogen gas by denitrifying bacteria.

Dependent variable
The variable you measure in an experiment.

Depolarisation
A decrease in the potential difference across a cell's membrane, making it less negative (i.e. more positive) than the resting potential.

Diabetes mellitus (Type I)
A condition in which blood glucose concentration can't be controlled properly because the body doesn't produce any insulin.

Diabetes mellitus (Type II)
A condition in which blood glucose concentration can't be controlled properly because the body doesn't produce enough insulin or the body's cells don't respond properly to insulin.

Differential reproductive success
Not all individuals have an equal chance of reproducing. Some individuals will have alleles that make them more likely to survive, and so reproduce and pass on their alleles.

Directional selection
Where individuals with alleles for characteristics of an extreme type are more likely to survive, reproduce and pass on their alleles.

Distribution
Where a particular species is within an area being investigated.

DNA polymerase
An enzyme that joins together the nucleotides on a new strand of DNA during DNA replication.

DNA probe
A short single strand of DNA that has a complementary base sequence to part of a target gene.

DNA sequencing
A technique used to determine the order of bases in a section of DNA.

Dominant allele
An allele whose characteristic appears in the phenotype even when there's only one copy.

Double-blind trial
A study involving a control group and an experimental group where neither the scientists involved nor the participants know which group the participants are in.

Ecosystem
All the organisms living in a particular area and all the non-living (abiotic) conditions found there.

Ectotherm
An animal that can't control its body temperature internally.

Effector
A cell that brings about a response to a stimulus, to produce an effect.

Electrochemical gradient
A concentration gradient of ions.

Electron transport chain
A chain of proteins through which excited electrons flow.

Endotherm
An animal that can control its body temperature internally by homeostasis.

Eutrophication
The process whereby nutrients build up in water, leading to the growth of large quantities of algae. This results in the death of plants, and the decomposition of dead plant matter causes the oxygen content of the water to fall, killing aquatic organisms.

Exon
A section of DNA that codes for amino acids.

FAD
A type of coenzyme involved in respiration. It transfers hydrogen from one molecule to another.

Fair test
A test in which only the independent variable has been allowed to affect the dependent variable.

Fast twitch muscle fibre
A muscle fibre that contracts very quickly but also gets tired quickly.

Follicle
A mammal's egg and its surrounding protective cells.

FSH (follicle-stimulating hormone)
A hormone released by the anterior pituitary gland that stimulates follicles to develop in the menstrual cycle.

Gel electrophoresis
A technique that allows DNA fragments to be separated on a gel according to size.

Gene
A section of DNA that codes for a protein (polypeptide) which results in a characteristic.

Gene expression
The transcription of a gene into mRNA and translation of the mRNA into a protein.

Gene pool
The complete range of alleles present in a population.

Gene technology
Techniques that allow the study and alteration of genes and their functions.

Gene therapy
Possible treatment option for genetic disorders and some cancers that involves altering defective genes inside cells.

Generator potential
The change in potential difference across a cell membrane due to the presence of a stimulus.

Genetic code
The sequence of base triplets (codons) in mRNA which code for specific amino acids.

Genetic disorder
An inherited disorder caused by an abnormal gene or chromosome.

Genetic engineering
The manipulation of an organism's DNA. Also known as recombinant DNA technology.

Genetic fingerprint
A DNA gel that shows the number of times repetitive, non-coding base sequences are repeated at different loci in an individual.

Genetic pedigree diagram
A diagram that shows how an inherited trait (characteristic) runs in a group of related individuals.

Genome
All the genetic material in an organism.

Genotype
The genetic constitution of an organism (the different alleles an organism has).

Geographical isolation
When a physical barrier, e.g. a flood, divides a population of a species, causing some individuals to become separated from the main population.

Geotropism (gravitropism)
The growth of a plant in response to gravity.

Glucagon
A hormone secreted by the pancreas that has an important role in raising blood glucose concentration.

Gluconeogenesis
The conversion of glycerol or amino acids to glucose, activated by glucagon.

Glycogenesis
The conversion of glucose to glycogen, activated by insulin.

Glycogenolysis
The conversion of glycogen to glucose, activated by glucagon.

Glycolysis
The first stage of aerobic respiration — here glucose is converted into pyruvate.

Greenhouse effect
The effect of greenhouse gases in the atmosphere which heat the Earth by absorbing outgoing energy, so that less is lost to space.

Gross productivity
The energy available to organisms that is absorbed by them.

Habitat
The place where an organism lives.

Hardy-Weinberg principle
A mathematical model that predicts that the frequency of alleles in a population won't change from one generation to the next provided that certain conditions are met.

Hereditary mutation
A mutation that's inherited from your parents.

Heterozygous
When an organism carries two different alleles for the same characteristic.

Homozygous
When an organism carries two copies of the same allele.

Host cell
Cells that are used to carry recombinant DNA.

Hyperpolarisation
An increase in the potential difference across a cell's membrane, making it more negative than the resting potential.

Hypothalamus
A part of the brain that controls body temperature.

Hypothesis
A specific testable statement, based on a theory, about what will happen in a test situation.

***In vitro* cloning**
When gene copies are made outside of a living organism using PCR.

***In vivo* cloning**
When gene copies are made within a living organism as it grows and divides.

Independent variable
The variable you change in an experiment.

Indoleacetic acid (IAA)
An auxin produced in the tips of shoots in flowering plants.

Insulin
A hormone secreted by the pancreas that has an important role in lowering blood glucose concentration.

Integrated system (in farming)
A type of pest control involving the use of chemical pesticides and biological agents.

Intensive farming
A type of farming which changes an ecosystem by controlling the biotic or abiotic conditions to make it more favourable for crops or livestock.

Interspecific competition
Competition between organisms of different species for the same resources.

Intraspecific competition
Competition between organisms of the same species for the same resources.

Intron
A section of DNA that doesn't code for amino acids.

Kinesis (kinetic response)
Non-directional (random) movement in response to a stimulus.

Krebs cycle
The third stage of aerobic respiration. It is a series of oxidation-reduction reactions that produces reduced coenzymes and ATP.

Leaching
The process in which water-soluble compounds in the soil are washed away, e.g. by rain.

LH (luteinising hormone)
A hormone released by the anterior pituitary gland that stimulates ovulation and the formation of a corpus luteum in the menstrual cycle.

Life expectancy
The age that a person born into a population is expected to live to.

Ligase
An enzyme that joins together the sticky ends of DNA fragments.

Light-dependent reaction
The first stage of photosynthesis. Light energy is absorbed by photosynthetic pigments and converted to ATP and reduced NADP.

Light-independent reaction (Calvin cycle)
The second stage of photosynthesis. Here ATP and reduced NADP (from the light-dependent reaction) are used to make glucose from carbon dioxide.

Limiting factor
A variable that can slow down the rate of a reaction.

Link reaction
The second stage of aerobic respiration where pyruvate is converted into acetyl coenzyme A.

Locus
The position on a chromosome where a particular allele is found.

Mean
The average of the values collected in a sample.

Medulla (oblongata)
A part of the brain that controls heart rate.

Meristem
A growing region of a plant, e.g. the roots and shoots, which contains totipotent stem cells.

Microarray
A glass slide with microscopic spots of different DNA probes attached to it in rows.

Monohybrid cross
A cross involving monohybrid inheritance which shows the likelihood of alleles (and so different versions of a characteristic) being inherited by offspring of particular parents.

Monohybrid inheritance
The inheritance of a single characteristic (gene) controlled by different alleles.

mRNA (messenger RNA)
A type of RNA that is the template for protein synthesis. It carries the genetic code from the DNA in the nucleus into the cytoplasm.

Multipotent stem cell
A stem cell only able to develop into a few types of cell.

Mutagenic agent
Something that increases the rate of DNA mutations.

Mutation
Any change in the DNA base sequence.

Myelin sheath
A layer of Schwann cells around a neurone that acts as an electrical insulator and speeds up conduction of nervous impulses.

Myofibril
A long, cylindrical organelle within a muscle fibre that's highly specialised for contraction.

Myosin
The protein that makes up the thick myofilaments in myofibrils.

NAD
A type of coenzyme involved in respiration. It transfers hydrogen from one molecule to another.

NADP
A coenzyme involved in photosynthesis. It transfers hydrogen from one molecule to another.

Natural selection
The process whereby a characteristic (allele) becomes common in a population because it makes an organism more likely to survive, reproduce and pass on the allele for that characteristic to its offspring.

Negative feedback mechanism
A mechanism that restores a level back to normal in a system.

Net productivity
The amount of energy that's available to the next trophic level in a food chain.

Neuromuscular junction
A specialised cholinergic synapse between a motor neurone and a muscle cell.

Neurotransmitter
A chemical that transmits a nerve impulse across a synapse.

Niche
The role of a species within its habitat, e.g. what it eats, and where and when it feeds.

Nitrification
The process in which ammonium compounds in the soil are changed into nitrogen compounds by nitrifying bacteria.

Nitrogen cycle
The conversion of nitrogen into a usable form and its movement through living organisms and the non-living environment.

Nitrogen fixation
The process in which nitrogen gas in the atmosphere is turned into ammonia by bacteria.

Oestrogen
A hormone released by the ovaries that stimulates the uterus lining to thicken in the menstrual cycle.

Oncogene
A mutated proto-oncogene that stimulates cells to divide uncontrollably.

Ovulation
The process in which an egg is released from its surrounding protective cells.

Oxidation
A chemical reaction where a molecule loses electrons, and may have lost hydrogen or gained oxygen.

Oxidative phosphorylation
The final stage in aerobic respiration. Energy carried by electrons, from reduced coenzymes, is used to make ATP.

Pacinian corpuscle
A type of receptor found in your skin which detects mechanical stimuli.

Palindromic sequence
A sequence of DNA bases that consists of antiparallel base pairs (base pairs that read the same in opposite directions).

PCR (polymerase chain reaction)
A technique used to make millions of identical copies of a DNA fragment in a few hours.

Peer review
Where a scientific report is sent out to peers (other scientists) who examine the data and results, and if they think that the conclusion is reasonable it's published.

Phenotype
The expression of the genetic constitution of an organism and its interaction with the environment (what characteristics an organism has as a result of its genes and the effect the environment has on them).

Photolysis
The splitting (lysis) of a molecule using light (photo) energy.

Photophosphorylation
The process of adding phosphate to a molecule using light energy.

Photosystem
A protein and photosynthetic pigment structure found in the thylakoid membranes of chloroplasts in plants and algae.

Phototropism
The growth of a plant in response to light.

Pioneer species
The first species to colonise an area during succession.

Placebo
A dummy pill or injection that looks exactly like the real drug, but doesn't contain the drug.

Plagioclimax
The climax community produced when succession is artificially stopped by human activities.

Polynucleotide
A molecule made up of lots of nucleotides joined together in a long chain.

Population
All the organisms of one species in a habitat.

Population growth curve
A graph showing the change in the size of a population over time.

Population growth rate
How much the size of a population increases or decreases in a year.

Positive feedback mechanism
A mechanism that amplifies a change away from the normal level in a system.

Potential difference
The voltage across a cell membrane.

Precise result
A result taken using a sensitive instruments that measure in small increments.

Predation
Where an organism (the predator) kills and eats another organism (the prey).

Prediction
See hypothesis.

pre-mRNA
A strand of mRNA that contains both introns and exons, before it has been spliced.

Primary succession
Succession which happens on newly formed or exposed land with no soil.

Primers
Short pieces of single stranded DNA that are complementary to the bases at the start of the DNA fragment you want.

Probability
How likely something is to happen.

Progesterone
A hormone released by the ovaries that maintains the thick lining of the uterus in the menstrual cycle, ready for the implantation of an embryo.

Promoter
A specific DNA site near to the start of target genes, to which specific transcription factors bind.

Proto-oncogene
A gene that produces proteins that make cells divide.

R

Receptor
A cell, or protein on a cell surface membrane, that detects a stimulus.

Recessive allele
An allele whose characteristic only appears in the phenotype if there are two copies present.

Recognition sequence
A specific palindromic sequence in DNA recognised by a restriction endonuclease.

Recombinant DNA
The name for DNA formed by joining together DNA from different sources.

Reduction
A chemical reaction where a molecule gains electrons, and may have gained hydrogen or lost oxygen.

Reflex
An automatic response to a stimulus.

Refractory period
The period following an action potential in which a neurone cell membrane can't be excited.

Reliable evidence
Evidence that can be consistently reproduced in independent experiments.

Repolarisation
The return of a cell membrane to its resting potential.

Repressor
A transcription factor that decreases the rate of transcription.

Reproductive isolation
When two individuals are unable to interbreed to produce fertile offspring.

Respiratory loss
The amount of energy lost to the environment when organisms use energy produced from respiration for movement or body heat.

Resting potential
The potential difference across a cell membrane when the cell is at rest.

Restriction endonuclease enzymes
Enzymes that recognise specific recognition sequences and cut DNA at these places.

Restriction map
A diagram of a piece of DNA showing where different recognition sites of restriction enzymes are found.

Reverse transcriptase
An enzyme that makes a DNA copy of RNA.

Ribosome
An organelle found in the cell cytoplasm that assembles proteins.

Ribulose bisphosphate carboxylase (rubisco)
An enzyme which catalyses the formation of glycerate 3-phosphate from carbon dioxide and ribulose bisphosphate (RuBP) in the light-independent reaction of photosynthesis.

RNA (ribonucleic acid)
A type of nucleic acid, similar to DNA but containing ribose instead of deoxyribose sugar and uracil instead of thymine.

RNA interference
The mechanism by which siRNA affects translation.

RNA polymerase
An enzyme that synthesises RNA from DNA.

S

Saltatory conduction
The process in myelinated neurones by which a nervous impulse travels between nodes of Ranvier.

Sample size
The number of samples in the investigation, e.g. the number of people in a drug trial.

Saprobiontic nutrition
A form of feeding in which a decomposer secretes extracellular enzymes onto dead organic matter then absorbs the products of digestion.

Sarcomere
A short contractile unit that's part of a myofibril, made up of overlapping myosin and actin filaments.

Schwann cell
The type of cell that makes up the myelin sheath around neurones.

Second messenger
A chemical that's produced inside a cell in response to a signal outside the cell. The chemical relays the signal to the inside of the cell.

Secondary succession
Succession which happens on land cleared of all plants but where the soil remains, e.g. after a forest fire.

Sex-linked characteristic
When the allele that codes for the characteristic is located on a sex chromosome (X or Y).

siRNA (small interfering RNA)
Double-stranded RNA molecules that can interfere with the transcription and translation of genes.

Sliding filament theory
The theory that myosin and actin filaments slide over one another to make sarcomeres contract.

Slow twitch muscle fibre
A muscle fibre that contracts slowly and can work for a long time without getting tired.

Speciation
The development of a new species.

Species
A group of similar organisms that can reproduce to give fertile offspring.

Splicing
The process by which introns are removed from pre-mRNA strands and exons are joined to form mRNA.

Stabilising selection
Where individuals with alleles for characteristics towards the middle of the range are more likely to survive, reproduce and pass on their alleles.

Stem cell
An unspecialised cell that can develop into other types of cell. They're also able to divide to form new cells.

Stem cell therapy
Using stem cells to treat or cure medical disorders.

Sticky ends
Small tails of unpaired DNA bases at each end of a DNA fragment.

Stimulus
A change in an organism's internal or external environment.

Succession
The process by which an ecosystem changes over time.

Summation
The process in which the effect of a neurotransmitter released from many neurones (or one neurone that's stimulated a lot in a short period of time) is added together.

Survival curve
A graph which shows the percentage of all the individuals that were born in a population that are still alive at any given age.

Synapse
A junction between a neurone and another neurone, or between a neurone and an effector cell.

Target cell
A cell that has specific receptors for a particular type of chemical, such as a hormone or a neurotransmitter.

Taxis (tactic response)
Directional movement in response to a stimulus.

Theory
A possible explanation for something

Tissue culture
Growing tissue artificially (*in vitro*).

Totipotent stem cell
A stem cell able to develop into any type of body cell.

Transcription
The first stage of protein synthesis in which an mRNA copy of a gene is made from DNA in the nucleus.

Transcription factor
Protein molecules that control the transcription of genes.

Transect
A line used to help measure how plants are distributed across an area, e.g. how species change from a hedge towards the middle of a field.

Transformed cell
A host cell that has taken up recombinant DNA.

Transformed organisms
Plants, animals or microorganisms that have had their genes altered by recombinant DNA technology.

Translation
The second stage of protein synthesis in which amino acids are joined together by ribosomes to make a polypeptide chain (protein).

tRNA (transfer RNA)
A type of RNA involved in translation. It carries the amino acids used to make proteins at ribosomes.

Trophic level
A stage in a food chain.

Tropism
The response of a plant to a directional stimulus.

Tropomyosin
A protein found between actin filaments attached to troponin. Together the two proteins help myofilaments move past each other.

Tumour
A mass of abnormal cells.

Tumour suppressor gene
A gene that slows the rate of cell division by producing proteins that stop cells dividing or cause them to self-destruct.

Valid conclusion
A conclusion that answers the original question and uses reliable data.

Variable
A quantity that has the potential to change, e.g. weight, temperature, concentration.

Vasoconstriction
Constriction (narrowing) of a blood vessel.

Vasodilation
Dilation (widening) of a blood vessel.

Vector (in gene technology)
Something used to transfer DNA into a cell, e.g. plasmids or bacteriophages.

Visual acuity
The ability to tell apart points that are close together.

Water potential
The likelihood of water molecules to diffuse into or out of a solution.

Acknowledgements

AQA Specification reference points are reproduced by permission of Assessment and Qualifications Alliance.

Data acknowledgements

Data used to construct the graph of daily CO_2 concentration on page 63 from School of GeoSciences, The University of Edinburgh.

Data used to construct the graph of yearly CO_2 concentrations on page 63 reproduced with kind permission from Atmosphere CO_2 at Mauna Loa Observatory, Scripps Institution of Oceanography, NOAA Earth System Research Laboratory.

Data used to construct the graph of temperature change over the last 1000 years on page 64 reproduced with kind permission from Climate Change 2001: The Scientific Basis, Contribution of Working Group I to the Third Assessment Report of the Intergovernmental Panel on Climate Change, SPM Figure 1. Cambridge University Press.

Data used to construct the graph of methane concentration on page 64 reproduced by permission of CSIRO Australia, © CSIRO. Also: MacFarling Meure, C. et al., Law Dome CO_2, CH_4 and N_2O ice core records extended to 2000 years BP. Geophysical Research Letters 2006; 33 (14), 10.1029/2006GL026152. Also: Etheridge, D. M. et al. Atmospheric methane between 1000 A.D. and present: evidence of anthropogenic emissions and climatic variability. Journal of geophysical research - Atmospheres 1998; 103(D13):15979-15993.

Data used to construct the graph of CO_2 concentration on page 64 reproduced with kind permission from U.S. Global Change Research Program, http://www.usgcrp.gov/usgcrp/nacc/background/scenarios/images/co2hm.gif

Data used to construct the graph of wheat yield on page 67 from Global scale climate-crop yield relationships and the impacts of recent warming. D. B. Lobell and C. B. Field. Environmental Research Letters 2 (2007) 014002 (7pp). IOP Publishing.

Data used to construct the graph of average global temperature on page 67 adapted from Crown Copyright data supplied by the Met Office.

Data used to construct the graph of global sea temperature on page 68 reproduced with kind permission from NASA Goddard Institute for Space Studies.

Diagram showing the distribution of subtropical plankton on page 68 reproduced with kind permission from Plankton distribution changes, due to climate changes - North Sea. (February 2008). In UNEP/GRID-Arendal Maps and Graphics Library. http://maps.grida.no/go/graphic/plankton-distribution-changes-due-to-climate-changes-north-sea.

Data used to produce graph on page 79 © I. Yassir, J. van der Kamp, P. Buurman and International Union of Soil Sciences (IUSS).

Data used to construct the graph on GLUT4 protein content on page 147 reproduced with kind permission from Diabetes: a journal of the American Diabetes Association; Stanford University. Copyright 2000. Reproduced with permission of American Diabetes Association.

Data used to construct the table on the role of protein and nucleic acid synthesis on page 177 reproduced with kind permission from Robert E. Click, D. P. Hackett. PNAS 1963; 50 (2):243-250.

Data used to construct the graphs on page 226 from S. Hacein-Bey-Abina et al. SCIENCE 302: 415-419 (2003)

Data used to produce the table on page 226 from A.C. Nathwani et al., Adenovirus-Associated Virus Vector–Mediated Gene Transfer in Hemophilia B: N Engl J Med 2011; 365:2357-2365

Photograph acknowledgements

Cover photo **Steve Gschmeissner**/Science Photo Library, p 1 **National Library of Medicine**/Science Photo Library, p 3 **Monty Rakusen**/Science Photo Library, p 4 **Cordelia Molloy**/Science Photo Library, p 7 (Fig. 1 top) **Steve Gschmeissner**/Science Photo Library, p 7 (Fig. 1 bottom) © **imagebroker**/Alamy, p 8 (middle) **mtomline**/iStockphoto, p 8 (bottom) **Mary Beth Angelo**/Science Photo Library, p 12 **Jeff Lepore**/Science Photo Library, p 14 **Martyn F Chillmaid**/Science Photo Library, p 15 (middle) **Nigel Cattlin**/Science Photo Library, p 15 (bottom) **Martyn F Chillmaid**/Science Photo Library, p 16 (top) **Philippe Psaila**/Science Photo Library, p 16 (middle) **Alexis Rosenfeld**/Science Photo Library, p 18 (top) **Duncan Shaw**/Science Photo Library, p 18 (middle) **Photostock-Israel**/Science Photo Library, p 22 Image Source/**Robert Harding**, p 25 (top) **Margaret Durrance**/Science Photo Library, p 25 (middle) **Peter Menzel**/Science Photo Library, p 32 **Dr. Kari Lounatmaa**/Science Photo Library, p 38 **Biophoto Associates**/Science Photo Library, p 41 **GAPS**/iStockphoto, p 43 **Dr. David Furness, Keele University**/Science Photo Library, p 57 **Frank Fox**/Science Photo Library, p 60 **Scott Camazine**/Science Photo Library, p 61 **David Aubrey**/Science Photo Library, p 62 **Cordelia Molloy**/Science Photo Library, p 70 (middle) **Dr. Jeremy Burgess**/Science Photo Library, p 70 (bottom) **Pasieka**/Science Photo Library, p 71 **Steve Gschmeissner**/Science Photo Library, p 72 **Robert Brook**/Science Photo Library, p 77 **Annie Haycock**/Science Photo Library, p 78 **Simon Fraser**/Science Photo Library, p 79 **Andrea Balogh**/Science Photo Library, p 80 (top) **Simon Fraser**/Science Photo Library, p 80 (middle) **Simon Fraser**/Science Photo Library, p 81 (Fig. 1 top) **Annie Haycock**/Science Photo Library, p 81 (Fig. 1 bottom) **Duncan Shaw**/Science Photo Library, p 82 (Fig. 2 top) **David Aubrey**/Science Photo Library, p 82 (Fig. 2 bottom) **kenxro**/iStockphoto, p 83 (top) **Bob Gibbons**/Science Photo Library, p 83 (bottom) **B.G Thomson**/Science Photo Library, p 85 (Fig. 3 top) **Colin Varndell**/Science Photo Library, p 85 (Fig. 3 bottom) **Adrian Bicker**/Science Photo Library, p 87 (top) **John Reader**/Science Photo Library, p 87 (bottom) **Reinhard Dirscherl, Visuals Unlimited**/Science Photo Library, p 93 (Fig. 2a) **Wim van Egmond, Visuals Unlimited**/Science Photo Library, p 93 (Fig. 2b) **J.C. Revy, ISM**/Science Photo Library, p 95 **Eye of Science**/Science Photo Library, p 105 **Michael W. Tweedie**/Science Photo Library, p 106 **Paul D Stewart**/Science Photo Library, p 114 **Ramon Andrade 3DCiencia**/Science Photo Library, p 116 **Medimage**/Science Photo Library, p 118 **Ray Simons**/Science Photo Library, p 119 **Eye of Science**/Science Photo Library, p 120 **Eye of Science**/Science Photo Library, p 124 (top) **Dr David Furness, Keele University**/Science Photo Library, p 124 (middle) **CMEAGB - UCBL1, ISM**/Science Photo Library, p 128 **Don Fawcett**/Science Photo Library, p 129 **Ed Reschke, Peter Arnold Inc.**/Science Photo Library, p 133 **Steve Gschmeissner**/Science Photo Library, p 134 **Thomas Deerinck, NCMIR**/Science Photo Library, p 138 **Dr Gladden Willis, Visuals Unlimited**/Science Photo Library, p 142 **Martin Shields**/Science Photo Library, p 152 Science Photo Library, p 153 (side) **Adam Jones**/Science Photo Library, p 153 (bottom) **Edward Kinsman**/Science Photo Library, p 157 **Conge, ISM**/Science Photo Library, p 172 **Ramon Andrade 3DCiencia**/Science Photo Library, p 180 **Mitchell Lewis, University of Pennsylvania Medical Center**/Science Photo Library, p 182 (Fig. 1) © **Jane Towle**, p 185 **Pascal Goetgheluck**/Science Photo Library, p 189 **Pasieka**/Science Photo Library, p 190 **G-I Associates**/Custom Medical Stock Photo/Science Photo Library, p 191 **Simon Fraser**/Science Photo Library, p 192 **Professor Miodrag Stojkovic**/Science Photo Library, p 193 (Fig. 4 top) **Dr. Tony Brain**/Science Photo Library, p 193 (Fig. 4 bottom) **CNRI**/Science Photo Library, p 193 (bottom) **Sinclair Stammers**/Science Photo Library, p 195 **Steve Gschmeissner**/Science Photo Library, p 196 **Chassenet**/Science Photo Library, p 202 **Robert Longuehaye, NIBSC**/Science Photo Library, p 205 **J.C. Revy, ISM**/Science Photo Library, p 206 (top) **Biozentrum, University of Basel**/Science Photo Library, p 206 (bottom) **Martin Shields**/Science Photo Library, p 209 **Makoto Iwafuji/Eurelios**/Science Photo Library, p 210 **International Rice Research Institute**, p 213 (middle) **TEK Image**/Science Photo Library, p 213 (bottom) **Larry Mulvehill**/Science Photo Library, p 216 **Peter Menzel**/Science Photo Library, p 219 **Sinclair Stammers**/Science Photo Library, p 222 **Patrick Dumas/Eurelios**/Science Photo Library, p 225 **Peter Menzel**/Science Photo Library.

Index

A

abiotic conditions 7, 8
abundance 13
accuracy 3
acetyl coenzyme A (acetyl CoA) 45
acetylcholine (ACh) 128, 129
acquired mutations 186-189
actin filaments 134, 135
action potentials 122, 123
  speed of conduction 124
activators 178
adaptations of organisms 8
ADP (adenosine diphosphate) 30
adrenaline 159
adult stem cells 196
aerobic respiration 29, 43-48
age-population pyramids 24, 25
alcoholic fermentation 49
allele frequencies 100
allele frequency patterns 104, 105
alleles 91
all-or-nothing principle of action potentials 123
ammonification 70
anaerobic respiration 29, 49
animal and plant breeding 215
anomalous data 5
answering data questions 231
answering essay questions 231
anticodons 169
anti-globalisation activists 210, 211
ATP (adenosine triphosphate) 29, 30, 48
ATP synthase 30
ATP-phosphocreatine (PCr) system 138
ATPase 30
autonomic nervous system 140
auxins 142-144

B

bacteriophages 205
baroreceptors 140
base triplets (codons) 168
beating trays 16
bias 4
biological agents 60
biotic conditions 7, 8
birth rates 21
blood glucose concentration 150, 157-160
blood pH 150
body temperature 149, 153-156
bone marrow transplants 195

C

Calvin cycle 32, 36, 37
cancer 187-190
captive breeding (conservation) 83
carbon cycle 62
carbon dioxide fluctuations 63, 64
causal relationships 5
cDNA 201
chain termination method 218
chance 234
chemical mediators 116
chemiosmosis 33, 47
chemoreceptors 140
chlorophyll 31, 39
cholinergic synapses 128, 129
chymosin 210
climatic climax communities 80
climax communities 78
codominant alleles 92
codons 168
coenzyme A 45
coenzymes
  in photosynthesis 31
  in respiration 43
collecting data 4, 233
command words 230
communities 10
conclusions 5, 232
cones 119, 120
confounding variables 3
conservation 81, 87
control experiments 4
control groups 4
control variables 3
correlations 5

cyclic AMP (cAMP) 159
cyclic photophosphorylation 34

D

death rates 21
decarboxylation 45
decomposers 54, 62
decomposition 62
dehydrogenation 46
Demographic Transition Model (DTM) 22
denitrification 71
dependent variables 3
depolarisation 122, 123
determining genetic relationships 214
determining genetic variability 214
diabetes 160
differential reproductive success 104
directional selection 105
distribution 13
DNA 167-169
  base sequencing 218, 219
  fragments 201
  ligase 205
  microarrays 222
  polymerase 202
  primers 202, 212
  probes 216, 221, 222
dominant alleles 92
double-blind trials 4
drug action at synapses 131

E

ecosystems 7
ectotherms 153
effectors 112, 133-137
electron transport chain 33, 47
embryonic stem cells 196
endotherms 153
energy (for muscle contraction) 138
energy transfers in ecosystems 54-56
ethanol 49

ethical considerations (of using stem cells) 196
ethical issues (when carrying out fieldwork) 18
eutrophication 71-73
evaluating evidence on conservation 85, 86
exam structure 230
exons 171

F

fair tests 3
fast twitch muscle fibres 139
fertilisers 61, 71
fluorescent tags 212, 216
food chains 54
food webs 54
forensic science 214
frequency (as a measure of abundance) 13
FSH (follicle-stimulating hormone) 161-163
fungicides 60

G

gel electrophoresis 213
genes 91, 167
gene cloning 205-207
gene expression 180
gene pools 100
gene sequencing 216
gene technology 201
gene therapy 224-226
generator potentials 117
genetic code 174
genetic counselling 222
genetic diagrams 93-97
genetic disorders 190, 191, 221
genetic engineering 209-211
genetic fingerprinting 212-215
  analysis 213
  uses of 214, 215
genetic pedigree diagrams 99
genetics 91
genetic screening 221, 222
genotypes 91
geographical isolation 106
geotropism 142, 143
germ line gene therapy 224
glasshouses 41

global warming 64, 65
  effects of 66-68
glucagon 157-159
gluconeogenesis 157, 158
glucose 29, 32, 37, 43, 157-160
glycerate 3-phosphate (GP) 36
glycogen 157
glycogenesis 157, 158
glycogenolysis 157, 158
glycolysis 43, 44
Golden Rice 210
gradient of a graph 235
graph skills 235
greenhouse effect 64
gross productivity 55

H

habitats 7
Hardy-Weinberg equations 100-103
Hardy-Weinberg principle 100-103
heart rate 140, 141
herbicides 60
hereditary mutations 186, 189-191
heterozygous 92
histamine 116
homeostasis 149
homozygous 92
hormonal system 114
host cells 206
humanitarians 210
hybridisation 216
hydrolysis of ATP 30
hyperpolarisation 122
hypothalamus 155, 156
hypotheses 1

I

identifying transformed cells 206
independent variables 3
indoleacetic acid (IAA) 143
inhibition (at synapses) 130
insecticides 60
insulin 157, 158, 160, 209, 210
integrated systems (of pest control) 60
intensive farming 59-61

interpreting data
  on auxins 143, 144
  on eutrophication 72, 73
  on gene expression 180
  on global warming 67, 68
  on limiting factors in photosynthesis 41, 42
  on nucleic acids 174, 175
  on organism distribution 19, 20
  on tissue culture 194
interpreting experimental data on nucleic acids 176
interspecific competition 10
intraspecific competition 11
introns 171
in vitro gene cloning 205, 207
in vivo gene cloning 205-207

K

kinetic responses (kineses) 111
Krebs cycle 45, 46

L

lactate fermentation 49
leaching 71
LH (luteinising hormone) 161-163
life expectancy 24
ligation 205
light-dependent reaction 32-34
light-independent reaction 32, 36, 37
limiting factors (in photosynthesis) 39-42
link reaction 45
locating genes 216
loci 91, 212

M

marker genes 206
mark-release-recapture 16, 17
medical diagnosis 215, 221
medulla (oblongata) 140
menstrual cycle 161-163
meristems 193
messenger RNA (mRNA) 168, 169, 201
methane 64, 65
mitochondria 43

model (scientific) 1
monohybrid crosses 93-95
monohybrid inheritance 93
   of codominant alleles 95
multiple allele crosses 97
multiple negative feedback
      mechanisms 151
multipotent stem cells 192
muscle contraction 136-138
muscles 133-139
mutagenic agents 185
mutations 184-191
   screening for 221, 222
myelination 124
myofibrils 133, 134
myosin filaments 134, 135

N

natural selection 104
negative controls 4, 233
negative correlations 5
negative feedback 150, 151
nervous system 112, 113
net productivity 55
neuromuscular junctions 129
neurones 112
neurotransmitters 128
   excitatory 130
   inhibitory 130
niches 7
nitrification 70
nitrogen cycle 70, 71
nitrogen fixation 70
nodes of Ranvier 124
non-cyclic photophosphorylation
      33, 34
nucleotides 167

O

oestrogen 161-163
   effect on gene transcription
      178, 179
oestrous cycle 161
oncogenes 187
optic nerve 119
ovaries 161-163
oxidation 31
oxidative phosphorylation 47, 48

P

Pacinian corpuscles 118
palindromic sequences 203
pancreas 157
parasympathetic nervous system
      140, 141
partial digests 218
PCR (polymerase chain reaction)
      202, 205, 212, 221
peer review 2
percentage cover (as a measure
      of abundance) 13, 14
pesticides 60
phenotypes 91
phosphorylation 30
photolysis 32
photophosphorylation 32
photoreceptors 119, 120
photosynthesis 29, 31-42,
      54, 62
photosystems 31
phototropism 142, 143
phylogenetics 214
pioneer species 77
pitfall traps 15
pituitary gland 161-163
placebos 4
plagioclimaxes 82
plant responses 142-144
plasmids 205, 209
polynucleotide strands 167
pooters 15
populations 10-12
   genetics 100
   growth curves 23
   growth rates 21
   human 21-25
   investigating 13-17
   sizes 10
positive correlations 5
positive feedback 151, 152
precision 3
predation 11, 12
predictions 1
pre-mRNA 171
primary succession 77, 78
probability 234
progesterone 161, 163
promoters 178
prostaglandins 116

protected areas (conservation)
      83, 84
protein synthesis 170-172
protocols (scientific) 2
proto-oncogenes 187
Punnett squares 94
pyramid diagrams 56-58
pyruvate 43-45, 49

Q

quadrats 14

R

radioactive tags 216
random number generators 13
random samples 13
receptors 112, 117-120
recessive alleles 92
recognition sequences 203
recombinant DNA 205, 209
redox reactions 31
reduction 31
reflexes 113
refractory period 123
reliability 3, 233
relocation (conservation) 83
repetitive, non-coding base
      sequences 212
repolarisation 122
repressors 178
reproductive isolation 106
respiration 43-49
respiratory loss 55
resting potentials 117, 121
restriction endonucleases 203
restriction maps 217
reverse transcriptase 201
ribosomes 168, 172, 173
ribulose bisphosphate (RuBP)
      36, 37
ribulose bisphosphate carboxylase
      (rubisco) 36
risk assessments (when carrying
      out fieldwork) 18
RNA 168
RNA polymerase 170, 171
rods 119, 120
running means 14

S

saltatory conduction 124
sample size 4, 233
sampling 13
saprobiontic nutrition 62
sarcomeres 134
saturation point 40
Schwann cells 124
scientific journals 2
secondary succession 79
second messengers 159
seedbanks (conservation) 82
sex-linked characteristics 96
    inheritance of 96, 97
shivering 154
sickle-cell anaemia 221
simple reflexes 113
simple responses 111
sinoatrial node (SAN) 140
skeletal muscle 133
sliding filament theory of
        muscle contraction 134
slow twitch muscle fibres 138
small interfering RNA (siRNA)
        179
sodium-potassium pumps 121
somatic gene therapy 224
spatial summation 130
specialised cells 192, 193
speciation 106
species 100
specific base pairing 167
splicing of pre-mRNA 171
stabilising selection 104
standard deviation 234
statistical significance 234
stem cells 192-196
stem cell therapies 195, 196
sticky ends 203, 205
stimuli 111
stretch-mediated sodium
        channels 118
substrate-level phosphorylation
        46
succession 77-79
    management of succession
        (conservation) 82
summation (at synapses) 130
survival curves 23
sweating 154
sympathetic nervous system
        140, 141
synapses 128-131

T

tactic responses (taxes) 111
temporal summation 130
theories 1, 2
thermoreceptors 155, 156
threshold levels (for action
        potentials) 117
tissue culture 193, 194
total digests 218
totipotent stem cells 192
transcription 170, 171
transcription factors 178
transects 15
transfer RNA (tRNA) 169
transformed organisms 209
    benefits 210
    concerns 210, 211
transforming cells 206
translation 172, 173
triose phosphate 36-38, 44
trophic levels 54
tropisms 142
tropomyosin 135
troponin 135
tumour suppressor genes 187

V

validity 2, 5
variables 3, 233
vasoconstriction 155
vasodilation 154
vectors 205
visual acuity 120

W

water potential of blood
        149, 150